THERMODYNAMICS

A Course Developed for Students in Engineering Colleges

BY

H. A. EVERETT

Head of Department of Mechanical Engineering
The Pennsylvania State College

SECOND EDITION — FIFTH PRINTING

D. VAN NOSTRAND COMPANY, Inc.

TORONTO   NEW YORK   LONDON

NEW YORK

D. Van Nostrand Company, Inc., 250 Fourth Avenue, New York 3

TORONTO

D. Van Nostrand Company (Canada), Ltd., 228 Bloor Street, Toronto

LONDON

Macmillan Company, Ltd., St. Martin's Street, London, W.C. 2

PRINTED IN U. S. A.

SCOTT PRINTING COMPANY
JERSEY CITY, N. J.

PREFACE TO SECOND EDITION

The acceptance of the new spectroscopic data on the specific heats of gases at high temperatures, emphasis on the application of the continuous flow principle to heat engines and a revision of the approach to the consideration of fluid flow constitute the major changes in this new edition. These together with several simplifications and the correction of typographical errors unfortunately inherent to any first edition will, it is hoped, produce a more readily taught and up to date text.

H. A. EVERETT.

January, 1941

PREFACE TŌ FIRST EDITION

This text is intended primarily for students in engineering colleges in this country, whose course in thermodynamics usually is taken during the second and third years of a four year curriculum. It assumes a preceding knowledge of the Calculus and a follow-up by the "applicational" or "professional" courses such as power plants, internal combustion engines, refrigeration, steam turbines, etc.

The order of subjects parallels closely the author's classroom presentation as developed over several decades of teaching. Considerable stress is laid on the kinetic theory explanation of heat, for, with all its defects, this theory permits the presentation of a very tangible picture of thermodynamic phenomena. Following this are gathered into one chapter the surprisingly few fundamental concepts vital to thermodynamic thinking. Next comes the application to our simplest fluid, the perfect gas and the consideration of actual engineering devices which use gases. Vapors are considered a narrowed portion of the gaseous phase and thus, together with practical applications, logically follow gases. A very brief and simplified chapter is devoted to the general mathematical relations—important though frequently shirked.

Special attention has been directed in the chapter dealing with gases to the departure of actual gases from the perfect gas and the charts which evaluate the change in the gas constant are original and have been found convenient. Also helpful within its limitations has been the temperature-entropy diagram developed for the diatomic gases and included in the chapter on gaseous mixtures.

A work of this sort presents little that is new; it consists mainly of the author's method of presenting the classical and neo-classical data and for such, meticulous acknowledgment has not been attempted. For the more modern material, however, a serious attempt has been made to give full credit and if omissions have occurred the author will welcome the opportunity to rectify them. Acknowledgment is due and gratefully rendered to his staff associates who have helped in many ways in the preparation of this text. In particular to Professor N. R. Sparks and Professor J. S. Doolittle for their invaluable assistance with problems, proof, and product.

H. A. Everett.

The Pennsylvania State College
State College. Pennsylvania
September, 1937

CONTENTS

CONTENTS

CHAPTER IV

CHAPTER V

CHAPTER VI

CHAPTER VII

CHAPTER VIII

CHAPTER IX

CHAPTER XIV

SYMBOLS

In General: Where possible, capital letters denote total quantities and small letters denote " specific " quantities or quantities per unit. Sometimes capital and small letters may distinguish units, as P may be pounds per sq. ft. and p lbs. per sq. in. or capitals may be values per mol. and small letters per pound.

p or P = pressure, absolute or gage (force per unit of area).

v = specific volume (volume per unit weight); V = Total Volume.

d or $\dfrac{1}{v}$ or v^{-1} = density (weight per unit volume).

c = specific heat, general.

c_p = specific heat at constant pressure, c_v = specific heat at constant volume.

k = ratio of specific heats = c_p/c_v.

Q = total quantity of heat supplied or rejected (i.e., in transit).

F = force, or pressure on a total area, total load.

M = molecular weight.

m = mass = w/g.

W = total quantity of work or mechanical energy, also total weight.

J = mechanical equivalent of heat.

A = $1/J$ or J^{-1} = heat equivalent of work, occasionally area.

t or (theta) = thermometric temp (θ is used when t is used for time).

T = absolute temperature.

S or s = entropy.

U or u = the internal or intrinsic energy.

U_k = the kinetic form or sensible heat.

U_p = the potential form or latent heat.

H or h = heat content, total heat, or enthalpy ($u + Apv$).

For these last three and any dealing with a fluid in different phases, subscripts are used to denote the phase as follows:

Subscript f denotes liquid at saturation pressure and temperature.

g denotes dry gas or vapor at saturation pressure and temperature.

For example:

h_f = heat content of one pound of saturated liquid.

h_g = heat content of one pound of dry saturated vapor.

h_{fg} = heat of vaporization, or the heat content change for the vaporization process of one pound of liquid.

x = quality of vapor, pounds of dry vapor per pound of mixture.

R = gas constant in equation, $pv = RT$.

R' = Universal gas constant = MR.

n = exponent of polytropic expansion in expression, pv^n = const.

eff. = efficiency.

N = revolutions per minute.

GREEK LETTER CHART

Form		English Equivalent	Name
A	α	a	Alpha
B	β	b	Beta
Γ	γ	g	Gamma
Δ	δ	d	Delta
E	ε	e (short)	Epsilon
Z	ζ	z	Zeta
H	η	e (long)	Eta
Θ	θ	th	Theta
I	ι	i	Iota
K	κ	k, c	Kappa
Λ	λ	l	Lambda
M	μ	m	Mu
N	ν	n	Nu
Ξ	ξ	x	Xi
O	o	o	Omicron
Π	π	p	Pi
P	ρ	r	Rho
Σ	σ	s	Sigma
T	τ	t	Tau
Υ	υ	u	Upsilon
Φ	φ	ph	Phi
X	χ	ch	Chi
Ψ	ψ	ps	Psi
Ω	ω	o	Omega

THERMODYNAMICS

CHAPTER I

ENERGY AND THE MECHANICAL THEORY OF HEAT

I–1. Thermodynamics.—Probably no branch of science has contributed more to the advancement of man's well-being and comfort than that dealing with the transformation of heat into mechanical work. As long as man was dependent solely upon his own muscles for overcoming resistances, his field was indeed limited and his material progress negligible. Even with the utilization of the efforts of captives and domestic animals, the total accomplishment was small, for muscular energy is, at best, a trivial reservoir to draw from. It was not until the possibility of obtaining mechanical work by means of heat was recognized, that the great strides in material progress were achieved. The realization that heat could produce mechanical energy, that it was, in fact, a form of energy, only needing proper devices to permit its transformation into useful work, opened a vista of such alluring possibilities as to warrant most serious efforts to understand, explain and utilize the various phenomena connected with it.

For the engineer the science of thermodynamics concerns itself mainly with one big project, viz., the transformation of heat energy into mechanical energy. How this is to be accomplished involves a knowledge of the properties of the working substance and the processes it undergoes. Much of the student's early efforts will be devoted to the finding of these data. It should be borne in mind, however, that a knowledge of these is but a step toward the ultimate goal, the production of the greatest amount of useful mechanical energy from a given supply of heat.

I–2. Energy.—The word energy comes from the two Greek words *en* and *ergon* meaning respectively *in* and *work*, it is frequently defined as *the ability to do mechanical work* and perhaps better by the converse statement that *work and anything obtainable from or convertible into work are forms of energy.** A precise or entirely satisfactory definition of energy does

* J. R. Partington, a Textbook of Thermodynamics.

1

not exist notwithstanding the enormous importance of energy in our every-day life, but the outstanding fact that energy is an aid to overcoming resistance perhaps constitutes our most general conception. It has been suggested that all human conceptions are capable of being divided into two broad groups one dealing with the composition of material things, or con-stitution of matter, and the other dealing with the behavior of matter or the energy concept. Conceptions of matter are reasonably tangible, energy conceptions are not so obvious even if we accept the dictum that *all that is not matter is energy.** Into this second group come the familiar mechanical, electrical, chemical, and heat energies and the various forms of energy due to wave motions in the air or ether, such as sound, light and radiant energy. It is essential, however, to note that throughout this text, it is with *energy* and its *transformations* that we shall be dealing.

Beside this general or family grouping, energy is divided by Mechanics into two specific subdivisions: *Kinetic*, or that due to the motion of the matter constituting the body and *Potential*, or that due to the position or configuration of the matter constituting the body.†

I–3. Energy Magnitudes Relative.—Measurements of energy are purely relative, that is, they are measured from some arbitrarily fixed datum. For example, in mechanics, kinetic energy, expressed by the product of the mass by one half the square of the velocity, is concrete only when the velocity is measured by comparing it with that of a body con-sidered at rest such as the surface of the earth. Similarly, potential energy or the product of mass by elevation is a definite quantity only when some selected reference plane, usually mean sea level, has been assigned the value zero for the measurement of elevations. The zero assumption is true in neither case, but since interest centers on the *change* of energy from one finite con-dition to some other, the origin of measurement is unimportant, so long as it be taken the same for both conditions. It is *differences* of energy rather than absolute values that enter into engineering calculations.

A force acting upon a body may produce two energy effects, a change in configuration, or, a change of motion. A change of configuration may mean a change of the parts of a body with reference to themselves such as a stretched spring, or a change of the body itself with respect to other bodies as a weight raised and fixed at some elevation, both of which are

---

* The science of chemistry deals mainly with phenomena of the first group while physics confines itself more particularly to the second group.

† According to Meyer, Kinetic Theory of Heat, the term *Potential Energy* was coined by Rankine in 1853 and the term *Kinetic Energy* by Lord Kelvin in 1867. Prior to these dates there had been much diversity of nomenclature, particularly with reference to the latter.

changes of *potential* energy.   A change of motion such as the setting of a body, or any of its parts, into motion, or any alteration of its velocity whether the body is considered as a unit or as an aggregation of units, corresponds to a change in its *kinetic* energy.

Example 1.—A man weighing 150 lbs. walks forward at the rate of 4 miles per hour in a train which is traveling at 30 miles per hour.

What is the kinetic energy of the man, (a) With respect to the train; (b) With respect to the surface of the earth?   The unit of mechanical energy, kinetic or potential, is the foot-pound or the energy required to raise a weight of one pound one foot vertically.

Solution.—It is understood that the speeds given above are relative to the immediate surroundings.

(a) Velocity of man relative to train is 4 miles per hour or 5.86 ft. per second.

Kinetic energy is $\frac{1}{2}m\,(\text{vel.})^2 = \frac{w\,(\text{Vel.})^2}{2g} = \frac{150\,(5.86)^2}{2\,(32.17)} = 80.2$ ft.-lbs. with respect to the train.

(b) Velocity of man relative to surface of the earth is $30 + 4 = 34$ miles per hour, or 49.9 ft. per sec.

Kinetic energy $= \frac{150\,(49.9)^2}{2\,(32.17)} = 5800$ ft.-lbs. with respect to the earth's surface.

Example 2.—A ten-pound weight rests on the floor of a room 40 ft. above the surface of the earth which, in turn, has an elevation 500 ft. above sea level.

Calculate the potential energy of the weight: (a) With the earth's surface as a datum plane; (b) Relative to sea level.

Solution.—(a) Potential energy is $mgl = Wl = 10\,(40) = 400$ ft.-lbs. with respect to earth.

(b) Potential energy $= 10\,(40 + 500) = 10\,(540) = 5400$ ft.-lbs. relative to sea level.

I–4.   Equivalence of Potential Energy, Kinetic Energy and Work.— These three terms are but three different names for the same thing, a fact hinted at in the definition of energy, as, "the ability to do work."   This can be proved by slightly manipulating the common mathematical statements of all three into expressions using the same terms, whereupon they become identical.

It is customary to consider the *potential energy* of an elevated body as the product of its weight and its elevation.

$$\text{Potential Energy} = \text{Weight} \times \text{Elevation.}$$

The weight of a body (W) is equivalent to the force which must be exerted to support it and thus partakes of the nature of a force, and thus,

$$\text{Potential Energy} = \text{Force} \times \text{Distance.} \tag{I–1}$$

By definition, *Work* is the product of force, and distance, or

$$\text{Work} = \text{Force} \times \text{Distance.} \qquad (\text{I--2})$$

Kinetic Energy is evaluated as the product of one half the mass and the square of the velocity

$$\text{Kinetic Energy} = \frac{m \text{ Vel.}^2}{2},$$

but, from the laws of freely falling bodies, Vel.$^2 = 2 \times$ Accel. $\times$ distance, and Mass $= \dfrac{\text{Force}}{\text{Accel.}}$, thus, Kinetic Energy may be written as,

$$\text{Kinetic Energy} = \frac{m \text{ Vel.}^2}{2} = \frac{\text{Force} \times 2 \times \text{Accel.} \times \text{Distance}}{\text{Accel.} \times 2}$$

$$= \text{Force} \times \text{Distance.} \qquad (\text{I--3})$$

Since (1), (2), (3), are identical, it is obvious that we are dealing throughout with but one quantity though it may appear under the names of potential energy, kinetic energy, or work, and all are mutually convertible. In other words, neglecting losses, work done stores up energy, and energy may give back work, foot-pound for foot-pound, and similarly the various forms of energy may be transformed from one to another at will.

The bob of a swinging pendulum furnishes an excellent illustration of the continued conversion of kinetic energy into potential energy and vice versa, for at the lowest point of its swing its energy is entirely kinetic, at the highest points its energy is entirely potential while at intermediate points its total energy is composed of the sum of both, each varying in amount but the sum of constant magnitude.

Example.—A 200-pound sphere is hoisted 50 ft. above the pavement to the fourth floor of a building. Subsequently, the weight falls from that position to the pavement.

Find: (*a*) The work expended in lifting the weight; (*b*) The potential energy possessed after hoisting (relative to pavement); and, (*c*) The kinetic energy in falling at the moment of contact with the pavement. (Neglect frictional losses.)

Solution.—(*a*) Work is Force $\times$ Distance $= 200 \times 50 = 10,000$ ft.-lbs. to hoist to position.

(*b*) Potential energy is $W \times l = 200 \times 50 = 10,000$ ft.-lbs. in raised position.

(*c*) Kinetic energy is $\dfrac{W \text{ (Vel.)}^2}{2g}$, where (Vel.)$^2 = 2gl$.

$$\text{(Vel.)}^2 = 2 \,(32.17)(50) = 3217.$$

$$\text{K. E.} = \frac{200 \,(3217)}{2 \,(32.17)} = 10,000 \text{ ft.-lbs.}$$

At the end of each swing it is at rest momentarily and the mass $\left(m = \dfrac{w}{g}\right)$, is at a distance l above the lowest point of its swing, therefore, possessing a potential energy of $w \times l$. Later, when at midswing, it has fallen the vertical distance l and thereby, in accordance with the laws of freely falling bodies, acquired a velocity of vel. $= \sqrt{2gl}$, and its corresponding kinetic energy $\left(\dfrac{m \text{ vel.}^2}{2}\right)$ is the same as the expression for potential energy, if for the value of vel. be substituted its value in terms of l,

$$\frac{m \text{ vel.}^2}{2} = \frac{m2gl}{2} = mgl = wl.$$

Neglecting friction, the work of hoisting a boulder onto the top of a cliff is exactly the same as the potential energy it acquires in the process and exactly the same as the kinetic energy it would possess if it fell freely back to its original position.

I–5. **Units of Force, Energy, and Work.**—The unit of force in American and British usage is the *weight of one pound* meaning by this, the force with which the earth attracts the *mass* of one pound. As gravity is not exactly the same over the whole earth, varying with both latitude and altitude, it is necessary for exact work to specify in the definition, the place to which it applies. If the latitude is taken at 45° and the altitude as mean sea level, then the value of gravity (g) is 32.173 ft. sec.^{2}

The variation of g, however, is very slight, and for engineering work corrections are rarely applied. The change due to latitude is from 32.0878 at 0° to 32.2577 at 90° and for altitude the correction for 1000 ft. elevation is but $-.0031$ ft. per sec.^{2}

The standard value of g adopted by the International Committee on Weights and Measures, 1901, was 980.665 cm. per sec.^{2} corresponding to 32.170 ft. sec.^{2}

When dealing with mechanical processes, the unit generally used for energy or work is, in the English system, the *foot-pound*, defined as the work which will raise one pound one foot high and in the Metric system the meter-kilogram or kilogrammeter (Kgm.).

$$1 \text{ ft.-lb.} = .1383 \text{ Kgm.}$$

Of late, there has been considerable effort spent toward the adoption of the C.G.S. system unit of work and energy, the Erg, or the Joule as it may be applied readily to all forms of energy.

$$1 \text{ ft.-lb.} = 1.3558 \text{ Abs. Joules} = 1.3554 \text{ Intl. Joules.}$$

$$1 \text{ Intl. Joule} = 0.73778 \text{ ft.-lb.}$$

I–6. The Mechanical Theory of Heat.—Much of the work of the early investigators in Thermodynamics was devoted to the evolution of a rational theory * of heat that should permit explanation of the phenomena experimentally produced, a searching for physical conceptions of heat action which should agree with actual results.

The early Caloric Theory, that heat was matter, an imponderable fluid which flowed from a body of high temperature to one of lower temperature, gave way to one based on the mechanics of the infinitesimal particles constituting the body, the sum of whose energies both Kinetic and Potential constituted the heat energy of the body. The inception of the theory is credited to Bernouilli in 1738 but was first presented in reasonably complete form by Clausius in a series of papers published about 1860 and assembled in book form in 1875.

A brief statement of the salient features is helpful for though there are places where this theory is insufficient, nothing has been brought forth which discredits the fundamental conceptions of the mechanical theory of heat, and, particularly for the beginner, it furnishes a foundation for analyses which permit tangible conceptions of otherwise intangible processes.

The Mechanical theory (frequently called also the Kinetic theory or the Dynamical theory of Heat) rests upon an accepted fact, one which is capable of experimental verification, namely, that heat may be converted into mechanical energy and, conversely that heat is generated when mechanical motion is destroyed by friction or otherwise. This experimental fact is commonly referred to as the First Law of Thermodynamics, and as such, will be discussed more fully later. It is mentioned here to emphasize the point that one is justified in considering heat as some form of energy and a form which is convertible into, or obtainable from, the everyday forms of mechanical energy with which we are familiar. The Mechanical theory of heat accepts the hypotheses of the atomic theory of *matter*, but its basic assumption is the attribution of masses, motions and attrac-

* *Theory* is defined as "The general or abstract principles of any body of facts" and any "theory" of heat may be considered as but an answer to the question, What IS heat?

tions to these infinitesimally small molecules, atoms, electrons, etc. They thus possess energy which is identical in character with the mechanical energy of finite bodies, and it is the aggregate of the energies of these ultramicroscopic units that constitutes *heat* as we understand it. Fortunately, most of the common heat phenomena (except radiation) can be explained by analogies to simple *molecular* mechanics so that energies *within* the molecule and within the atom need not be considered as contributing to the final effect except as especially noted.

The simple conception of matter as being composed primarily of molecules each of which behaves in general like a spherical unit, while not strictly accurate in the light of modern research, best serves the purpose for the first explanation of the various heat phenomena and for this the following hypotheses as to molecular characteristics are customarily accepted.

1. The molecules are moving at very high velocities and without any frictional resistance.

2. They are moving in all directions and with all sorts of velocities and both velocities and directions are continuously being interrupted and changed by frequent collisions one with another.

3. In these encounters, the duration of which is extremely brief compared with the time the molecule is free, they follow perfectly the laws of elastic impact.

4. The length of the path traveled between encounters, called the free path, varies greatly but the average, mean free path, is always large compared with the size of the molecule itself.

5. Notwithstanding these heterogeneous motions, the entire aggregation of molecules is in a state of dynamic equilibrium and all molecules are influenced by an intermolecular attractive force similar to gravity.

Much has been written on this subject* and any detailed presentation of the mechanical theory of heat lies outside the scope of this book. However, its basic conceptions are simple and if accepted with the realization that they are illustrative or explanatory, afford helpful mental picturizations of heat phenomena. Figure 1 gives a pictorial representation of the successive positions of seven molecules of a perfect gas after each of a series of equal time intervals has elapsed. The current position of each molecule is indicated by the solid black circle and its previous position is indicated by a light circle. The circles are serially numbered, corresponding to the successive positions.

To simplify the presentation, motion is assumed to take place only

* The Brownian movements, see any good text on Physics.

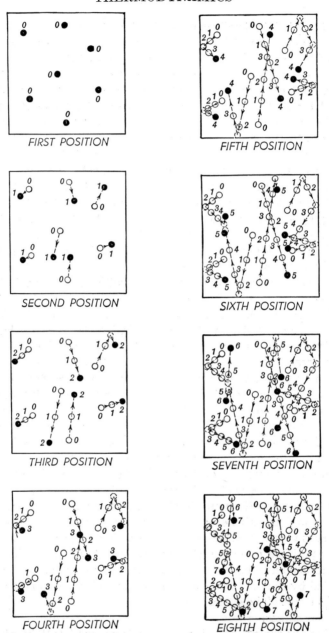

FIG. (1–1a–b). Diagrammatic illustration of the movements of molecules of a perfect gas as shown by their positions after several successive equal time intervals. Motion assumed restricted to one plane.

in the plane of the paper, though actually the molecules would be moving in truly random directions.   Different velocities have been assigned each molecule and the locations after collisions are plotted in agreement with the laws of elastic impact.   If projected as a quick running series the frames would constitute a moving picture, a sort of ultra-microscopic bird's-eye view of the molecular activity always going on in every gas.   Actually the effect of such molecular activity for the liquid phase can be observed if water to which very fine dye particles have been added be examined under a powerful microscope.   The dye particles, though very small, are excessively large compared to the molecules but are batted around by the molecules much as a large pushball would be moved over the campus by a mob of students.   The comparatively large size of the dye particle, and accompanying greatly reduced velocity, allow it to be visible as a tiny speck rapidly darting hither and thither.   While such an experiment does not show the molecules themselves it does give evidence of their activity. Motion pictures have been taken from which the velocities have been computed and the results agree with those computed from purely theoretical reasoning.

Differences in phase, solid, liquid, and gaseous, correspond to differences in mean free path and velocities of the aggregation, and in the gaseous phase there are many points of similarity between the actions of these infinitesimal bodies and the celestial bodies of the great planetary systems. In gases under normal pressures and temperatures, the molecules are far apart, the mean free path is great, and the motion of each is nearly rectilinear, while in liquids where they are much nearer together, and, therefore, feel the attractions of their neighbors more strongly, their paths are orbital and the molecules wander about through the aggregation trying to rotate about each other, but interrupted by the many collisions.   In the solid state, the motion is oscillatory, of smaller amplitude, and with the mean positions practically stationary, no free wandering, Fig. (I–2). Throughout all phases, or states, however, the translatory motions of the molecules tend to disrupt the equilibrium and this is balanced by the intermolecular attractive force (frequently called cohesion) of the body, provided the state is stable, as in liquids and solids.   In the case of gases where the intermolecular distances are great and the attractive force nearly negligible, the balance must be supplied by the restraining effect of the walls of the containing vessel.

Liquids and gases contain progressively more energy than the solid phase of the substance, as is proven by the fact that energy is required for the transformation.   If a body in the solid phase has its molecular activity

increased, a point will be reached where the molecules will be moving with
sufficient velocity to break through the restraint of their immediate neighbors and continue on until, curbed by the joint effects of their new neighbors, they move in the orbital or free wandering paths characteristic of the
liquid phase. Similarly, the passage to the gaseous phase occurs when the
velocities become sufficient for the molecules near the surface of the liquid
to be projected into the space above, where they will continue in rectilinear,
or nearly rectilinear, paths to all intents unaffected by their fellow molecules.

The change in the mean distance apart of two neighboring molecules
(the cube root of the total volume divided by the total number of molecules)
corresponds to the change in volume which the substance undergoes and is

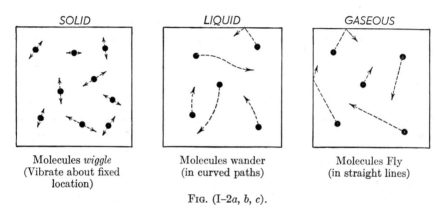

SOLID	LIQUID	GASEOUS
Molecules *wiggle* (Vibrate about fixed location)	Molecules wander (in curved paths)	Molecules Fly (in straight lines)

Fig. (I–2a, b, c).

usually slight for the transition from solid to liquid and great for the
transition from liquid to gas, amounting in the case of water, for example, to
a volumetric expansion of about 1600 for the change into steam at atmospheric pressure.

The velocities of the molecules are always extremely great, for example,
the mean velocities (square root mean Square) of the molecules of Oxygen,
Nitrogen, and Hydrogen at 68° F. are 1570, 1670 and 6250 feet per second
respectively.   In other words, the average Hydrogen molecule moves
nearly a mile and a quarter and bumps adjacent molecules about ten
thousand times in one second.

Molecular velocities are functions of the temperature of the substance
and thus vary widely, but the size of the molecule is the same for all
substances in the gaseous phase though they may possess various molecular
weights.

TABLE OF MOLECULAR DIMENSIONS

APPROXIMATE VALUES OF THE MEAN FREE PATHS, VELOCITIES AND DIAMETERS

Gas	Velocity at 0° C., cm./sec.	Mean Free Path at Atmos. Pres., cm.	Molecular Diameter,* cm.
Argon (A)...............	4.1×10^4	10.0×10^{-6}	3.2×10^{-8}
Helium (He).............	13.1×10^4	28.5×10^{-6}	2.9×10^{-8}
Mercury (Hg)............	....	....	3.0×10^{-8}
Hydrogen (H_2)...........	18.4×10^4	18.3×10^{-6}	2.6×10^{-8}
Nitrogen (N_2)............	4.9×10^4	9.4×10^{-6}	2.8×10^{-8}
Oxygen (O_2).............	4.6×10^4	10.0×10^{-6}	2.6×10^{-8}
Carbon Monoxide (CO)...	4.9×10^4	9.3×10^{-6}	3.5×10^{-8}
Carbon Dioxide (CO_2).....	3.9×10^4	6.3×10^{-6}	3.2×10^{-8}
Water (H_2O).............	7.1×10^4	7.2×10^{-6}	2.6×10^{-8}

* The column of molecular diameters was obtained by averaging the values obtained by various methods and reported by Loeb in "Kinetic Theory of Gases," Appendix II. The other data are taken from "Physical and Chemical Constants," by Kaye and Laby.

I–7. **Energy Changes Due to Addition of Heat.**—It is a basic truth that when heat is added to any substance the only results that follow are (1) a change in the true heat energy that the body possesses, meaning by

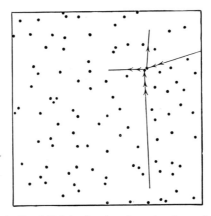

FIG. (I–3). Diagram by Lord Kelvin showing, to scale, size and spacing of molecules in cross-section of cube of air measuring 0.64×10^{-6} cm on a side.

that the total of the kinetic and potential energies of its component particles; and (2) the accomplishment of external work by the substance altering its volume against the existing external pressure. Denoting the internal energy by U and the work done by W this may be expressed mathematically as

$$dQ = dU + \frac{dW}{J},\qquad (\text{I--4})$$

which might be written in finite form as

$$_1Q_2 = U_2 - U_1 + \frac{_1W_2}{J},\qquad (\text{I--4a})^*$$

where the subscripts 1 and 2 refer to the initial and final states.

$\int_1^2 dU$ or $U_2 - U_1$ expresses the increase in the *true* or *intrinsic energy possessed by the substance.* This title is more commonly shortened to **Intrinsic Energy,** and Intrinsic Energy may very well be defined as the *total energy which a substance possesses by virtue of the motions and relative positions of its component particles.*†

Its change for any case may be evaluated by subtracting from the total amount of heat which has been supplied to produce the given change, the thermal equivalent of the external work done by the substance.

$$dU = dQ - \frac{dW}{J}.\qquad (\text{I--5})$$

It should be noted that while both dQ and dU are heat quantities and are expressed in the same dimensions, thermal units, nevertheless, they represent very different conceptions. The first designates the amount of heat energy *supplied to* a body and the second represents the increment of the energy that *is within* the body, its intrinsic energy.

The heat supplied to a body (Q) may or may not increase the amount of energy *contained in* that body just as the water supplied to a reservoir and water-wheel may or may not increase the amount of water *in* the reservoir, since the quantity supplied is subdivided into two distinct portions, one going to build up the level or the reservoir and the other to pass on through the water-wheel and do work external to the reservoir. Similarly, the *heat supplied to* a body $(_1Q_2)$ which expands and pushes

---

* Because dQ and dW are imperfect differentials their complete integration cannot be stated without further information. It is customary, however, to indicate the result of the integration as $_1Q_2$ or $_1W_2$, which signifies the heat supplied, or work done, between states 1 and 2, when the path by which the change has been affected is known.

† The word particles is here used in the general sense and is intended to include molecules, atoms, electrons, nuclei and other subatomic units.

aside some external force will not be equal to the increase in energy which the body itself experiences $(U_2 - U_1)$ (its increase in intrinsic energy) except when none has been passed on in the form or external work ($_1W_2 = 0$).

Example.—Five hundred B.t.u. (defined in paragraph III-5) of energy in the form of heat are supplied to a metallic bar which, as a result, expands, raises a weight, and does 77,826 ft.-lbs. of external work.

Find the increase in intrinsic energy.

Solution.—The change in intrinsic energy is equal to the heat supplied minus the external work done.

$$U_2 - U_1 = 500 - \frac{77,826}{778.26} = 500 - 100 = 400 \text{ B.t.u.}$$

I-8. Intrinsic Energy Dual In Its Nature.*—In harmony with our conception of heat as the mechanical energy of the constituent particles, any increase in the Intrinsic Energy may consist of an increment in both the molecular *kinetic* energy and the molecular *potential* energy. The first is the result of the increase in the molecular velocity, and the second is the result of the increased distance between molecules where they have been forced into a new state of aggregation against the intermolecular attractive forces. Denoting the molecular energy of the kinetic form by U_k and of the potential form by U_p,

$$dU = dU_k + dU_p \quad \text{or} \quad U = U_k + U_p.$$

Example.—The intrinsic energy of a substance is increased 400 B.t.u., of which 350 B.t.u. increases the molecular potential energy of the substance.

By how much is the molecular kinetic energy increased?

Solution.—The intrinsic energy of a substance is composed of the sum of the molecular potential and molecular kinetic energies.

Increase in molecular K. E. = $400 - 350 = 50$ B.t.u.

I-9. Sensible and Disgregation Heat Energies.—The effect of heat on our physical senses is the sensation which follows the touching of a hot body. What actually takes place is that when the molecules of the hand are laid against the more rapidly moving molecules of the hot substance they are suddenly accelerated and this sudden change or shock is transmitted through the nervous system to the brain flashing to it a warning to withdraw the hand before disruptive velocities have been attained. Obviously, the greater the speed with which the molecules of the hot substance are moving the greater will be the impact or shock when they strike against

---

* Intrinsic Energy is called by some writers Internal Energy; the terms are synonymous.

the touching body. This form of heat, due to the *motion* of the molecules and perceptible to our sense of touch, is termed **Sensible Heat** and will be denoted by U_k. It is nothing other than the Kinetic energy of all the infinitesimal particles constituting the body.

The other form, that of the potential energy stored up by virtue of the positions or configuration of the molecules, is not so obvious, it has been called *Heat of Disgregation* or preferably *Intrinsic Energy of Disgregation* and will be denoted by (U_p). It becomes of importance only during changes of phase or state such as from a liquid to a vapor where a closely knit molecular aggregation is torn apart into one of greater intermolecular distances, or for the process of melting from a solid to a liquid; a change where the energy supplied to a given molecular aggregation becomes sufficient to disrupt the existing equilibrium and force the system into a new sort of dynamic equilibrium. For example, to change a pound of ice at 32° F. into water at that same temperature requires 144 times as much heat as that necessary to raise a pound of water one degree (F.) of temperature. Thus, with no attendant rise in temperature, this heat has been spent in changing the state of the substance and most of it has gone into rearranging the molecules in spite of their mutual attractions. The heat energy added apparently disappears but really becomes latent and this term is frequently applied to designate the entire amount of heat supplied to a body to produce the change of phase, such as Latent Heat of Fusion and Latent Heat of Vaporization. Thus, a more detailed statement of equation (I–5) becomes,

$$_1Q_2 = (U_{k2} - U_{k1}) + (U_{p2} - U_{p1}) + \frac{_1W_2}{J}. \tag{I-6}$$

Translating this into words, when heat is added it may cause an increase in the sensible heat, an increase in the disgregation energy and do external work.

A perfect gas is assumed to have no intermolecular attractive forces, therefore, no energy can be used for tearing the structure apart $U_{p2} - U_{p1} = 0$, or $dU_p = 0$, and equation (I–6) becomes,

$$_1Q_2 = U_{k2} - U_{k1} + \frac{_1W_2}{J}, \quad \text{or} \quad dQ = dU_k + \frac{dW}{J}, \tag{I-7}$$

but only for a Perfect Gas.

An increase in sensible heat is always evidenced by an increase in temperature, while an increase in disgregation energy is shown only by a change of phase.* A thermometer may, as its name implies, serve as a measuring device for *sensible* heat, but is utterly valueless as a measurer of changes in disgregation energy, since the entire amount of heat supplied during any change of phase (Latent Heat) goes solely into changing the structure and does not increase the temperature. Temperature is variously measured but always by the effects produced in different measuring bodies by the kinetic energies of the particles composing the body to be measured, these effects may be volumetric expansion, change in electrical resistance, optical effects and others, but they all serve solely as mechanisms for measuring this particular form of molecular energy, namely sensible heat.

* When dealing with actual fluids undergoing expansion there may be appreciable change in disgregation energy, but usually it is so slight compared with that which accompanies a change of phase as to be entirely negligible.

CHAPTER II

THE MECHANICAL THEORY APPLIED TO GASES

II–1. Mechanical Theory Most Readily Applied to Gases.—The Mechanical, or Kinetic, theory of heat has been most satisfactorily applied to the gaseous phase, largely because that particular phase lends itself most readily to analytical treatment. The perfect gas has its molecules traveling in rectilinear paths and in many actual gases, at normal temperatures and pressures, the departure of the molecular paths from this is so slight that little error is introduced by assuming them straight. Thus, quantitative predictions for actual gases may be made by the statistical method applied to a hypothetical "Perfect" gas, and these have been verified experimentally. When the paths become orbital as in the liquid state, the difficulty of mathematical analysis is enormously increased and quantitative results are seldom obtainable.

There are some phenomena which seem in disaccord with the mechanical theory, but, generally, as an aid to mental picturization of heat processes it is invaluable, and while the science of Thermodynamics rests on no assumptions of the mechanical theory and can be developed quite independently of it, it is today, particularly for beginners, as useful an adjunct to correct thermal thinking as it was when first presented.

II–2. The Statistical Method.—In discussing a group of units which are behaving in a heterogeneous manner, such as the molecules of a gas, shooting about in various directions with all sorts of velocities, it is impossible to predict the actions of any one individual and only by taking averages are we able to analyze what is taking place. This, dealing with averages, determined from the statistics of a large number of individuals, is called the statistical method.

For example, life insurance companies using the statistics from a large number of cases, are able to predict with remarkable accuracy the probable life of individuals of various ages. This does not mean that they know the term of life of one individual but that they do know with reasonable certainty the average term of life of a large group of similar individuals of the same age.

The statistical method applied to molecular mechanics enables us to analyze the mass action of the haphazard and unpredictable individual molecule and predict changes of the group by considering the action of an average molecule or a group made up of molecules acting in harmony with the law of averages.

II–3. Pressure and Temperature.—The pressure which a gas exerts on the walls of a containing vessel is the reaction which they experience as a result of the continuous bombardment of the gas molecules. Just as the lid of a corn popper tends to be lifted by the impacts of the rapidly flying kernels of popcorn, the walls of the containing vessel must withstand a force due to the shock of the countless tiny molecules as they strike the wall and rebound. Pressure is a force, specific pressure is a force, per unit of area. We customarily deal with specific pressures and our conception of such is the total of these molecular impacts over a unit area.

The conception of temperature is quite different. Temperature is a measure of the *sensible* heat of a body, therefore, of the kinetic energy of its molecules and thus, indirectly, of its molecular velocity. It is a measure of the hotness of a body and to our senses, is the sting which follows the touching of a body whose molecules are moving faster than those of our finger. If we were to place our finger over a hole in a tank containing a gas at a high pressure but at a low temperature, the effect would be different from that if the gas were at low pressure but at a high temperature. The predominant effect on our senses would be that of *pressure* in the first case, and that of *hotness* (sensible heat) or high *temperature*, in the second; sensations transmitted to our brain by muscular and nervous stimuli, respectively. In the first case, there would be a larger number of slower molecular bumps; in the second, a smaller number of faster molecular bumps.

II–4. The Perfect Gas and Actual Gases.—The truly **Perfect** gas is a purely hypothetical substance, for none such actually exists. Moreover, the criteria for defining this *perfection* differ according to the method by which the thermodynamic analysis is attempted. If considered from the experimental point of view, the *Perfect* gas is one that follows exactly the experimental laws of Boyle, Charles, and Joule,* and has a constant specific heat, while, if defined in accordance with the kinetic theory, the *perfect* gas is one whose molecules conform to the following three postu-

---

* Boyle's Law; at constant temperature the pressure varies inversely as the volume; $(PV)_T$ = const. Charles' Law; at constant volume the pressure varies directly as the temperature; $(P)_v$ = const. $\times T$. or at constant pressure the volume varies directly as the temperature; $(V)_p$ = const. $\times T$. Joule's Law; the intrinsic energy of a perfect gas is a function of its temperature. $u = fT$.

lates: (1) They move with perfect freedom except during encounters, thus traveling in straight lines and with uniform velocities between collisions, (2) the time of actual collision is negligible compared with the time of free travel, and (3) the dimensions of the molecule are negligible compared with the length of the free path.*

Actual gases conform exactly to none of these assumptions, but for many (including the so-called Permanent gases—Oxygen, Nitrogen, and Hydrogen) the divergence is so slight throughout the range usually dealt with, that but little error results from using relations derived by the help of these simplifying assumptions. It is important, however, to have in mind these underlying hypotheses whenever applying the *perfect* gas laws and equations to *actual* gas problems.

II–5. Pressure Exerted by a Perfect Gas.—Since the pressure which a gas exerts upon the wall of the containing chamber is due to the molecules bumping against those sides, there should be a fixed relationship between pressure and the translational velocity of the molecules. Consider the effect produced by a single molecule moving parallel to the X axis of the cube $OXYZ$, Fig. (II–1). If its mass is m, and the x component of its

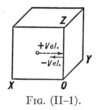

Fig. (II–1).

velocity is Vel._x, then the time consumed in passing from one side of the chamber to the other is:

$$t = \frac{OX}{\text{Vel.}_x}.$$

The number of collisions per unit time of this molecule with the side ZOY is:

$$\frac{\text{Vel.}_x}{2OX}.$$

The force resulting from these collisions is given by: $F = ma$, where a is the change in the velocity per unit time. The change in velocity per

* The distinction is sometimes made of calling the first conception a **Perfect** gas and the second conception an **Ideal** gas, but there is little uniformity of nomenclature and frequently the terms are used interchangeably, the assumptions are equivalent for both.

collision is 2 Vel.$_x$. Then, the total change in velocity per unit time, or the acceleration, experienced by the molecule is

$$\frac{\text{Vel.}_x}{2OX} \cdot 2\,\text{Vel.}_x = \frac{(\text{Vel.}_x)^2}{OX}.$$

The force on the side ZOY produced by each molecule is:

$$F = ma = \frac{m(\text{Vel.}_x)^2}{OX}.$$

The pressure (force per unit of area) acting on the face ZOY, and due to the action of this single molecule is then

$$P = \frac{m(\text{vel.}_x^2)}{OX} \div (OZ \times OY) = \frac{m(\text{vel.}_x^2)}{\text{Vol. of cube}}.$$

The above expression is for one particular molecule moving parallel to the X axis, but the motion of a molecule moving in any direction can be resolved into components parallel to the coordinate axes and this expression may be considered as representing the motion along the X axis of a molecule moving in any direction. For a group of molecules moving at random the total effect on the plane ZOY will then be the sum of the individual effects along OX which will be the sum of the individual masses multiplied by the *average* of the *squares* of all the different X velocities.

Representing the total number of molecules by N, the sum of the masses of all the molecules in the cube is Nm, and denoting the *velocity of mean square* * by VEL.$_x$, then,

$$P = Nm\frac{(\text{VEL.}_x^2)}{\text{Vol. of cube}}.$$

The relationship between the velocity of *one molecule* moving in any direction and its components along the coordinate axes, is,

$$(\text{vel.}^2) = \text{vel.}_x^2 + \text{vel.}_y^2 + \text{vel.}_z^2,$$

and, similarly, the *velocity* of *mean square* may be resolved, as

$$\text{VEL.}^2 = \text{VEL.}_x^2 + \text{VEL.}_y^2 + \text{VEL.}_z^2$$

Since the motion of this average molecule takes place equally in all directions, these components are equal and

$$\text{VEL.}^2 = 3(\text{VEL.}_x)^2.$$

* The velocity equal to the square root of the average of the squares of all the velocities.

Furthermore, if the cube be considered as containing a unit *mass* of gas, the expression becomes

$$P = \frac{(VEL.)^2}{3v'}. \tag{II–1}$$

where v' is the volume occupied by a unit mass of the gas.

For a unit *weight* this becomes

$$P = \frac{(VEL.)^2}{3gv} = \frac{(VEL.)^2}{96.6v}, \tag{II–2}$$

where v is the volume occupied by a unit *weight* of the gas, its specific volume.

Example.—Compute the pressure exerted by one pound of each of the following gases at a temperature of 68° F. and a volume of 5 cu. ft.: (a) Oxygen; (b) Nitrogen; (c) Hydrogen.

Solution.—(Molecular velocities from Art. I–6.)

(a) Molecular velocity of Oxygen at 68° F. = 1570 ft. per second.

$$O_2 \text{ pressure} = \frac{(1570)^2}{3\,(32.2)\,(5)} = 5100 \text{ lbs. per sq. ft.}$$

(b) Molecular velocity of Nitrogen at 68° F. = 1670 ft. per second.

$$N_2 \text{ pressure} = \frac{(1670)^2}{96.6\,(5)} = 5770 \text{ lbs. per sq. ft.}$$

(c) Molecular velocity of Hydrogen at 68° F. = 6250 ft. per second.

$$H_2 \text{ pressure} = \frac{(6250)^2}{96.6\,(5)} = 81,000 \text{ lbs. per sq. ft.}$$

II–6. Absolute Zero of Temperature.—As sensible heat is but the kinetic energy of the molecules, and temperature, the measure of the sensible heat, the temperature of any body of gas is directly related to the velocity of its molecules. The kinetic energy of one molecule is $\frac{m(vel.)^2}{2}$ and the total molecular kinetic energy or sensible heat of the entire body is the sum of the kinetic energies of all its particles, or $\sum \frac{m(vel.)^2}{2}$. As just stated, this can be represented by $\frac{Nm(VEL.)^2}{2}$, where N is the total number of molecules under discussion and (VEL.) represents the velocity of mean square. Thus, since Nm represents the mass of the body, it is obvious that the temperature or measure of the sensible heat depends upon the translational velocity * of the molecules and upon that alone. A correct thermometer, therefore, would be one which recorded the true average kinetic energy of the molecular aggregation in which it was placed.

The common mercurial thermometer records, not temperatures but *differences* of temperature, and these by the physical changes wrought by the change in molecular velocities. The increase in the kinetic energy of the molecules of mercury has the effect of increasing its volume, thus causing the thread in the stem to rise and record a "higher" temperature. For such a device, the selection of a zero may be made purely on grounds of convenience, and has no effect on computations as measurements of differences are independent of the origin. Actually there are several accepted starting points, such as the temperature of melting ice which is used for the centigrade scale, or the temperature of a mixture of ice salt and water under certain conditions which serves as the zero for the Fahrenheit scale.† They are both artificial datum points for the measurements of *differences* of temperature and have no physical significance.

It is quite obvious, then, that if we are interested in knowing the *true* or *absolute* temperature, the measurement would have to be made from a datum point of zero kinetic energy of the molecules. Doing this, we should have a scale on which readings would correctly represent the sensible heat of the perfect gas, it would thus be an *absolute* scale and temperatures measured according to it would be *absolute temperatures.* Thermodynamically speaking, *there is no temperature except the absolute temperature.* The absolute temperature may, of course, be expressed in either Centigrade, Fahrenheit, or other units, for that is but selecting a preferred size of unit for measurement from the absolute zero.

The best experimental evidence to date indicates the absolute zero of temperature as lying 459.6° and 273.1° below the zeros of the Fahrenheit and Centigrade scales respectively, thus the conversion necessary to obtain absolute temperature is

$$T = t + 459.6° \text{ (Fahrenheit)}$$
$$T = t + 273.1° \text{ (Centigrade)}.$$

* This is strictly true only in monatomic gases, for such the molecules can possess only translatory motion, as they behave like frictionless spheres. In diatomic and polyatomic gases the molecules may also possess spinning motions, hence for these gases the sensible heat depends upon the sum of the kinetic energies due to translation and rotation.

† The lowest temperature that Fahrenheit could obtain at the time he made his thermometer.

When temperatures are quoted, they should be completely defined as: 53.2° F. or 512.8° F. abs.: 42.0° C. or 315.1° C. abs.

Example.—What is the absolute temperature in Fahrenheit degrees of a substance whose temperature is: (a) 175° F.; (b) −40° F.?

Solution.—(a) $T = 175 + 459.6 = 634.6°$ F. abs.

(b) $T = -40 + 459.6 = 419.6°$ F. abs.

II–7. Characteristic Equation of a Perfect Gas.—The absolute temperature of a perfect gas is a measure of the average kinetic energy of its molecules and, therefore, is proportional to the mean square of the velocities of translation.*

Thus, T is proportional to $(Vel.)^2$, or $T = $ Const. $\cdot$ Vel.² Substituting this in equation (II–2) we have,

$$P = \frac{\text{const.} \times T}{96.6\,v},$$

whence

$$Pv = RT$$

or,

$$PV = WRT, \tag{II–3}$$

where P is the pressure in pounds per square foot, v is the volume in cubic feet occupied by one pound of the gas, T is the absolute temperature in Fahrenheit degrees, and R is a constant determined for the particular gas under discussion.

An equation such as this which connects one characteristic property of a fluid with two others is called a Characteristic Equation or Equation of State. The above is the characteristic equation of a perfect gas.

Example.—Determine the pressures exerted by one pound of: (a) Oxygen; (b) Nitrogen; (c) Hydrogen, at 68° F. and at a volume of 5 cu. ft. R for Oxygen $= 48.27$, R for Nitrogen $= 54.9$, R for Hydrogen $= 767.56$.

Solution.—(a) O_2 pressure $= \dfrac{48.27\,(527.6)}{5} = 5{,}093$ lbs. per sq. ft.

(b) N_2 pressure $= \dfrac{54.9\,(527.6)}{5} = 5{,}792$ lbs. per sq. ft.

(c) H_2 pressure $= \dfrac{767.56\,(527.6)}{5} = 80{,}978$ lbs. per sq. ft.

* See footnote, p. 21.

II-8. Heating by Compression.—When a gas is compressed in a non-conducting cylinder, it becomes heated because the energy that is being supplied to push the piston in against the gas pressure is being spent in knocking the molecules back from the face of the piston with increased velocities, just as when playing baseball the batter hits a pitched ball.

Let Fig. (II-2) represent a cylinder and piston of non-conducting material filled with a perfect gas. The piston is tight fitting, but without friction and when in the position first shown its weight is just balanced by the impacts of the molecules bombarding the under side. If a gradually increasing force be applied the piston will move downward. During the process every molecule striking the face of the piston will bound back from it with the downward component of its velocity increased by the amount of the velocity of the piston. While this increase is very little for a single impact, as the velocity of the piston is very small compared with that of the molecule, the molecule strikes many times in a second and the total of these tiny increments may become large. The increased molecular velocities result in increased kinetic energies, therefore, increased sensible heat and temperature and the amount of this increase is exactly equal to the mechanical energy spent in pushing the piston down, for no energy has entered or left the gas in any other way.

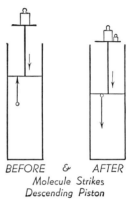

BEFORE   &   AFTER
Molecule Strikes
Descending Piston
Fig. (II-2).

Because no heat, as such, is supplied during the process, Q of equation (I-4a) is zero and the equation becomes

$$0 = U_2 - U_1 + \frac{_1W_2}{J} \quad \text{or,} \quad 0 = dU + \frac{dW}{J}, \tag{II-4}$$

and the work that is done during the (adiabatic) compression has all gone to increasing the intrinsic energy of the gas.

If instead of the compression taking place in a non-conducting cylinder as just described, the bottom of the cylinder had been made of some conducting material that would have allowed heat energy to be transferred through, the withdrawal of heat could have been so regulated that the molecular velocities, thus, the temperature, would have remained the same. Then, there would have been no change in the intrinsic energy or sensible heat, dU becomes zero and equation (I-4a) would read $_1Q_2 =$

$\dfrac{_1W_2}{J}$, or $dQ = \dfrac{dW}{J}$ and *the work done during the (isothermal) compression would have been equal to the heat energy transferred to the outside source.* Thus, again, an illustration of the conversion of mechanical energy into heat, though, in this case, the increment of molecular energy of the gas within the cylinder was passed on through the bottom to some external body as fast as it was produced.

Example.—10,000 ft.-lbs. of work are done on a perfect gas, (*a*) Within a nonconducting cylinder; (*b*) Without change in the temperature of the gas.

For each case, find the increase in intrinsic energy and the heat rejected.

Solution.—(*a*) The heat supplied is equal to the change in intrinsic energy plus the heat equivalent of the work done. In this case, no heat is supplied ($dQ = 0$), and the work done is at the expense of the intrinsic energy, or,

$$U_2 - U_1 = -\left[\frac{-10{,}000}{778.3}\right] = 12.85 \text{ B.t.u.}$$

(*b*) Since there is no change in temperature, the molecular kinetic energy comprising the intrinsic energy of a *perfect* gas, does not change, that is, $U_2 - U_1 = 0$. Therefore, $-\dfrac{_1W_2}{J} = -{_1Q_2} = \left[-\dfrac{10{,}000}{778.3}\right] = -12.85$ B.t.u., which signifies that 12.85 B.t.u. must be withdrawn from the gas.

II–9. Work Done by Expansion.—Considering the converse of the foregoing processes, we would have, from analogy to the first, the pushing out of the piston without the molecules receiving any outside assistance. The piston is forced outward by the molecular bombardment but each molecule leaves the piston face with its velocity reduced correspondingly. The molecules continue their bombardment throughout the process, following up the piston as it moves out, but growing feebler as their kinetic energy is expended in doing the mechanical work, external to the gas, of pushing the piston along. The conception assumes equilibrium throughout the process, i.e., the opposing forces on the two sides of the piston the same at all times, as might be accomplished if the weights on the piston were automatically adjusted to make the total load on the piston become less as it moved outward. As before, since no heat is supplied, ${_1Q_2} = 0$, and equation (II–4) becomes, $U_1 - U_2 = \dfrac{_1W_2}{J}$, or $-dU = \dfrac{dW}{J}$, which states that, *for an expansion taking place in a non-conducting cylinder (adiabatic) any external work performed is done at the expense of the intrinsic energy of the working substance.*

Similarly, from analogy to the second type of compression, when the expansion takes place in a cylinder so arranged that heat may be supplied continuously and at such a rate that the molecules suffer no loss in energy from their bombardment of the moving piston, then the external work is done, not at the expense of the intrinsic energy of the gas, but at the expense of the heat energy supplied *to* the gas.   Furthermore, because the intrinsic energy (therefore, temperature) of the gas remains constant, $dU = dU_k$ $= 0$, equation (4a) becomes $_1Q_2 = \dfrac{_1W_2}{J}$ or, $dQ = \dfrac{dW}{J}$, and, *the heat energy supplied to a perfect gas during a constant temperature* (isothermal) *expansion is equal to the external work done.*

Example 1.—The intrinsic energy of a perfect gas expanding in a non-conducting cylinder decreases by 50 B.t.u.

Find the external work done.

Solution.—For an adiabatic process, $dQ = 0$, and thus, $dU = -AdW$, or $U_2 - U_1 = -A_1W_2$.

$$-_1W_2 = J(U_2 - U_1) = 778.3 \,(50) = 38{,}930 \text{ ft.-lbs.}$$

Example 2.—Fifty B.t.u. of heat are supplied to an expanding perfect gas without changing its temperature.

Find the external work done.

Solution.—For an isothermal process (perfect gas), $dQ = AdW$, or

$$_1Q_2 = A_1W_2$$
$$_1W_2 = J_1Q_2 = 778.3 \,(50) = 38{,}930 \text{ ft.-lbs.}$$

CHAPTER III

FUNDAMENTALS

III-1. General.—Most of the derivations and conclusions of Thermodynamics are arrived at by the manipulation of a surprisingly few fundamental conceptions and processes, but the knowledge of these should be as ingrained in the mind of the student as the letters of the alphabet. This is particularly true of the special terms used to describe certain processes which simply must be memorized. In what follows, an attempt is made to present these fundamentals in concrete form, so assembled that they may be readily assimilated. They are perfectly general, i.e., apply to any substance in any state.

The theory of thermodynamics rests upon three fundamental supports or hypotheses, the First and Second Laws and the Thermodynamic Assumption. The first two deal with energy concepts and the third with the mathematics of analysis.

III-2. Nomenclature of Common Thermal Processes.—Thermal processes fall into two broad groups, those during which the working substance receives or rejects heat from, or to, external bodies and those during which the working substance receives no heat, as such. In the first group, all three members of the general equation, $dQ = dU + \dfrac{dW}{J}$, may vary; while in the second, since dQ is zero, the number of variables is reduced to two.

Changes of the first group are classified according to the manner in which the heat is supplied and there are three common processes, each named after the property that remains constant during the change. (1) Changes at *Constant Volume*, also called Isometric or Isovol. (2) Changes at *Constant Pressure*, also called Isopiestic or Isobaric. (3) Changes at constant temperature, almost universally called *Isothermal*.

Changes of the second group are all called **Adiabatic**. The word was coined by Rankine, who derived it from the Greek word, diabatic, meaning " passing through," and a, the prefix of negation, thus meaning " *no passing through*." As used, it is applied broadly to all changes that occur without the addition (or subtraction) of heat, as such, to the working substance.

26

Clausius aptly defines it as, *"any change occurring within an envelope impermeable to heat."*

In practice, it is customary to differentiate adiabatic changes into two groups, those which proceed in an orderly way, without turbulence or friction of the working substance (reversible processes, such as the expansion of a gas in a non-conducting cylinder when the piston moves smoothly outward), and those carried out with the fluid undergoing a disorderly chaotic, or turbulent transition (irreversible processes). Some writers confine the use of the term adiabatic to reversible processes only; we shall use it, however, always in the broad sense, as defined above, applying it to any change occurring within an envelope impermeable to heat.

In addition to these special processes enumerated above, it is customary to assume when dealing with perfect gases, that *any* orderly change has the pressure-volume relationship, represented by the equation, $p_1v_1^n = p_2v_2^n = $ const., and that n is constant for the particular process under consideration. As, by modification of the value of the exponent n this equation may be made to give the pv relationship for *all* the common changes, it is called the *Polytropic* equation, and *Polytropic Processes* are those that follow this equation.

The word *cycle* signifies a series of events, thus a series of thermal processes may constitute a cycle. As commonly used, it is applied to the successive changes undergone by the working substance. When the substance periodically returns to its initial state the cycle is termed a closed or completed cycle.

By change of phase, is meant the radical change in molecular aggregation corresponding to a change from solid to liquid, or from liquid to gas.

III-3. **The First Law of Thermodynamics.**—The First Law of Thermodynamics is a formal statement of an experimental fact, namely, that *heat and mechanical energy are mutually convertible and in a fixed quantitative relationship,* or, that *every unit of heat requires for its production and produces by its disappearance a definite number of units of mechanical energy or work.*

This is in effect a somewhat specialized statement of the general law of the Conservation of Energy, that energy may neither be created nor destroyed but may be converted from one form to another, restricting the consideration to but the two forms in which we are particularly interested, namely, heat and mechanical energy.

Example 1.—In a certain machine, 20 Hp. are expended in overcoming mechanical friction.

What is the resulting heat production per hour?

Solution.—Thermal equivalent of a Hp.-hr. is

$$\frac{33{,}000 \text{ ft.-lbs.} \times 60 \text{ min.}}{778.3 \text{ ft.-lbs. per B.t.u.}} = 2544 \text{ B.t.u.}$$

Heat produced by 20 Hp. = 20 (2544) = 50,880 B.t.u. per hour.

Example 2.—A heat engine transforms 1000 B.t.u. per minute into work. What Hp. is developed?

Solution.—(1) 1000 B.t.u. per min. = 1000 (778) = 778,000 ft.-lbs. per min.

$$\text{Hp.} = \frac{778{,}000}{33{,}000} = 23.6 \text{ Hp.}$$

(2) 1000 B.t.u. per min. = 60,000 B.t.u. per hr., equivalent to

$$\frac{60{,}000}{2{,}544} = 23.6 \text{ Hp.}$$

III-4. The Second Law of Thermodynamics.—While the First Law is a statement of an experimental fact, and capable of direct proof it makes no mention of the relative facility with which work may be transformed into heat and heat into work. The Second Law extends the conception of heat action by indicating that though the *work into heat* transformation is easy and in fact inevitable, the converse process of converting heat into work is difficult and beset with limitations. The Second Law is stated in many ways but for present purposes, the following will suffice:

Any self-acting machine cannot completely and continuously transform all the heat supplied to it into mechanical work. *

This statement is a negation and hence incapable of direct proof.

Just as the First Law was a specialized form of the general law of the *conservation* of energy, the Second Law is a specialized form of the general law of the *degradation* of energy which, as enunciated by Lord Kelvin, stated that " the result of any natural (unassisted) change, or transformation, of energy, is to leave the energy in its final form less available for doing useful work."

III-5. Units.— *Volume (V).*—The unit of volume is the cubic foot.

Pressure (P).—The unit of pressure is the pound per square foot. Pressures are also frequently stated in pounds per square inch or in atmospheres. One atmosphere at standard Barometric pressure of 29.929 inches of mercury at 32° F. is equivalent to 14.696 pounds per square inch and one inch of mercury is equal to 0.4912 pound per square inch.

Temperature (T).—The unit of temperature is the degree on the Fahrenheit thermometric scale.

* As stated by Clausius, "Heat cannot, of itself, pass from a colder to a hotter body."

Work (W).—The unit of work is the foot-pound, or the energy required to raise a weight of one pound through a height of one foot at standard latitude.

Heat.—The unit of heat is called a British thermal unit (B.t.u.) and is best defined in energy units. So defined, it is equal (by international agreement) to 778.3 foot-pounds.* It is approximately equal to the heat required to raise the temperature of one pound of water one degree F. which was originally the method by which it was defined. The fact that when so defined the unit had a different value for different temperatures and also was influenced by the latitude of the laboratory, led to the abandonment of such an experimental unit and the substitution of a definition in terms of energy. Furthermore, defining the heat unit in terms of energy automatically pegs the **Mechanical Equivalent of Heat** at that defining figure (778.3 ft.-lbs.) instead of the several evaluations previously existing, values which differed only in being reported in B.t.u. of different energy content.

Power (Hp.).—The unit of power is the Horsepower, defined as 33,000 foot-pounds of work per minute, or 550 foot-pounds per second. It is equivalent to 2544 B.t.u. per hour or 42.40 B.t.u. per minute. Another unit much used in electrical work is the kilowatt and this is equivalent to 3413 B.t.u. per hour or 56.88 B.t.u. per minute.

III–6. Properties.—The identification as well as the manipulation of the various substances is predicated upon a knowledge of the properties inherent to the substance and their relation one to another. A *property*

* There are in use today three types of B.t.u., (1) the single temperature B.t.u., (2) the mean B.t.u., and (3) the energy defined B.t.u.

(1) The single temperature B.t.u. was defined as the amount of heat necessary to raise one pound of water one degree Fahr. at some specified temperature, as 59°–60° or 68°–69° and was used by the earliest writers, though without agreement on the temperature at which the unit was defined. Accordingly as the specific heat of water varies materially, there was corresponding variation in the defined unit and each writer had to state the experimental conditions governing the B.t.u. used.

(2) To minimize this difficulty the use of a mean B.t.u. was proposed by Davis, which was defined as 1/180 of the heat required to raise one pound of water from 32° F. to 212° F. while at atmospheric pressure. This brought some order out of the chaotic situation and was adopted for most of the steam tables published in this country. A slight modification was proposed in 1928 by Osborne, Stimson and Fiock of the U. S. Bureau of Standards, whose definition read "1/180 of the difference in the heat content (enthalpy) of one pound of water in the saturated liquid state at 32° F. and 212°.F."

(3) Striking at the root of the matter, the International Steam Table Conference held at London in 1929 avoided all the vagaries of the substance and experimentation and defined the unit of heat directly in energy terms by defining the calorie as 1/860 International Watt-hours, which by proper conversion is equivalent to defining the B.t.u. as 778.3 ft.-lbs.

may be defined as a characteristic quality of a thing, accordingly when the properties of a working medium come up for discussion they must be characteristic of the given substance and of the given state. Moreover, for any particular substance any true property is a function of the state in which the substance exists and a function only of that state. For example, a gas is stated as existing at a certain pressure and temperature. These define its state. Whenever the gas exists at this state it will always possess that pressure and that temperature; therefore, these may be classed as true properties. Pressure, Volume, Temperature and Intrinsic Energy are some of the true properties.

The word *specific* is used to indicate that consideration has been limited to a *unit* instead of a total or general quantity, and thus specific properties are the property evaluated for a unit of weight, or area, or mass, etc., as the case may be.

The volume occupied by *one pound* of the substance is called the *Specific Volume* and is expressed in cubic feet. It will be denoted by v.

In cases where the total volume instead of the volume of one pound is dealt with, it will be denoted by V. The total volume is always equal to the product of the weight and the specific volume, $V = Wv$.

When the pressure is expressed in pounds per square *foot*, it is called the *Specific Pressure* and will be denoted by P. It is customary to assume that the pressure is a hydrostatic pressure such as a fluid exerts upon the sides of the containing vessel, consequently the pressure is considered to be that exerted *by* the substance rather than that exerted *on* the substance.

Similarly, when dealing with unit quantities one should speak of specific density (the weight in pounds of one cubic foot), specific entropy (the entropy of one pound of a substance), specific intrinsic energy (the intrinsic energy of one pound), etc. However, common custom has, illogically enough, dropped the term specific as applied to these particular properties and uses the longer descriptive phrase given in the parentheses. For example, if it is customary to speak of the intrinsic energy of one pound and the specific volume, it would be equally correct to speak of the specific intrinsic energy and the volume of one pound, and more correct to use the term specific for both.

The heat required to raise the temperature of *one* pound of the substance *one* degree, expressed in B.t.u.'s is called the *Specific Heat*. If the Specific Heat is constant, the heat supplied is equal to the product of the Specific heat and the temperature rise, $_1Q_2 = Wc(T_2 - T_1)$, if the Specific heat is variable, then calculus must be used, and $_1Q_2 = W \int_1^2 c\,dT$. When the change of temperature occurs at constant volume or at constant pressure, the constant property is indicated by a subscript as c_v or c_p for the Specific Heat at constant volume and Specific Heat at constant pressure, respectively.

III–7. **The Thermodynamic Assumption.**—One of the basic supports of the modern thermodynamic theory is the assumption that the state of any substance is definitely fixed when any *two* of its independent properties are fixed, i.e., that there may be but *two* independent variables in the thermodynamic equations. This implies that a knowledge of any *two* independent properties will permit the determination of all the other properties. This is a mathematical assumption and warranted only by the fact that it has never been disproven and that when deductions contrary to this assumption are made they lead to conclusions inconsistent with experimental facts. It is this assumption that permits the expression for perfect gases that $T = fpv$ which leads, with the help of experimental data, to the characteristic equation, $pv = \text{const.} \times T$. Furthermore, this assumption is equivalent to the statement that all substances may be represented in space by *surfaces* when plotted on three coördinate axes, these axes being any three characteristic properties. Such a surface is termed a Characteristic Surface.

A substance may have as many properties as we care to define, but fixing any two independent properties completely fixes all the others. If, for example, we were to specify the intrinsic energy and the Pressure, the state of a gas would be as completely defined as if we had specified the volume and the pressure.

III–8. **Compound Properties.**—The four properties discussed so far, P, V, T, and U, possess physical significance. However, accepting the definition of a property as a characteristic quality of state, it is possible to create any number of additional properties by combinations of these. Two such deserve mention at this time, heat content (enthalpy) H defined as $U + APV$ and entropy (S), the change of which is defined as $dS = \dfrac{dQ}{T}$ for any orderly process. Both of these will be dealt with in extenso later but are mentioned here simply to call attention to the fact that they are true properties, functions of state only, and may be treated in exactly the same manner as any of the four properties originally mentioned. They do not have the clear-cut physical significance of the others but are useful and widely used. The list of commonly used properties is thus augmented to six, as follows:

Pressure.........	P	Intrinsic energy....	U
Volume........	V	Heat content......	H
Temperature....	T	Entropy..........	S

III–9. Point and Path Functions.—If the state of a substance can be represented by a point on a pair of coordinate axes, the properties so represented are called *Point Functions*. Any property of a substance that depends solely upon the state of the substance and not upon the manner by which that state was achieved is called a *function of the state* and is obviously a point function. For example, p, v, T, and similar characteristic properties are all functions of the state, or point functions. Variation of their magnitudes from one state to another is obtained by the simple difference between their initial and final conditions. Differentials of point functions are exact and we may write

$$\int_1^2 dv = v_2 - v_1.$$

There are other magnitudes, however, that are not function of the state alone but are functions of the transitional process itself. These are affected by the route or path by which the change is made and are termed *Path Functions*. For example, if it were required that heat be added to a substance originally at T_1 sufficient to raise its temperature to a final temperature of T_2. The quantity of heat required, Q, will be greater if the transition occurs at constant pressure than if it occurs at constant volume. Q then is a function of the transition, a path function, it is not a property and its magnitude cannot be determined by the simple difference between its values at the two states. It is true that the integral of dQ may be evaluated, if the path be sufficiently well known, but the knowledge of this path is essential. dQ is not an exact differential and for such functions we must write

$$\int_1^2 dQ = {}_1Q_2.$$

The path functions most commonly met with are, the quantity of heat (Q) supplied to the body to effect a given change, and the work (W) performed by the substance during the change.

All of the true properties are point functions, their differentials are exact, and integration between limits consists of the simple difference between the value at the two states, for example:

$$\int_1^2 dU = U_2 - U_1 \quad \text{or} \quad \int_1^2 dP = P_2 - P_1, \text{etc.}$$

The integration of the general equation

$$dQ = dU + \frac{dW}{J}$$

can only be written as

$$_1Q_2 = U_2 - U_1 + \frac{_1W_2}{J}$$

and can only be definitely evaluated when the path by which the changes have occurred is known.

Recapitulating, Q and W are path functions and $\int_1^2 dQ$ or $\int_1^2 dW$ must be written as $_1Q_2$ or $_1W_2$. The properties P, V, T, U, H, S, however, are point functions and $\int_1^2 dP$ or $\int_1^2 dV$, etc., may be written as $P_2 - P_1$ or $V_2 - V_1$, etc.

III-10. Allowable Substitutions for dQ and dW.—In the general energy equation

$$dQ = dU + \frac{dW}{J}$$

the first and last terms are path functions and it is often convenient to substitute for them equivalent terms involving the properties of the working substance.

By definition, the specific heat, c, is

$$c = \frac{dq}{dt}$$

and the change of entropy, for a reversible process, dS, is

$$dS = \frac{dQ}{T}.$$

Hence,

$$dQ = Wc\,dt = T\,dS,$$

and any of these terms may be used interchangeably.

Useful work is most commonly achieved by the expansion of the working fluid overcoming a resistance, as when steam in the cylinder of a steam engine pushes the piston outward, for such cases, $W = \int P\, dV$, as may be proved if we consider a cylinder filled with an elastic fluid and fitted with a leakproof but frictionless piston. If the resisting force is just equal to that exerted by the working substance on the other side of the piston,

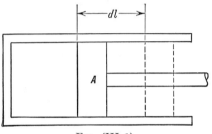

Fig. (III–1).

there will be no motion, but if the resistance be slightly less, the piston will move outward and work external to the fluid will be done. Work is equal to the force, times the distance moved, and the increment of work, dW is

$$dW = Fdl \text{ (where } l \text{ represents a linear distance).}$$

The force is equal to the product of the pressure and the area of the piston (A). $F = PA$. The increment of volume of the working substance will be,

$$dV = Adl$$

from which,

$$dl = \frac{dV}{A}$$

Thus,

$$dW = PA\,\frac{dV}{A} = PdV$$

and

$$_1W_2 = \int_1^2 PdV.$$

III–11. **Significance of the Area Under a Curve on the PV Plane.—** If a curve be drawn, using P and V for the coördinate axes, the area under it is represented by the integral of PdV between the initial and final states.

$$_1\text{Area}_2 = \int_1^2 PdV.$$

But, it has just been shown that

$$_1W_2 = \int_1^2 PdV.$$

Thus, it follows that $_1\text{Area}_2 = _1W_2$, provided the curve correctly represents the change. This may be stated as, *the area under any curve representing a change on the PV plane is equal to the external work done during that change.*

The selection of P and V as coördinates for graphs of thermal changes thus serves a double purpose; it gives a pictorial representation of the change and also permits the measurement of the work involved in the process. If the curve proceeds from left to right, as in Fig. (III–2), the area is positive and represents work done *by* the gas, as in an expansion, and conversely if the final condition lies to the left of the initial, the area is negative and indicates work done *on* the gas as in a compression.

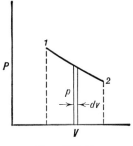

Fig. (III–2).

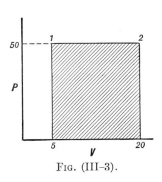

Fig. (III–3).

Example 1.—A gas undergoes a change from $p_1 = 50$ lbs. per sq. in., $V_1 = 5$ cu. ft.; to $p_2 = 50$ lbs. per sq. in., $V_2 = 20$ cu. ft.

Sketch the process on P–V coördinates and find the work done by calculating the area beneath the curve.

Solution.—This change will be represented by a horizontal straight line on the P–V diagram. The area beneath the curve is rectangular of an altitude $P = 144 \ (50) = 7200$ lbs./sq. ft., and a base $V_2 - V_1 = 20 - 5 = 15$ cu. ft.

Area beneath the curve = Work = 7200 (15) = 108,000 ft.-lbs.

Example 2.—A gas expands, the pressure and volume maintaining a straight line relationship, from $p_1 = 75$ lbs. per sq. in., $V_1 = 4$ cu. ft.; to $p_2 = 15$ lbs. per sq. in., $V_2 = 18$ cu. ft.

Sketch the process on P–V plane and find the work done by calculating the area beneath the curve.

Solution.—The area beneath this curve will be trapezoidal, and will be equal to the base times the mean altitude.

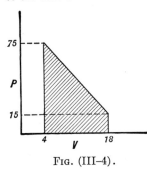

FIG. (III–4).

Base = 18 − 4 = 14 cu. ft.

Mean altitude = $\dfrac{75 + 15}{2}$ = 45 lbs. per sq. in.

or 6480 lbs. per sq. ft.

Area beneath the curve = Work = 14 (6480) = 90,700 ft.-lbs.

III–12. Reversibility.—It is important to obtain a clear conception of what constitutes *perfection* in any process whereby heat is transferred or transformed. To provide this, the criterion of reversibility was advanced by Carnot. This stated, in effect, that the test as to *perfection* of any process should be the obvious one of reversing it and examining the result to see if the original state of the substance and all coöperating agencies had been restored. It is obviously a test for perfection in any transformation whether it be exchanging a dollar bill into pennies at some bank or transforming heat energy into useful work.

As applied to thermodynamic processes we say any process is reversible if it is one that can be reversed and the substance pass back through all the stages through which it originally passed, and with its surroundings, be in exactly the same condition at each corresponding intermediate stage.

Obviously, the process must be one of continuous equilibrium and for a heat-work transformation, such as an adiabatic expansion of a perfect gas, the continuously balanced expansion constitutes a *perfect* transformation of heat energy into useful work. If doubted, start the process in the opposite direction work will be transformed into heat and everything will be returned to its original condition, thus there can have been no loss or degradation of energy. Thermodynamic reversibility is thus the *criterion of perfection* when considering any heat-work transformation.

III–13. Entropy.—In any subject developed analytically, there are expressions which, occurring repeatedly, deserve to be dignified by special names, and in thermodynamics there are many such. Clausius proposed and used in his writing an important thermodynamic quantity which is extremely helpful in understanding and evaluating thermal changes. He called it **Entropy,** coupling the Greek word *"trope,"* meaning transformation, to the first syllable of the word *energy.*

He defines it thus, "If for any reversible process any element of heat taken in (positive or negative) be divided by the absolute temperature at which it is taken in, the result is equal to the corresponding change of entropy."

Stated mathematically, this is, $\dfrac{dQ}{T} = dS$ (for reversible process) where dS represents the change in entropy and the other symbols have their customary meaning.

It should be noted that this definition is a definition of *change of entropy* not of *entropy*, moreover, while the entropy of one pound of substance in any given state is a perfectly definite numerical quantity, just as is the intrinsic energy, we are not interested in the absolute value but in the differences corresponding to any change, so for convenience in computation some point is arbitrarily chosen as the starting point or zero of entropy.

The entropy change for any reversible adiabatic process is zero, since by definition, $dS = \dfrac{dQ}{T}$ and for adiabatic action, $dQ = 0$, thus, $dS = 0$.

Hence for *any reversible adiabatic change the entropy remains constant.* Such changes are frequently called Isoentropic or Isentropic.

Further discussion of entropy will be reserved for a later chapter but it may be noted in passing that if the defining equation be slightly rewritten as $dQ = TdS$, it is apparent that both temperature and entropy appear as component factors in expressing the magnitude of any heat energy supplied from outside sources. Energy is necessarily a two-factor quantity whether it be mechanical energy with factors of $\left\{ \begin{matrix} \text{mass and velocity squared} \\ \text{force and distance} \\ \text{weight and elevation} \end{matrix} \right\}$ or heat energy with the factors of temperature and entropy. If we wish to classify these factors into intensity and extensity (or distribution) types there will be one of each in every form of energy considered. If the analogy be applied to heat energy we might classify temperature as the intensity factor and entropy as the extensity factor.

The important thing at present, however, is the fact that a definition of entropy change is simply *the ratio of heat supplied to the absolute temperature at which it is supplied when considering any reversible process,* i.e., any heat-work transformation that is perfect.

Example.—With the temperature remaining at 200° F., 60 B.t.u. are supplied to a substance during a reversible process.

Find the change in entropy.

Solution.— $t = 200°$ F. $T = 200 + 460 = 660°$ F. abs.

$$dS = \frac{dQ}{T}, \quad S_2 - S_1 = \frac{{}_1Q_2}{T}.$$

$$S_2 - S_1 = \frac{60}{660} = 0.091 \text{ unit of entropy.}$$

III–14. Significance of the Area Under a Curve on the TS Plane.— The area under any curve drawn with temperature and entropy as coördinate axes is equal to the integral of TdS between the initial and final states.

$$_1\text{Area}_2 = \int_1^2 TdS.$$

By definition, the change of entropy is,

$$dS = \frac{dQ}{T}$$

thus,

$$dQ = TdS$$

and,

$$_1Q_2 = \int_1^2 TdS.$$

Therefore, $_1\text{Area}_2 = {}_1Q_2$, and we have that, *The area under any curve representing a reversible change on the temperature-entropy plane is equal to* the heat supplied or rejected during that change.

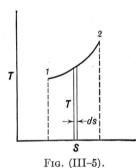

As in the case of the use of P and V for coördinates, the selection of temperature and entropy as axes for graphs of thermal changes, serves a double purpose since such graphs not only serve as pictorial illustrations of the change, but in addition, the area under such a curve has the significance just mentioned.

If the curve proceeds from left to right, as in Fig. (III–5), the area is positive and indicates that heat has been *supplied* to the working substance and conversely if the final

Fig. (III–5).

condition lies to the left of the initial, heat has been *taken from* the working substance.

III–15. Graphical Representation of Changes of State.—Graphs showing the various thermal changes are of great service in clarifying mental conceptions of the processes themselves, and their relationship one to another. They are most frequently drawn on the PV and TS axes because these coördinates have the additional merit of evaluating the area between the graph and the horizontal axis. However, any pair of properties may serve as coördinate axes and, as there are six properties commonly used (P, V, T, U, H, S), there are correspondingly thirteen other sets of coördinate axes which would indicate the changes quite as well as the P-V and T-S axes except for the bonus of the extra information mentioned above.

In sketching approximate graphs of thermal changes three questions should be answered before beginning each graph, proceeding from some chosen starting point representing the initial state, does the graph progress, (1) *upward* or *downward*, i.e., does the property denoted by the ordinate increase or decrease, (2) *to the right* or *to the left*, i.e., does the property denoted by the abscissa increase or decrease, and (3) is it *straight* or *curved*, i.e., is the equation connecting the coördinate properties of the first degree or not.

Answers to the first two are usually obvious, bearing in mind that adding heat is also adding entropy. The answer to the third can come only from a knowledge of the property relations of the coördinates.

Example.—For a heat addition process taking place at constant volume, determine the trend of graphs showing the relations between any two of the following properties—P, V, T, U, H, and S.

For an analysis of these graphs, the following fundamental equations should be considered: $(dQ)_v = dU$; $dS = \dfrac{dQ}{T}$; and $(dH)_v = dU + \text{Avdp}$.

Solution.—There will be fifteen sets of coördinate axes possible as follows:

(1) *P-V Plane.*—Heat supplied at constant volume must increase the intrinsic energy. More specifically, since the disgregation heat cannot be increased, the heat supplied must go to increase the sensible heat, that is, the molecular kinetic energy, resulting in greater molecular velocities. This being so, with the same number of molecules impinging upon the same surface at higher velocity, the pressure must increase.

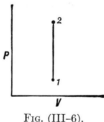

Fig. (III-6).

There is no change in volume.
The curve proceeds up vertically.

*(2) *P–T Plane.*—The pressure increases as of (1). An increase in sensible heat as of (1) is indicated by a rise in temperature.

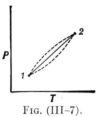

Fig. (III–7).

*(3) *P–U Plane.*—The pressure increases. Heat supplied results in an increase in intrinsic energy.

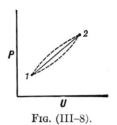

Fig. (III–8).

These curves trend upward and to the right. Whether they are straight or curved cannot be determined without knowledge of the equations giving the relation between P and T and P and V for a constant volume heating, hence the graphs dotted to show alternative paths.

*(4) *P–H Plane.*—The pressure increases. Heat content changes by $dU + AVdP$, both terms of which are increased.

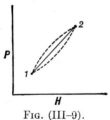

Fig. (III–9).

*(5) *P–S Plane.*—The pressure increases. The entropy also increases because of the addition of heat.

Curve is upward and to the right.

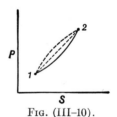

Fig. (III–10).

The curve is upward and to the right, the inclination, in general, being less than that of the *P–U* curve.

(6) *V–T Plane.*—Volume remains constant. Temperature increases as in (2).

Curve is a horizontal line from left to right.

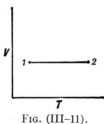

Fig. (III–11).

(7) *V–U Plane.*—Volume is constant. Intrinsic energy increases as in (3).

Curve is horizontal from left to right.

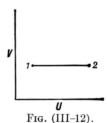

Fig. (III–12).

* See footnote p. 42.

(8) *V–H Plane.*—Volume is constant. Heat content increases as in (4).

Curve is horizontal and from left to right.

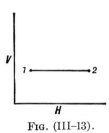

Fig. (III–13).

(9) *V–S Plane.*—Volume is constant. Entropy increases as in (5).

Curve is horizontal and from left to right.

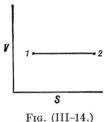

Fig. (III–14.)

*(10) *T–U Plane.*—Temperature increases as in (2). Intrinsic energy increases as in (3).

Curve trends upward and to the right.

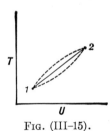

Fig. (III–15).

*(11) *T–H Plane.*—Temperature increases as in (2). Heat content increases as in (4).

Curve trends upward and to the right.

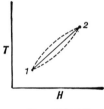

Fig. (III–16).

*(12) *T–S Plane.*—Temperature increases as in (2). Entropy increases as in (5).

Curve trends upward and to the right.

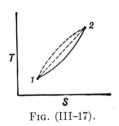

Fig. (III–17).

* See footnote p. 42.

*(13) *U–H Plane.*—Intrinsic energy increases as in (3). Heat content increases as in (4). It should be noted that, for each increment, the change in H exceeds that for U by $A\,VdP$.

Curve is upward and to the right.

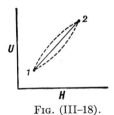

Fig. (III–18).

*(14) *U–S Plane.*—Intrinsic energy increases as in (3). Entropy increases as in (5).

Curve is upward and to the right.

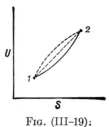

Fig. (III–19).

*(15) *H–S Plane.*—Heat content increases as in (4). Entropy increases as in (5).

Curve trends upward and to the right.

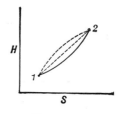

Fig. (III–20).

III–16. Work of Process and Work of Cycle.—If a substance originally in the state (1) expands by some regular process, as when smoothly forcing out a piston, to the final state (2), the work external to the substance done by the expansion is $_1W_2 = \int_1^2 PdV$ and this is represented by the area 0, 1, 2, 3. This is the work of the process only, viz., the expansion from 1 to 2.

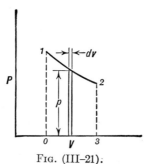

Fig. (III–21).

As a cycle is simply a series of processes, the net work for the entire cycle is equal to the algebraic sum of the work done during each process. For example, the net work of a cycle such as is shown by Fig. (III–22) is equal to the $\int PdV$ carried around the entire cycle in the order in which the events occur. $W_{\text{Cycle}} = _0W_1 + _1W_2 + _2W_3 + _3W_0$. If the direction

* Path is not definitely shown, since the curvature depends upon property relations which, in turn, are dependent upon the substance under consideration. The full lines show the general form the path would have if the substance were a perfect gas.

of the process is from right to left, the sign of the result will be negative but the algebraic sum of all will correctly give the net work of the cycle both in sign and amount.

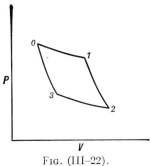

Fig. (III–22).

If the cycle be one that is bounded by two lines of constant pressure, as in Fig. (III–23), the net area becomes

$$\int_0^1 PdV + \int_1^2 PdV + \int_2^3 PdV = P_1(V_1 - 0) + \int_1^2 PdV + P_2(0 - V_2)$$

$$= \int_1^2 PdV + P_1V_1 - P_2V_2.$$

Fig. (III–23).

For such a cycle the net area by vertical integration and therefore the work, is equal to $-\int_1^2 VdP$

$$W_{\text{Cycle}} = -\int_1^2 VdP, \quad \text{or} \quad = +\int_2^1 VdP.$$

III–17. Significance of $\int PdV$ and $\int VdP$—The $\int PdV$ signifies the work done during any regular process.* It represents the area under the single curve 1, 2, of the figure (III–21), the summation of the infinitesimal vertical strips between the limits of V_2 and V_1, and thus *the work of the process only.*

If instead of integrating horizontally the integration be performed vertically between pressure limits, the area between the curve and the P axis will be given by $-\int_1^2 VdP,\ \left(\text{or} \int_2^1 VdP\right)$. The contour of this area as 0, 1, 2, 3 of Fig. (III–23) is the same as the ideal cycle of many heat engines and thus the area 0, 1, 2, 3, or $-\int_1^2 VdP$ represents the *work of the entire cycle* for such cycles as are bounded at top and bottom by lines of constant pressure.

To summarize, we have

$$\text{For the } \textit{Process, } W_{\text{Proc.}} = \int_1^2 PdV.$$

$$\text{For the } \textit{Cycle, } W_{\text{Cycle}} = -\int_1^2 VdP.$$

with the reservation for the latter, that the cycle must have constant pressure terminal processes.

III–18. Relative Steepness of Adiabatic and Isothermal Lines.—For reversible changes and at a given state. The adiabatic is steeper than the isothermal on both the PV and TS sets of coördinate axes. In Fig. (III–24) (a), the curve a–b represents an adiabatic expansion of a perfect gas from P_1 to P_2 and the curve (ad) represents an isothermal expansion between the same pressure limits and starting from the same initial state. During the adiabatic expansion no heat was added and the temperature dropped, while throughout the isothermal expansion heat was being added continually in order to keep the temperature from

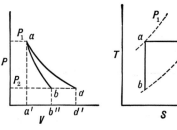

Fig. (III–24) (a) Fig. (III–24) (b)

---

* Meaning by that one without impact, or internal turbulence, i.e., are reversible process where the fluid may be considered to be in equilibrium throughout, both internally and with its opposing force.

dropping. Obviously at the final pressure the volume will be larger for the higher temperature and the point (d) of the isothermal will lie to the right of the point (b) of the adiabatic. This will be true for any pressure drop and thus the curve (ad) diverges to the right and has less slope than the adiabatic (ab).*

On the temperature-entropy plane, Fig. (III–24) (b) a similar relationship holds, though more pronounced. For the adiabatic expansion, $dQ = 0$ and thus $\int TdS = 0$. The area under the curve (ab) must then be zero,

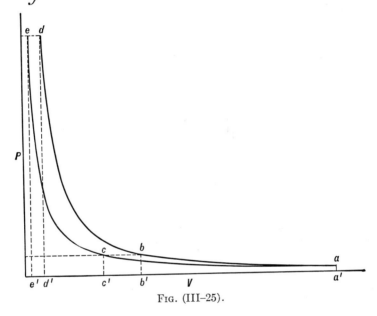

Fig. (III–25).

and (ab) a vertical straight line. The isothermal is a horizontal straight line and thus of less slope than the adiabatic.

The relation on the P–V plane is of more practical interest than that on the T–S plane, because the area under a curve on the P–V plane indicates the amount of work done on the substance during the change. For moderate compressions the area under the isothermal curve is greater than under the steeper curve; $acc'a'$ is greater than $abb'a'$, Fig. (III–25). For

* The slope of the curve on the PV plane representing a reversible adiabatic expansion for any fluid is actually k times the slope of the curve representing the isothermal expansion, where k is the specific heat ratio, c_p/c_v. This is shown by the expression, $\left(\dfrac{dp}{dv}\right)_s = k \left(\dfrac{dp}{dv}\right)_\tau$ derived in Chap. XIV.

large compressions, however, while the isothermal curve is less steep than the adiabatic at the initial pressure, its slope increases more rapidly as the compression progresses, which tends to offset the initial divergence, and the area under the complete isothermal curve may be less than that under the adiabatic. This is shown in Fig. III–25, where the area under the isothermal $aee'a'$ is less than that under the adiabatic $add'a'$. This does not violate the earlier statement as to relative steepness of these two curves, because the terminal points are not at the same state.*

III–19. **Relative Steepness of Constant Volume and Constant Pressure Lines.**—The relationship on the PV plane Fig. (III–26a) is at once

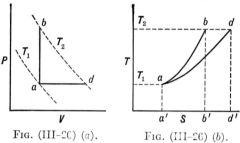

Fig. (III–2C) (a).   Fig. (III–2C) (b).

apparent as the constant volume line ab is a vertical straight line of greater slope than the horizontal line ad representing the constant pressure change.

More interest, however, centers on their graphs on the T–S plane. For this, Fig. (III–26) (b), consider the substance (a perfect gas) in state a, to have heat added to it at constant volume until it reaches the final temperature, T_2. The heat energy supplied has all gone into increasing the intrinsic energy, since no external work has been done $(dQ = dU + AdW)$.

Next consider the substance in state a, to be heated at constant pressure until it reaches the same final temperature, T_2, at d and, therefore, same intrinsic energy as before. More heat energy will have to be supplied, for external work must be done in addition to the same increase of intrinsic energy. Since more heat has been added, the area $a'add'$ will be larger than the area $a'abb'$ and the curve ad will lie to the right of the curve ab.

* "Two thermal lines of the same kind, such as two adiabatics or two isothermals can never cut each other on the three coördinate surface in space which represents the characteristic equation, for such a point of intersection would signify that the single point then had two values of this property represented as constant on each curve, for example two temperatures. Sometimes, however, their curves on one of the planes, being simply the projection on that plane of the actual curves on the true surface, may intersect, as when part of the surface overlies another portion. This is true for water when close to the freezing point (from 32° F. to 39° F.), as pointed out by Rucker in 1874. The curves themselves. however, do not actually intersect in space."

Thus the constant volume line is steeper than the constant pressure line on the temperature entropy plane. *

III–20. Gibbs' Thermodynamic Potentials.—Willard Gibbs presented † three mathematical quantities as useful adjuncts for facilitating thermodynamic computations. He gave them the general name of "Thermodynamic Potentials" and all have found wide acceptance and are in general use. They are as follows:

$$\text{The Psi Function } (\psi) = U - TS \qquad \text{(III–1)}$$
$$\text{The Chi Function } (\chi) = U + APV \qquad \text{(III–2)}$$
$$\text{The Zeta Function } (\zeta) = U - TS + APV \qquad \text{(III–3)}$$
$$= \chi - TS \qquad \text{(III–4)}$$

It should be noted that these are definitions in terms of finite quantities, not infinitesimals, and are simply arbitrary combinations of definite properties. Thus they are all functions of the state only, or point functions. The first (ψ) was originally proposed by Helmholtz (called by him the "Free Energy") and is particularly useful in the thermodynamic consideration of chemical phenomena pertaining to solutions.

The other two have found favor in the thermodynamic treatment of engineering problems, especially the Chi Function (χ) which has been so widely used as to be christened with a special name. It has been called variously Heat Content, Total Heat, Enthalpy and Thermal Potential, all of which, except the last, are misnomers and in some instances actually misleading in their significance. The Chi Function is useful in predicting the amount of work that can be done under certain conditions and the velocity of efflux of expanding vapors and gases.

The third, the Zeta Function (ζ), is useful in discussing the equilibrium of different phases of a given substance such as arise in the expansion of wet steam. Values of it are included in the recent tabulation of the properties of steam published by some British authors.

The first and third of these are of secondary importance in engineering work and consideration of them can be reserved till later. The second, however, the Chi Function, is of vital importance and must be discussed here.

The Thermodynamic Potential, Chi (χ) [Enthalpy].

The second of Gibbs thermodynamic potentials (the Chi Function) is

---

* The slope of the constant volume line is actually k times that of the constant pressure line, $(k = c_p/c_v)$, as is shown by the relation derived in Chap. XIV.

† Vol. 1 of his Scientific Papers.

of great value in engineering and has been given many names by others than Gibbs. It is denoted by H and is *defined* by the mathematical relationship $H = U + APV$, where A is the reciprocal of the mechanical equivalent of heat $(1/J)$ and the other terms have their customary significance. This definition may be expressed in words if preferred, as the sum of the intrinsic energy and the heat equivalent of the pressure volume product, but it should be borne in mind that it is essentially a mathematical property of purely arbitrary creation, the existence of which is warranted solely by its usefulness in simplifying analytical and numerical work and has no particular physical significance. Subsequent to Gibbs' original presentation numerous attempts were made to assign to it a name conveying some physical concept, such as Total Heat and later Heat Content. Both were misnomers, as it is neither the total heat energy spent to achieve a given state nor the heat energy contained in the substance.

More recently the term Enthalpy (accent on the second syllable) has been coined and has received considerable acceptance. This terminology possesses the rather negative merit of not being a misnomer but has little to recommend it otherwise. In current usage *heat content* and *enthalpy* are synonymous and may be used interchangeably. They are both names for Gibbs' Chi Function, defined as $U + APV$.

As both the intrinsic energy and the Apv product are determined by the state alone, it follows that the enthalpy (heat content) (h) is a function of the state only, therefore a point function and a perfect differential, and it is correct to write $\int_1^2 dh = h_2 - h_1$.

It is a most useful property and the types of problems where it is particularly helpful are: (1) in predicting the work of the cycle $\left(\int vdp\right)$ for certain types of heat engines; (2) evaluating the heat supplied for constant pressure processes $\left(\int c_p dt\right)$; and (3) in determining the work done in devices which operate on the continuous flow principle such as steam turbines.

The defining equation is

$$H = U + APV.$$

Differentiating,

$$dH = dU + APdV + AVdP,$$

but

$$dU + APdV = dQ;$$

hence

$$dH = dQ + AVdP. \qquad \text{(III–5)}$$

This is of interest as it clearly shows that the change in enthalpy (or heat content) is equal, in the general case, to *more* than the simple *heat supplied* ($_1Q_2$).

Two special cases are of immediate interest, 1, when the change occurs without the addition of heat, and 2, when it occurs with the pressure remaining constant.

If *adiabatic action* be assumed, $dQ = 0$, and

$$dH = AVdP;$$

integrating,

$$H_2 - H_1 = A \int_1^2 VdP$$

or, for an adiabatic expansion, *the difference in the enthalpy (heat content) is equal to the work of the cycle* (provided the cycle be of the form discussed in par. (III–16).

Reverting again to equation (III–5),

$$dH = dQ + AVdP,$$

the last term becomes zero if the process be restricted to one of *constant pressure*, in which case

$$dH = (dQ)_p = c_p dt$$

or,

$$H_2 - H_1 = (_1Q_2)_p = \int_1^2 c_p dt,$$

which states that *the difference in enthalpy (heat content) is equal to the heat supplied when (and only when) the process has been one of constant pressure.*

Example 1.—For a given state, the intrinsic energy of one pound of a substance is 350 B.t.u., based on an arbitrary zero point; the pressure is 75 lbs. per sq. in., and the volume is 3 cu. ft.

What is the enthalpy (heat content) h, based on the same zero point?

Solution.—

$$h = U + APv = 350 + \frac{75\,(144)\,(3)}{778} = 350 + 41.65 = 391.65 \text{ B.t.u.}$$

Example 2.—One pound of a substance undergoes a process at constant pressure in which the intrinsic energy is increased 150 B.t.u., and the external work done is 40,000 ft.-lbs.

What is the increase in enthalpy (heat content)?

Solution.—$dh = dU + APdv + AvdP$.

In this case, $AvdP = 0$, and $dh = du + APdv$, or

$$h = (U_2 - U_1) + A_1W_2 = 150 + \frac{40,000}{778} = 150 + 51.4 = 201.4 \text{ B.t.u.}$$

Example 3.—A cycle consists successively of the following processes: constant pressure expansion, adiabatic expansion, constant pressure compression, and constant (0) volume compression. The decrease in enthalpy (heat content) of 1 lb. of working substance during the adiabatic expansion is 50 B.t.u.

Find the work of the cycle.

Solution.—$dh = dq + AvdP$.

Since, for an adiabatic, $dq = 0$, $dh = AvdP$. That is, $h_1 - h_2 = AW_{\text{cycle}}$.

Cycle work = 50 (778) = 38,900 ft.-lbs.

III–21. Heat Engines.—A heat engine is a device for converting heat energy into mechanical energy or useful work. It must have four essential elements, the *working substance*, a *source* for supplying heat, a *receiver* for the rejected heat (frequently called the refrigerator) and a *mechanism* for transforming the available heat into work.

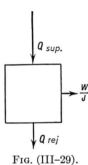

Fɪɢ. (III–29).

Figure (III–29) is a diagrammatic representation of a heat engine, a device *to which* the heat $Q_{\text{sup.}}$ is supplied, *by which* the work W is done and *from which* the unused heat, $Q_{\text{rej.}}$, is rejected. By the Law of the Conservation of Energy, the incoming and outgoing energies must be equal, hence,

$$Q_{\text{sup.}} = \frac{W}{J} + Q_{\text{rej.}} \qquad \text{(III–6)}$$

and also

$$\frac{W}{J} = Q_{\text{sup.}} - Q_{\text{rej.}}$$

Furthermore since efficiency (Eff.) may be generally defined as Output ÷ Input,

$$\text{Eff.} = \frac{Q_{\text{sup.}} - Q_{\text{rej.}}}{Q_{\text{sup.}}} = \frac{AW}{Q_{\text{sup.}}}. \qquad \text{(III–7)}$$

These equations are fundamental and apply to any and all heat engines.

So far it has been tacitly assumed that the heat engines were "perfect," i.e., without friction or other energy losses, but the treatment holds for all engines, perfect or actual, if the expression for external work be considered as *including all energy losses* as well as the net or useful work. The principal losses are those due to friction and radiation, hence,

$$Q_{\text{sup.}} - Q_{\text{rej.}} = \frac{W}{J} + \text{Losses.} \qquad \text{(III–8)}$$

Example.—A heat engine receives 10,000 B.t.u. per min., and rejects 6,500 B.t.u. per min.

Find: (a) the work done per minute; (b) the thermal efficiency; (c) the power delivered.

Solution.—

(a) $W = (Q_{\text{sup.}} - Q_{\text{rej.}}) J = (10,000 - 6500) \, 778 = 2{,}723{,}000 \text{ ft.-lbs./min.}$

(b)   Eff. $= \dfrac{(Q_{\text{sup.}} = Q_{\text{rej.}})}{Q_{\text{sup.}}} = \dfrac{10{,}000 - 6500}{10{,}000} = \dfrac{3500}{10{,}000} = 0.35.$

(c)   Power $= \dfrac{2{,}723{,}000}{33{,}000} = 82.5 \text{ Hp.}$

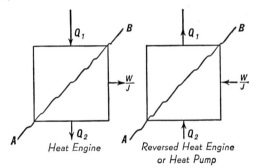

Heat Engine   Reversed Heat Engine
or Heat Pump

Fig. (III–30).

III–22. Reversed Heat Engine.—As a heat engine is a device for converting heat energy into useful work there must be always a complete balance of the incoming and outgoing energies and when diagrammatically indicated as in Fig. III–29 the sum of the vectors representing the outgoing energy $\left(Q_2 \text{ and } \dfrac{W}{J}\right)$ must equal the vector representing the incoming energy (Q_1). The diagram may be imagined as balancing about the irregular line $A - B$ (Fig. III–30) separating the incoming from the outgoing energies. Furthermore all these energies may be supplied or rejected reversibly. If the directions of all the energy transfers were reversed there should result a *reversed heat engine* which instead of receiving heat and producing useful work would receive work and produce heat at the higher of the temperature levels between which the engine was working. In other words the reversed heat engine would have become a *heat pump*.

The usefulness of any device is measured by the manner in which it accomplishes its assigned task. Pumps have two types of tasks, withdrawal and delivery, as exemplified in the bilge pump for a ship and a fire pump, and the classification and evaluation of the unit are dependent upon the service to which it is put. Similarly a reversed engine or heat pump may be considered as a *heating* or a *refrigerating* unit when the objective sought is the *delivery* of Q_1, or the *abstraction* of Q_2 respectively.

The foregoing are exact statements and complete for all *isolated* heat engines, by which is meant those operating with a *fixed quantity* of working substance. For such, the energy transfers are solely in the form of heat energy transmitted (Q) and external work performed $\left(\dfrac{W}{J}\right)$.

There are, however, many devices which, instead of operating with a fixed quantity of working substance which is repeatedly energized and de-energized, operate by *continuously receiving* working substance of high energy content and *continuously exhausting* this working substance with its energy reduced by the amount of the external work performed.

For such devices obviously the total ingress of energy cannot be simply the heat energy (Q) transmitted to the working substance but must include any additional energy that the working substance has brought in by virtue of its flow into the machine. The most important are, the work done on it in forcing it into the engine against the initial pressure, and its kinetic energy of flow in the supply pipe, hence the total incoming energy consists of the intrinsic heat energy (U), the work of pushing the working substance of volume, V, into place against the initial pressure, P, and the kinetic energy of approach, or

$$E_1 = U_1 + AP_1V_1 + \frac{KE_1}{J}$$

$$= H_1 + \frac{KE_1}{J}$$

III–23. Isolated Action Compared with Continuous Flow.—Usually the analysis of the performance of a heat engine is made considering the plant as a whole as the device to which heat is supplied and from which useful work is derived. For example a steam power plant constitutes a heat engine in the sense that the fuel burned under the boiler supplies the heat ($Q_{sup.}$) to the working fluid (steam) which provides useful work by expanding in the cylinder of the engine and then gives up heat ($Q_{rej.}$) to the cooling water of the condenser whence the condensed steam is returned by the feed pump to the boiler for a new supply of heat.

In such a system, complete in itself and isolated for convenience of consideration, the thermodynamic history of one pound of the working fluid throughout a complete circuit constitutes the cycle of the heat engine and would be approximately as follows. In the boiler there is a heating at constant pressure as the heat is supplied to convert the pound of water

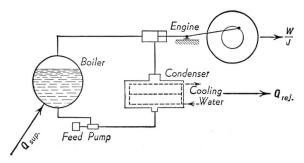

FIG. (III–31).

into steam with consequent increase in volume $(a - b)$, (Fig. III–32) the steam then undergoes no change until it has reached the cylinder where it expands, pushing the piston ahead of it $(b - c)$ and doing useful work. After expansion the steam passes to the condenser where it is condensed back to water and its volume shrivels at constant pressure $(c - d)$ after which the feed pump forces it into the boiler at practically constant volume $(d - a)$ ready to receive another load of heat and repeat the circuit. Considered in such a manner the heat engine is not simply the steam engine cylinder, it is the *whole plant* and the cycle shown in Fig. III–32 is the true cycle or thermodynamic history of one pound of the working fluid throughout one complete circuit. The heat supplied and the heat rejected are those which the working substance takes on in the boiler and rejects in the condenser and the useful work (W/J) is the horsepower developed in the engine cylinder (ihp) and the efficiency is the ratio of this to the heat supplied.

There are many instances, however, where a less general and more detailed consideration is desirable as, for example, when scrutiny of the engine itself or of the condenser might be necessary. When such segregation is made, it is important that it be clearly understood that the working fluid flowing continuously around the circuit of the plant possesses energy of flow due to this hydraulic action which must be taken account of. It must be added to the heat energy coming to the steam engine or other selected part and must also be added to that store of heat energy which the outgoing fluid takes with it as it leaves the engine. When considering the system as a whole this is not necessary as equilibrium of flow exists, but when considering only a portion of the circuit such allowances must be made. Thus the energy brought in to the cylinder of the steam engine comprises the heat energy carried in by the steam (U) *plus* the energy of

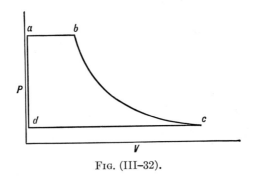

FIG. (III–32).

entrance of the flowing stream (not steam). This energy of entrance consists mainly of the kinetic energy due to the velocity of approach plus the work done in pushing the steam into the cylinder at constant pressure up to the point where it is cut off from the boiler (PV/J).

The velocity of flow to and from the engine is kept nearly the same by designing the supply and exhaust lines to have proper diameters, thus eliminating need for considering changes in kinetic energy and thus there remains for the "energy supplied" term only the expression, $U + PV/J$, which will be recognized at once as the property (H) enthalpy previously defined (p. 31). Hence, for analyses of continuous flow machines, the work done is equal to the difference in the enthalpy of the fluid supplied to and rejected from the machine.

Recapitulating, for any isolated system or *complete heat engine,* the difference between the *heat supplied* and the *heat rejected* is *equal* to the *external work done,* (plus losses) whereas, for any device which operates with a *continuous flow* of the working fluid passing through it, *the difference in that* property termed enthalpy, as measured for the incoming and outgoing fluid, is *equal* to the *external work done* plus losses.

Isolated Action,

$$Q_{\text{Supplied}} - Q_{\text{Rejected}} = W/J. + \text{losses} \qquad \text{(III–8)}$$

Continuous Flow,

$$H_{\text{Incoming}} - H_{\text{Outgoing}} = W/J. + \text{losses} \qquad \text{(III–9)}$$

In the *isolated* system there is no flow of working fluid to or from the system and only energy in the form of heat is supplied and rejected. In *continuous* flow devices there is the added energy due to flow which must be considered. If the action is adiabatic and the engine perfect (W) represents the net or useful work, if non-adiabatic and the engine imperfect it must be considered as including all rejections (or accessions) of energy from (or to) the working fluid.

Continuous Flow.—Such a large number of engineering devices operate in a manner susceptible to analysis by the continuous flow principle that it constitutes one of the most useful tools of modern thermodynamics. It will be dealt with in more detail later in the chapter on Flow of Fluids, but the presentation here of its essential features will be helpful.

The outstanding feature is that for any flowing fluid the total thermodynamic energy which it possesses is its intrinsic energy (U) plus the work done to bring it into the pipe against the existing pressure (PV). The sum of these $\left(U + \dfrac{PV}{J}\right)$ will be recognized as the Enthalpy (or Heat Content or Total Heat).

Consider next any mechanical device which operates by virtue of a continuous supply of the motivating fluid and assume no leakage of fluid. The total energy approaching will be the kinetic energy of the flowing stream plus the thermodynamic energy, H, and similarly for the exhaust. The only change which can have occurred between entrance and exit will be due to the energy abstracted by the machine and delivered to external agents plus any heat given up to jackets or lost by radiation, etc., therefore,

$$\left(\frac{KE}{J} + H\right)_1 - \left(\frac{KE}{J} + H\right)_2 = \frac{{}_1W_2}{J} + \text{Heat Losses}$$

and in its broadest sense this holds for any and all thermodynamic devices which receive and exhaust a continuous supply of working fluid. It applies to steam engines, air compressors, refrigerating machines, turbine nozzles, etc., etc. If for any of these the enthalpy of the working fluid at entrance and exit are known, the difference can be attributed only to energy which has left the fluid in the form of useful work or heat losses. It can even be made to include internal combustion engines if there be added another term to both supply and exhaust to cover the chemical energy (approximate heating value) of the mixture.

Diagrammatic representation of some of these are shown in Fig. (III–33) with the various energy quantities represented as vectors.

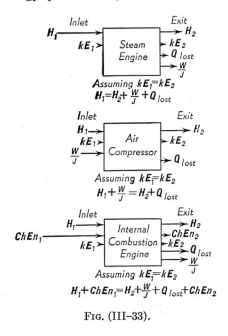

FIG. (III–33).

Continuous flow implies that the flow be steady, in a state of dynamic equilibrium, and that the apparatus itself shall not serve as an energy absorber or reservoir. Such devices as steam turbines, where the steam is continuously and steadily supplied, and the unit is in a stable thermal state throughout, lend themselves excellently to this type of analysis.

Similarly centrifugal air blowers operating conversely, i.e. receiving work and delivering the working substance at a higher energy level, are very conveniently analyzed. Even devices which at first appear to function with the flow intermittent, or cyclical, may be considered as continuous flow devices provided the points of observation for the initial and final states are sufficiently remote from the place where the fluctuations occur to be unaffected. For example, while the detailed cylinder action of a steam engine can not be analyzed properly, its functioning as a whole can be correctly studied if the initial and terminal states be selected at the main steam and exhaust lines sufficiently remote from the engine itself not to feel the fluctuations caused by the successive momentary bites by which the cylinder is fed.

Other devices susceptible to treatment by the continuous flow method are boilers, condensers, heat engines, compressors, etc., also the flow through nozzles and the effect of throttling, where the fluid passes adiabatically from a region of high pressure to one of lower pressure doing no useful work as in passing through a reducing valve, are very simply dealt with if continuous flow is assumed.

When it is desirable to consider single processes or any isolated member such analyses must be made by the general thermodynamic energy equation, $dQ = dU + \dfrac{dW}{J}$. Any cycle is composed of a series of processes and frequently the entire cycle may be studied by isolating each process and analyzing it by the foregoing equation.

Possibly one might generalize to the extent of saying that when single processes are involved equation (III–8) is usually used but when complete machines are under consideration, or even portions of machines where steady flow exists, such cases are most conveniently discussed using equation (III–9).

To illustrate, consider the case of an air compressor which is taking in 1500 cu.ft. of atmospheric air per minute and delivering this compressed to 90 lb per sq in. absolute. The temperature of the entering air is 70 F and the temperature of the air leaving the compressor is 346 F. The jacket water carries away 1770 Btu per minute.

From the central portion of figure III–33 and assuming equal kinetic energies for the entering and leaving air stream,

$$H_1 + \frac{W}{J} = H_2 + Q_{\text{Lost}}$$

The enthalpy for a perfect gas is, $h = c_p T$ and for this case the heat lost (Q_{Lost}) is very nearly the heat carried off by the jacket water (1770 Btu per min.) The weight of air taken in is, $1500 \div 13.35 = 112.3$ lb per min., where 13.35 is the specific volume of air at 14.7 p.s.i. and 70 F.

The specific heat of air (c_p) is close to 0.24, hence,

$$H_1 = 112.3 \times 0.24 \times (460 + 70) = 14280 \text{ Btu}$$

$$H_2 = 112.3 \times 0.24(460 + 346) = 21720 \text{ Btu}$$

using these values,

$$\frac{W}{J} = 21720 - 14280 + 1770 = 9210 \text{ Btu per min.}$$

$$W = 7,165,000 \text{ ft lb per min.}$$

This is equivalent to 216.7 horsepower and is the power required to drive the air compressor.

This agrees with the figure obtained by a step by step calculation of the cycle as given later (Art. IV–6).

CHAPTER IV

GASES

IV-1. Early Experimental Laws of Gases.—The structure of the modern theory of thermodynamics was built largely upon a group of laws propounded by the early chemists as a direct result of their experimental investigations of the so-called permanent gases. By aid of the modern conception of heat, as the energy of the component particles of the substance, it is possible to arrive at the same laws by an entirely different line of reasoning, but it is important that one be familiar with these early experimental laws and their application.

Boyle's Law.—As a result of his experiments on the behavior of various gases when pressure and volume were permitted to change but the temperature kept constant, Boyle announced the following law as governing the action of the *perfect gas.* **When the temperature of a given weight of a perfect gas is kept constant, the product of the pressure and the volume is a constant, i.e., the volume varies inversely as the pressure.** This may be expressed mathematically by the equation,

$$pv = \text{const.}, \quad \text{or} \quad p_1v_1 = p_2v_2 = \text{const.} \quad \text{For Isothermal Changes.}$$

Charles' Law.—Similarly it was found, when a given quantity of gas was kept at constant volume and heated, or cooled, that the *change* in pressure was directly proportional to the *change* in temperature, that is, for every degree F that the temperature was raised, or lowered, the pressure of the gas was increased, or decreased by a constant amount. It may be formally stated as, **When a given weight of a perfect gas is heated, or cooled, at constant volume the change in pressure is proportional to the change in temperature** $(\Delta p \propto \Delta t)_v$.

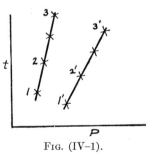

Fig. (IV-1).

This was another way of saying that the graph showing the change was a straight line when plotted on the tp coördinate axes as is shown for two different gases 1 2 3 and 1'2'3' in Fig. (IV-1).

59

If instead of the volume being kept constant the heating or cooling be carried out with the pressure kept constant, the graph on the *tv* plane is a straight line and the Law may be stated, ***When a given weight of a perfect gas is heated or cooled at constant pressure the change in volume is proportional to the change in temperature*** $(\Delta v \ \alpha \ \Delta t)_p$.

Graphs on this plane for several different gases are shown in digrammatic form in Fig. (IV–2). When the actual experimental evidence was assembled in this form it was apparent that the extrapolation of all the graphs tended to focus in a single point on the *t* axis. This could have but

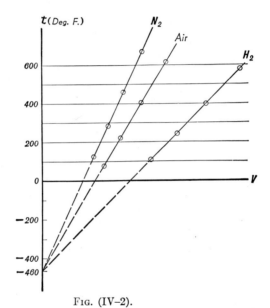

Fig. (IV–2).

one meaning; *that temperature had an absolute zero of measurement.* It was clearly recognized that the zero of the scale actually used for measuring temperatures (Fahrenheit) was a purely arbitrary one, but whether there was or was not a *true* scale with a correct or absolute zero for its origin was unknown until after the enunciation of Charles' Law.

Stating Charles' Law mathematically we have, for constant volume changes, $\left(\dfrac{P_1}{P_2}\right)_v = \left(\dfrac{T_1}{T_2}\right)_v$ or $[P\alpha T]_v$ and for constant pressure changes $\left(\dfrac{V_1}{V_2}\right)_p = \left(\dfrac{T_1}{T_2}\right)_p$ or $[V\alpha T]_p$, that is, for changes occurring at constant pressure, the volume is proportional to the absolute temperature and for changes taking place at constant volume the pressure is proportional to the absolute temperature.

As previously mentioned the best evaluation of the zero of the absolute scale of temperature is 459.69 Fahrenheit degrees below the zero of that scale, or 273.16 Centigrade degrees below the zero of the Centigrade scale. Expressions for the conversion of temperatures on these scales to absolute temperatures are,

$$\text{Fahrenheit scale, } T = t + 459.69°,$$

$$\text{Centigrade scale, } T = t + 273.16°.$$

Reasoning strictly according to the extrapolation of Charles' Law, the concept of absolute zero would be that temperature where the perfect gas produced zero pressure and occupied a space of zero volume, conceptions which seem preposterous unless viewed in the light of the kinetic theory of heat. According to this, it might be logical to expect that the complete cessation of molecular action at the absolute zero of temperature would result in a cessation of the molecular impacts on the walls of the containing vessel and thus zero pressure, also that the cessation of all molecular and sub-molecular activity might result in a shrivelling of material structure to the density of the atomic nucleus with corresponding volume of unbelievable minuteness.

Such speculations, however, are purely academic and the gross extrapolation of the few experimental points used for developing Charles' Law was entirely unjustifiable except that it directed attention to the possibility of temperature being a true property, a function of state only, at a time when the multiplicity of arbitrary thermometric scales in use (Fahrenheit, Celsius, Réaumur, etc.) tended to mask the fact that they all had one important point in common, namely, an absolute zero.

Joule's Law.—After it had been definitely proven that heat was a form of energy and that this energy might be of both the kinetic and potential forms (sensible heat and latent heat), Joule pronounced the dictum, since known as Joule's Law, that in the case of the perfect gas, *all* the intrinsic energy was in the *kinetic* form. As stated by him the law was, *"The intrinsic energy of a perfect gas depends only upon the temperature and is independent of volume."*

The broadest statement of the effect of adding heat is that of the general energy equation,

$$dQ = dU + dW/J. \tag{IV-1}$$

As previously mentioned, this can be made a more detailed statement by subdividing the intrinsic energy into its two forms, kinetic and potential thus,

$$dQ = dU_k + dU_p + dW/J \tag{IV-2}$$

Of these two, only the kinetic form or sensible heat was admittedly a function of the temperature, thus Joule in presenting his law had to prove that when undergoing any change, no energy is spent in pulling apart (disgregating) the molecular aggregation, therefore no energy is stored up in the potential form as disgregation or latent energy of the molecular group. In other words, dU_p must be proved to be equal to zero for any change of a perfect gas.

In order to do this Joule took two large receivers and immersed them in a bath of water, the one contained air at a pressure of 22 atmospheres and from the other he had exhausted all the air possible. The two receivers, A and B, were connected together with a pipe having a closed stop-cock (C). Immersed in the bath was a thermometer.

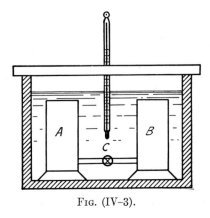

Fig. (IV–3).

Joule reasoned that with such an apparatus if the stop-cock were opened the air would rush from the high-pressure vessel to the empty one, doing no external work on the way, thus dW would be zero. If, further, the thermometer did not change, it would indicate two things: that there had been no heat added to or taken from the surrounding water and that there had been no change in the sensible heat of the air, thus both dQ and dU_k would be zero. This was exactly what happened and thus with three terms of the equation equal to zero the fourth, dU_p must also be zero, which indicated that there was no energy spent in changing molecular aggregation from one of close proximity, as in the high-pressure state, to one of greater remoteness in the low-pressure and increased volume of the final state. Therefore all the heat energy in a perfect gas consisted of the kinetic form or sensible heat.

$$dU = dU_k. \tag{IV-3}$$

Stated somewhat differently, there had been a change, without heat having been supplied or any work done, and thus the intrinsic energy must have remained the same. The temperature had remained the same though the pressure and volume had changed, therefore the intrinsic energy depended solely upon the temperature, and any change in pressure and volume had no effect upon the intrinsic energy unless there was a change of temperature.

While Joule's Law holds true for the perfect gas, actual gases show some departure from it and undergo a slight change in temperature when expanded as just described, the departure is negligible, however, for the so-called permanent gases for ordinary changes of pressure.

The general equation for the effect of adding heat

$$dQ = dU_k + dU_p + dW/J$$

when limited to the consideration of perfect gases thus becomes,

$$dQ = dU_k + dW/J. \tag{IV-4}$$

The experiment was later carried out with a somewhat different form of apparatus in which the bath was separated into three portions, A, B, and C, surrounding each of the elements of the air container. A sketch of this form is shown in Fig. (IV-4). With this it was noted that the bath around A was cooled and that around B was warmed by an equal amount. This fulfilled expectations as the gas in A should become cooler because of the work it does in expanding against the rising pressure in B and the gas in B should be heated by the work of compression done upon it, and the conversion of the energy of its eddying motion back into heat. Thus for the whole system there should be no gain or loss of heat.

Actually, however, the entire bath underwent a very small drop in temperature at first attributed to experimental inaccuracy. Later experiments, developed to study this more carefully, showed the change in temperature to be actually existent and to be attributable to the departure of actual gases from the assumptions made for the *perfect* gas, in that some energy was used in doing disgregation work. A discussion of these later experiments will be given farther on in this chapter (Art. IV–21) under the heading of " Joule's Law and Actual Gases."

In addition to the foregoing laws proposed as the result of experimental observation by Boyle, Charles and Joule, there are two others, which will be mentioned here but discussed in more detail later, the laws of Avogadro

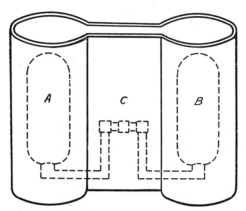

FIG. (IV–4).　Apparatus used to demonstrate Joule's Law.

and Dalton. *Avogadro's Law* states that equal volumes of perfect gases under the same conditions of temperature and pressure contain the same number of molecules. *Dalton's Law* states that when a mixture of two or more gases (or vapors) is contained in a vessel, the resulting total pressure on the sides of the vessel is equal to the sum of the partial pressures that would be exerted by each gas if it occupied the vessel separately at the same temperature, but with none of the other gases present.

Example 1.—A gas exists initially at a pressure of 90 lbs. per sq. in. abs., and a volume of 5 cu. ft.

If the volume be increased to 15 cu. ft. without change in temperature, what is the final pressure?

Solution.—Boyle's Law will apply here.

$$P_1V_1 = P_2V_2 \qquad P_2 = \frac{P_1V_1}{V_2} = \frac{90\,(5)}{15} = 30 \text{ lbs. per sq. in.}$$

Example 2.—Initial conditions of a gas are as follows: $P_1 = 20$ lbs. per sq. in. abs., $V_1 = 10$ cu. ft., $t_1 = 40°$ F. Without change in volume, the pressure is increased to 80 lbs. per sq. in. abs.

What is the final temperature?

Solution.—Charles' Law applies.

$$P_1/P_2 = T_1/T_2 \qquad T_2 = \frac{P_2 T_1}{P_1} = \frac{80\,(40 + 460)}{20} = 2000°\text{ F. abs.}$$

or

$$2000 - 460 = 1540°\text{ F.}$$

Example 3.—A gas initially at $P_1 = 20$ lbs. per sq. in. abs., $t_1 = 40°$ F., $V_1 = 10$ cu. ft., is increased in volume to 40 cu. ft. without change in pressure. What is the final temperature?

Solution.—Charles' Law applies.

$$V_1/V_2 = T_1/T_2 \qquad T_2 = \frac{V_2 T_1}{V_1} = \frac{40\,(40 + 460)}{10} = 2000°\text{ F. abs.}$$

or

$$2000 - 460 = 1540°\text{ F.}$$

IV–2. Definition of Perfect Gas.—All the foregoing laws apply only to the *perfect gas* a term coined by these early workers which was intended to take the *almost* out of their experimental evidence. For example, the graphs of Charles' Law were *almost* straight lines, the pv product in Boyle's work was *almost* a constant and the change in temperature in Joule's experiment was *almost* zero. It was decided that these slight deviations were due to some unknown imperfection of the gas and that if the gas were truly *perfect* it would conform *exactly* to the proposed law. Thus it was decided to fit the man to the coat and enunciate these laws as governing the action of that purely hypothetical substance, the *perfect gas.*

As already mentioned (see Art. II–4), there are two criteria for defining it, the experimental and the molecular. According to the first it is *any gas that conforms exactly to the laws of Boyle, Charles and Joule, and also has constancy of specific heats.* According to the second, it is *any gas that conforms exactly to the postulates of the kinetic theory of heat* (given in Art. I–6).

The assumption of a perfect gas permits the use of a single expression for the action of many gases instead of individual expressions for each. No actual gas is perfect in the above sense but for many, through the range of conditions usually met with, the divergence is so slight as to be of insignificant importance. Exceptional conditions, such as extreme ranges of pressure or temperature, may involve great divergence or render perfect gas laws inapplicable.

IV–3. The Characteristic Equation of a Perfect Gas.—An equation connecting one property with two others is known as a *characteristic equation* for that substance. The possibility of writing such an equation rests upon a fundamental assumption that thermodynamic equations may contain but two independent variables, an assumption justified by the results.

The properties most commonly combined to form a characteristic equation are Pressure, Volume and Temperature. We have already derived such an equation for a perfect gas, using only the mechanical theory of heat (Art. II–7), but it may be derived quite independently by combining the mathematical statements of the purely experimental laws of Boyle and Charles. Boyle's Law states that, at constant temperature, the pressure of a perfect gas varies inversely as the volume, or that, pv = const. at const. t. Charles' Law states that, at constant pressure, the volume of a perfect gas varies directly as the absolute temperature, or that, v/T = const. at const. p. Let a unit weight of gas be contained in a cylinder fitted with a tight fitting but frictionless piston and let the gas change from the condition of p_1, v_1, and T_1 to the final condition p_2, v_2, and T_2. The change, however, is made in two steps, first to an intermediate condition x, keeping the temperature constant and then to the final condition 2, keeping the pressure constant.

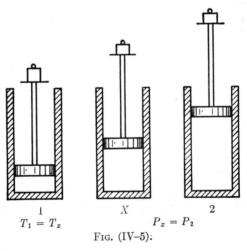

$$\begin{array}{ccc} 1 & X & 2 \\ T_1 = T_x & & P_x = P_2 \end{array}$$

Fig. (IV–5):

By Boyle's Law,

$$p_1 v_1 = p_x v_x, \qquad\qquad\qquad \text{(IV–5)}$$

but

$$p_x = p_2,$$

then

$$p_1 v_1 = p_2 v_x \quad \text{or} \quad v_x = \frac{p_1 v_1}{p_2}. \qquad\qquad \text{(IV–6)}$$

By Charles' Law,

$$v_x/T_x = v_2/T_2,$$

but

$$T_x = T_1,$$

then

$$v_x T_2 = v_2 T_1 \quad \text{or} \quad v_x = \frac{v_2 T_1}{T_2}. \tag{IV-7}$$

Equating (6) and (7),

$$\frac{p_1 v_1}{p_2} = \frac{v_2 T_1}{T_2},$$

or

$$\frac{p_1 v_1}{T_1} = \frac{p_2 v_2}{T_2} = \text{constant},$$

and

$$Pv = RT, \tag{IV-8}$$

where P is the pressure in pounds per square foot, v is the *specific* volume (volume of one pound) in cubic feet, T the absolute temperature in Fahrenheit units and R is a constant, defined for any given state by $\dfrac{Pv}{T}$.

If more than one pound of gas is under consideration it may be more convenient to write equation (14) as follows:

$$PV = WRT \tag{IV-9}$$

where V is now the total volume, w is the weight of gas under consideration, and the other letters have the same significance as before.

In doing numerical problems there are three common errors: (1) failure to add atmospheric pressure (14.7 lbs.) to gage pressures, (2) failure to multiply pressures that are given in pounds per square inch by 144 to get them into pounds per sq. ft., and failure to add 460° to the Fahrenheit temperature in order to obtain the absolute temperature. Try to avoid these.

Value of Constant R.—In the above equation, IV-7, the constant R may be evaluated for any particular gas by substituting the correct physical values for P, V, and T consistently taken for any single condition of the gas. For example, for oxygen, which is, of the permanent gases, the one for which we have the most accurate data, the specific volume (volume of

1 lb.) at 32° F. and standard atmospheric pressure is $\dfrac{1}{0.08921}$ cu. ft.*

$$R = \frac{Pv}{T} = \frac{14.696 \times 144}{491.6 \times 0.08921} = 48.26.$$

Values of R for other gases are given in the following table:

IV-4. Universal Gas Constant.—In the characteristic equation the constant R may be evaluated for any particular gas by substituting the correct values for P, v, and T, taken consistently for any single state, as was done for oxygen in the preceding paragraph. A more general conception is obtained by modifying the expression to take account of the molecular characteristics of the gas.

If the equation is written in the form,

$$v = \frac{RT}{P}$$

and both sides multiplied by the molecular weight, M, then

$$Mv = \frac{MRT}{P}.$$

The term, Mv, is the volume of M units by weight (M pounds) of gas and by Avogadro's Law this is the same for *all* perfect gases when at identical conditions of temperature and pressure, $M_1v_1 = M_2v_2 = $ const. It is the volume of another unit of quantity, the mol. A mol is *defined* as M pounds (or M grams) of a fluid. †

Using foot and pound units, the volume of one mol at atmospheric pressure and 32° F. may be taken as 359 cubic feet.‡

* "A Review of the Densities of Various Gases," U. S. Bureau of Standards, 1924.

† By Avogadro's Law equal volumes of different gases existing at the same pressure and temperature, contain the same number of molecules. As each molecule weighs M units, the weights of equal volumes of different gases will be proportional to their molecular weights, M_1, M_2, M_3, etc. Thus, if amounts of each gas exactly proportional to their molecular weights were taken, the resulting volumes would all be equal, $M_1v_1 = M_2v_2 = M_3v_3 = $ const. This is the reason for the existence of the mol as a unit of quantity; it is really a unit of number of molecules (2.749×10^{26}) like the dozen, though the definition is simply M pounds of the gas.

‡ The experimental determination of the volume of one mol differs slightly, according to the gas used. For several gases most closely approximating the action of the perfect gas, the value at 32° F. and atmospheric pressure is as follows: Argon 358.5, Helium 359.1, Hydrogen 359.2, and Oxygen 358.7. The average of these is 358.9.

TABLE I

Name of Gas	Symbol or Formula	Atoms per Molecule	Molecular Weight		Density, lb. per cu. ft., 32° F., 14.7 lbs. per sq. in.	Specific Volume, cu. ft. per lb., 32° F., 14.7 lbs. per sq.in.	R, 32° F., 14.7 lbs. per sq. in.	MR (using exact molecular weight)	Instantaneous Specific Heats at 32° F. and 14.7 lbs. per sq. in.		
			Approximate	International (1928)					c_p	c_v	$k = \dfrac{c_p}{c_v}$
1 Air	......	...	29.0	28.97	0.08072	12.389	53.347	1545.5	0.24	0.1715	1.40
2 Argon *	A	1	39.9	39.91	.11133	8.982	38.676	1543.5	.1269	.076	1.67
3 Acetylene	C_2H_2	4	26	26.0154	.07323	13.656	58.802	1529.75	.3913	.315	1.242
4 Ammonia †	NH_3	4	17	17.0311	.04813	20.790	89.522	1524.64	.52	.415	1.253
5 Carbon dioxide	CO_2	3	44	44.0	.12342	8.102	34.887	1535.0	.2028	.1577	1.286
6 Carbon monoxide	CO	2	28	28.0	.07804	12.814	55.176	1544.93	.2484	.1786	1.398
7 Ethylene	C_2H_4	6	28	28.0308	.07866	12.713	54.742	1534.46	.3573	.2865	1.247
8 Helium *	He	1	4	4.00	.01114	89.767	386.54	1546.13	1.251	.754	1.659
9 Hydrogen	H_2	2	2	2.0154	.00561	178.253	767.56	1546.92	3.140	2.155	1.457
					Saturated						
10 Mercury ‡	Hg	1	200.6	200.61	.25233	3.963	....	....	0.025	0.015	1.67‡
11 Methane	CH_4	5	16	16.0308	.0447	22.376	96.35	1544.57	.54	.4164	1.297
12 Nitric oxide *	NO	2	30	30.008	.08373	11.943	51.426	1543.19	.231	.167	1.38
13 Nitrogen (chemical)	N_2	2	28	28.016	.07807	12.809	55.156	1545.25	.2484	.1785	1.392
14 Nitrogen (atmospheric)§	N_2	2	28	28.16	.07846	12.745	54.879	1545.4	.2486	.1777	1.399
15 Nitrous oxide *	N_2O	3	44	44.016	.12342	8.102	34.887	1535.57	.226	.174	1.30
16 Oxygen	O_2	2	32	32.0	.08921	11.2095	48.266	1544.51	.2175	.1554	1.399
17 Sulphur dioxide	SO_2	3	64	64.065	.18273	5.473	23.567	1509.8	.187	.156	1.199

NOTE: Unless otherwise noted, all values for molecular weight, density, and specific volume are from International Critical Tables, Vol. III, 1928. Values for specific heat, except as noted, from the work of Goodenough and Felbeck based on $J = 777.64$. For $J = 778.3$, these values will be slightly lower.

* Specific heat values from work of Landolt and Bornstein (1923).
† Bureau of Standards Circular No. 142 (1923).
‡ Density and specific volume at 14.7 lbs. per sq. in. abs., dry and saturated. Specific heats for superheated Hg vapor. All values from "Properties of Mercury Vapor," by L. A. Sheldon (General Electric Co.).
§ By atmospheric nitrogen is meant the residue left from atmospheric air after the abstraction of oxygen. It consists mainly of nitrogen but has traces of CO_2, Argon, Helium, etc.

Rewriting the characteristic equation as,

$$MR = \frac{P \times Mv}{T},$$

the first term, MR becomes a constant applicable to one mol of *any* perfect gas, thus a **universal gas constant,**

Using the value of R previously determined for oxygen and the molecular weight of 32, the evaluation of the Universal Gas Constant is, $32 \times 48.260 = 1544$. The average of the values for Argon, Helium, Hydrogen, Nitrogen, and Oxygen is 1545.3. In this text we shall use the value 1545. The Characteristic equation for *any* perfect gas then becomes,

$$Pv = \frac{1545T}{M}, \tag{IV-10}$$

where the letters have their customary significance of,

P = pressure, in pounds per square foot.

v = the volume of one pound (the specific volume) in cubic feet.

M = the molecular weight of the gas under discussion.

T = the absolute temperature in Fahrenheit degrees.

Example 1.—A gas has a molecular weight of 45.
What is the specific volume at 20 lbs. per sq. in. and 140° F.?
Solution.—

$$R = 1545/45 = 34.35 \qquad v = RT/P = \frac{34.35\,(140 + 460)}{20\,(144)} = 7.15 \text{ cu. ft.}$$

Example 2.—Find the volume of a mol of any gas at 70° F. and 12 lbs. per sq. in. abs.
Solution.—

$$Mv = MRT/P = \frac{1545(70 + 460)}{12(144)} = 474 \text{ cu. ft.}$$

Example 3.—From data in Table I, find the apparent molecular weight of air.
Solution.—

$$R = 53.35 \qquad M = 1545/53.35 = 29$$

or

$$M\,(12.39) = 359 \qquad M = 359/12.39 = 29$$

IV-5. Characteristic Surface.—The characteristic equation for a perfect gas, commonly written $Pv = RT$, contains three variables, only two of which can be independent. It may therefore be represented geometrically by a surface on a set of three coördinate axes along each of which one of these variables is measured to some scale. Such a surface is commonly called the Characteristic Surface and is shown in Fig. (IV–6). As the number of independent variables is limited to two, there can be but one characteristic surface for any given gas and every point representing a state of the gas must lie on this surface. For example, at a given pressure and volume there can be but one temperature, or for a given temperature and pressure there can be one, and only one, volume. The representation of any change occurring at constant temperature will be

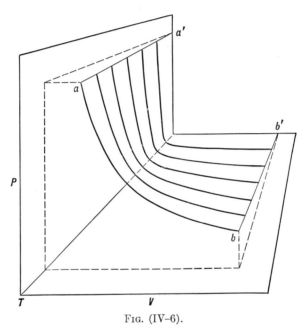

FIG. (IV–6).

shown by the line cut out of this surface by a plane perpendicular to the T axis as ab and $a'b'$. Making T constant in the characteristic equation gives pv = const., thus these isothermal curves are rectangular hyperbolae (or hyperbolas) when shown on the PV plane. Similarly, for constant pressure and constant volume changes, the lines cut from the surface by planes perpendicular to the P and V axes respectively are straight lines, aa^1 and bb^1, when shown on their planes of projection as they should be from the mathematical statement of Charles' Law,

$$(v)_p = \text{const.} \times T, \quad \text{and} \quad (p)_v = \text{const.} \times T.$$

Characteristic equations in terms of other properties can be formulated and would have corresponding geometrical surfaces when plotted on coördinate axes representing these properties. However, such have little interest other than the fact that they would all be *surfaces*, since the basic assumption limiting the number of independent variables to two holds good regardless of the properties involved.

IV–6. Specific Heat.—By the term Specific Heat, which is really a contraction of Specific Heat-capacity, is meant the amount of heat required to produce a change of one degree of temperature in a unit weight of the substance. In English units it is the number of B.t.u's necessary to raise one pound of the substance one degree Fahrenheit.*

If the specific heat is constant, the heat supplied to a unit weight is equal to the product of the specific heat and the temperature change,

$$_1Q_2 = Wc(T_2 - T_1). \tag{IV–11}$$

If it is variable, the heat supplied is

$$Q = W \int_1^2 c\,dt$$

and always

$$c = \frac{dQ}{W \times dt} = \frac{dq}{dt},$$

or

$$c\,dt = dq.$$

As previously pointed out the addition of the heat, dq, may cause a change in the intrinsic energy, du, of the body and may do work, $\dfrac{dw}{J}$,

$$dq = du + \frac{dw}{J}.$$

Substituting $c\,dt$ for dq and Pdv for dw,

$$c\,dt = du + \frac{Pdv}{J}, \tag{IV–12}$$

or for total weight,

$$W \times c\,dt = dU + \frac{PdV}{J}, \tag{IV–13}$$

* It is sometimes defined as the ratio of the thermal capacity of the substance to the thermal capacity of an equal mass of water at some definite temperature accepted as standard. Since there is no accepted standard temperature, this definition is not as precise as the one given.

and this is quite as general a form of the fundamental energy equation as equation (IV–1).

The intrinsic energy, U, is a true property, a function of the state only, but the work done, $\int PdV$, depends upon the path by which the change is effected; thus, in general, there may be any number of specific heats for a given gas, dependent upon the manner in which the heat, q, is supplied or rejected.

The specific heats for two processes are of particular importance, namely, when the heat is supplied at constant volume and when it is supplied at constant pressure, c_v and c_p respectively.

At Constant Volume.—When the volume remains constant, no heat energy is spent in doing external work (as $dv = 0$) and the total amount of heat supplied goes into increasing the intrinsic energy. Equation (2) IV–8 then becomes

$$(dq)_v = c_v dt = du + 0.$$

As du is perfect differential this integrates into the form,

$$\int c_v dt = u_2 - u_1, \tag{IV–14}$$

which is true for *any* substance. When restricted to perfect gases, for which it has been assumed that the specific heats are constant, this becomes

$$c_v(T_2 - T_1) = u_2 - u_1. \tag{IV–15}$$

This gives an evaluation for the specific heat at constant volume in terms of the change in intrinsic energy, or conversely, for the *intrinsic energy change*, an evaluation in *terms of the specific heat at constant volume*. This is convenient, as the specific heat is a quantity readily determined experimentally, whereas the intrinsic energy is not. Thus the intrinsic energy change may be measured always by $\int c_v dt$ regardless of the path by which the change was effected. When dealing with gases, we may *at any time* substitute $\int c_v dt$ for du * and, in the case of perfect gases,

* Strictly the expression is as follows:

$$du = c_v dT + \left[T\left(\frac{dP}{dT}\right)_v - P \right] dv;$$

however, except for gases near the vapor phase *or* at extremely high pressures where the inter-molecular distance is much reduced the second term, is negligible. A similar statement holds for dh.

$c_v(T_2 - T_1)$ for $u_2 - u_1$. Stated differently, as intrinsic energy is a true property of the substance, the amount by which it changes is independent of the manner in which the change is made and having found the amount of the change by some route which is well known, then the same change accomplished by any other route will have the same change of intrinsic energy.

At Constant Pressure.—Consider next the case of heat supplied at constant pressure, then $(dq)_p = c_p dt$ and the general equation becomes

$$c_p dt = du + \frac{Pdv}{J},$$

or substituting $c_v dt$ for du, we have

$$\int c_p dt = \int c_v dt + \int \frac{Pdv}{J} \qquad \text{(IV–16)}$$

This expression is true for a constant pressure change of any fluid. For a perfect gas the specific heats are constant, hence the integrations can be performed, resulting in

$$c_p(T_2 - T_1) = c_v(T_2 - T_1) + \frac{P(v_2 - v_1)}{J}.$$

Difference of Specific Heats.—Substituting RT for Pv,

$$c_p(T_2 - T_1) = c_v(T_2 - T_1) + \frac{R}{J}(T_2 - T_1),$$

whence,

$$c_p - c_v = \frac{R}{J}. \qquad \text{(IV–17)}$$

This is an important perfect gas relation and useful in the solution of many problems.

Example 1.—Three pounds of a perfect gas undergo a change of state during which the temperature increases 250° F.
If $c_v = 0.3$, what is the change in intrinsic energy?
Solution.—$dU = W(c_v)dt$

$$U_2 - U_1 = W(c_v)(T_2 - T_1) = 3 \,(.3)\,(250) = 225 \text{ B.t.u. increase.}$$

Example 2.—If R for the above gas is 60, how much heat would be required to raise the temperature 50° F. at constant pressure?
Solution.—$(dQ)_p = W(c_p)dt$

$$c_p - c_v = R/J, \quad c_p = R/J + c_v = 60/778 + 0.3 = .077 + .3 = 0.377.$$

$$(_1Q_2)_p = W(c_p)(T_2 - T_1) = 3 \,(.377)\,(50) = 56.6 \text{ B.t.u. supplied.}$$

IV.–7. Molal Specific Heat.—When the unit of quantity is taken as the mol (M pounds), the specific heat is called the molal specific heat. It is sometimes denoted by

$$\gamma = Mc. \tag{IV–18}$$

Writing equation (IV–17) in this form,

$$Mc_p - Mc_v = \frac{MR}{J} = \frac{1545}{778.3} = 1.985. \tag{IV–19}$$

Thus, for perfect gases, the difference of the molal specific heats is a constant (1.985), and independent of the gas, that is for *any* perfect gas it requires 1.985 B.t.u.s more, to raise the temperature of one mol one degree F. when the heating is at constant pressure than when it is at constant volume.

It is interesting to note that this relationship is true whether the specific heats are independent of the temperature or not.

For a heating at constant pressure

$$c_p dt = c_v dt + \frac{Pdv}{J}. \tag{IV–20}$$

Differentiating the characteristic equation ($Pv = RT$), for a constant pressure change, $Pdv = Rdt$ and substituting, in (IV–20),

$$c_p dt - c_v dt = \frac{R}{J} dt \quad \text{or} \quad c_p - c_v = \frac{R}{J},$$

multiplying by M,

$$Mc_p - Mc_v = \frac{MR}{J} = 1.985,$$

which is true whether the specific heats are constant or of the form,

$$c = a + bT + cT^2, \text{ etc.}$$

Example 1.—From data in Table I, calculate the molal specific heats —Mc_p and Mc_v—for oxygen at 14.7 lbs. per sq. in. abs. and 32° F.
Solution.—$M = 32 \qquad c_p = 0.2175$

$Mc_p = 32 (.2175) = 6.96$ B.t.u. per mol per deg. F.

$Mc_v = Mc_p - 1.985 = 6.96 - 1.985 = 4.975$ B.t.u. per mol per deg. F.
or
$Mc_v = Mc_p - MR/J = 6.96 - 1545/778.3 = 4.975.$

Example 2.—Four mols of oxygen are heated at constant volume through a temperature range of 150° F.

Find the heat supplied.

Solution.—

$$(_1Q_2)_v = Mc_v(T_2 - T_1) \text{ (Number of mols)} = 4.975 \ (150) \ (4) = 2985 \text{ B.t.u.}$$

IV-8. Choice of Coördinate Axes.—A graphical representation of any change experienced by a gas can be made on any pair of coördinate axes desired, provided the coördinates chosen are functions of the state only, such as pressure, volume, temperature, intrinsic energy, heat content, or entropy. It is possible then to represent a change on any of the fifteen planes defined by these coördinates but two planes stand out as preeminently useful because in addition to picturing the change, the relation between the coördinates themselves is such that the areas between the curve and the axes have a physical significance. These outstanding pairs are the pressure-volume and the temperature-entropy axes. On the former, as explained in Art. III-11, the area between the curve and the v-axis represents the external work done during the process and on the latter the heat supplied for the process (see Art. III-14). Thus these axes are almost invariably selected for drawing the graphs of the changes discussed.

IV-9. Graphs of the Common Thermal Processes for Gases.— Consider the graphs of a perfect gas when passing through the common thermal changes in an orderly or reversible manner; those occurring at constant volume, at constant pressure, at constant temperature (isothermally) and adiabatically (at constant entropy).

The only constant volume change that can occur is when the substance receives or rejects heat. The graphs for the heating of a perfect gas at constant volume are shown at a in the adjacent figure. The answers to the questions are, for the PV axes, (1) upward, as the pressure increases, (2) neither to the right nor left, hence vertical, as the volume remains constant, and (3) straight, as the PV relation is of the first degree ($V_1 = V_2$). For the TS axes the graph goes (1) upward, as the temperature has risen, (2) to the right, as heat and thus entropy has been added, and (3) curved, as the equation connecting temperature and entropy is not of the first degree, $\left(S_2 - S_1 = Wc_v \log \dfrac{T_2}{T_1}\right)$. For a cooling the numbers 1 and 2 should be transposed.

Similarly, a heating at *constant pressure* (therefore an expansion) is shown by the graphs of b. If the numbers were transposed it would show a compression.

For the case of an *Isothermal* expansion (Fig. c), first consider the TS plane for which the answers are obviously, (1) neither upward nor downward, as T is constant, (2) to the right because heat is added to produce any isothermal expansion, and (3) a straight line.

On the PV plane, the volume increases, the pressure drops, as it is an expansion, thus the graph goes downward and to the right. It is a curved line because the equation representing the change ($PV = $ const.) is that of a rectangular hyperbola. For a *compression* the transposition of the numbers will make the graph applicable.

In a similar manner the graph of an *Adiabatic* change (reversible) is developed and shown in Fig. *d*. Here no heat, thus no entropy, was added and the graph on the TS axes is a vertical line. From 1 to 2 represents an

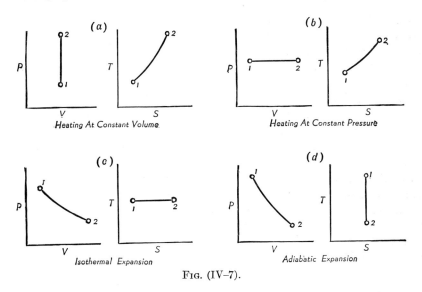

Fɪɢ. (IV–7).

expansion and transposing these, the graph would represent a *compression*. It is a curve on the PV axes as the equation for the adiabatic change ($PV^n = $ const.) is not of the first degree.

As pointed out earlier (Art. III–18), for a given point, the slope of the adiabatic is steeper than that of the isothermal and also the slope of the constant volume line is steeper than that of the line of constant pressure. This is true on both sets of coördinate axes and is most readily remembered if the comparison be made on the coördinate axes where the graphs show as straight lines. For example, on the PV plane it is obvious that the vertical (constant volume) line stands up steeper than the horizontal (constant pressure) line, and the same relation exists on the TS plane. Similarly, the vertical (adiabatic) line on the TS plane is steeper than the horizontal (isothermal) line, a relationship also true for the PV plane.

IV–10. Changes of State for a Perfect Gas.—When a gas undergoes a change from one state, having the properties, p_1, v_1, T_1, to another state, in which it has the properties, p_2, v_2, T_2, that change usually also involves the energy relations, q, u, and w, dealt with in the general energy equation, and most of the numerical problems consist of the determination of the final properties or the energy changes involved, in some clearly defined change.

Any *two* independent properties completely define the state of a gas, if these are known the third may be found from the characteristic equation, $Pv = RT$. If, knowing the original state, but *one* final property, together with the *path* from the original state, be known, the problem is still solvable, since another property for the final state can be determined from the data given by the path. To illustrate, consider a change from an initial state, p_1, v_1, T_1, to a final pressure p_2, by a constant volume path. Then $v_2 = v_1$ and two of the three final characteristic properties are known.

As already mentioned, there are four principal paths or routes by which changes are considered as proceeding, (1) constant volume, (2) constant pressure, (3) constant temperature (isothermal) and (4) adiabatic (thermally isolated). For these four a knowledge of the relation between p, v, T, of the initial and final states is essential. In addition to this, changes in other properties such as entropy, intrinsic energy, and heat content are important. Furthermore, the energy changes involved are of the utmost importance. Stated differently, we must be able to determine the heat supplied, the work done, and the change in the six common properties: Pressure (p), volume (v), temperature (t), intrinsic energy (u), entropy (s), and heat content (h), for these four common changes.

This might seem at first glance to be a rather formidable list, totaling as it does some thirty or more items, but further consideration will show that in several instances one expression holds for all types of change. This is true of the expression for intrinsic energy and also of that for heat content. Furthermore, there are other cases where the character of the change immediately imposes the condition of zero on certain variations, as in the case of the isothermal, where $dt = 0$, the adiabatic, where $dq = 0$, and the constant volume, where $dw = 0$.

As already shown, the general expression for the change in intrinsic energy is, $\int c_v dt$. For the perfect gas the specific heat is constant and

this becomes, $c_v(T_2 - T_1)$, thus for *all changes* of a *perfect gas* the following
is true.
$$u_2 - u_1 = c_v(T_2 - T_1).$$

Treating the general expression for change is heat content (enthalpy)
as $\int c_p dt$, in a similar manner it becomes, $c_p(T_2 - T_1)$, hence for *all
changes* of a *perfect gas* the following is true.
$$h_2 - h_1 = c_p(T_2 - T_1). \tag{IV-21}$$

IV-11. Constant Volume and Constant Pressure Processes. *Constant
Volume Change.*—For any change the characteristic equation may be
written,
$$\frac{P_1 v_1}{T_1} = \frac{P_2 v_2}{T_2} = R.$$

When the volume remains constant this becomes
$$\left(\frac{P_1}{T_1}\right)_v = \left(\frac{P_2}{T_2}\right)_v = \text{const.}$$

The *heat supplied* is
$$(dq)_v = c_v dt \quad \text{or} \quad (_1q_2)_v = c_v(T_2 - T_1). \tag{IV-22}$$

The *work done* $\left(\int P dv\right)$ is zero, as $dv = 0$, and the *change of intrinsic
energy* (since $u_k = u$ for a perfect gas) is from equation (IV-14),
$$du_k = c_v dt \quad \text{or} \quad u_{k1} - u_{k2} = c_v(T_2 - T_1). \tag{IV-23}$$

Constant Pressure Change.—For a change occurring at constant pressure
the pv property relationship is obtained by similarly modifying the characteristic equation. This becomes, when p is constant,
$$\left(\frac{v_1}{T_1}\right)_p = \left(\frac{v_2}{T_2}\right)_p = \text{const.}$$

The *heat supplied* is
$$(dq)_p = c_p dt \quad \text{or} \quad (_1q_2) = c_p(T_2 - T_1). \tag{IV-24}$$

The *work done* is
$$_1w_2 = \int_1^2 P dv = P \int_1^2 dv = P(v_2 - v_1), \tag{IV-25}$$

and, as before, the *intrinsic energy change* is
$$u_{k2} - u_{k1} = c_v(T_2 - T_1). \tag{IV-26}$$

Example 1.—Five pounds of air at 30 lbs. per sq. in. abs. and 35 cu. ft., are supplied with 400 B.t.u. of heat while the volume remains constant.

Find the change in each of the properties P, V, T, U, H, and also the work done and heat supplied.

$Solution.$—$T_1 = \dfrac{P_1V_1}{W(R)} = \dfrac{144\ (30)\ (35)}{5\ (53.35)} = 567°\ F.\ abs.$

$_1Q_2 = W(c_v)(T_2 - T_1)$ $\qquad T_2 - T_1 = \dfrac{_1Q_2}{W(c_v)} = \dfrac{400}{5\ (.171)} = 468°\ F.$

$T_2 = 567 + 468 = 1035°\ F.\ abs.$

$U_2 - U_1 = W(c_v)(T_2 - T_1) = 5\ (.171)\ (468) = 400\ B.t.u.$

$H_2 - H_1 = W(c_p)(T_2 - T_1) = 5\ (.24)\ (468) = 562\ B.t.u.$

$\dfrac{p_2}{p_1} = \dfrac{T_2}{T_1},\quad p_2 = \dfrac{T_2 p_1}{T_1} = \dfrac{1035\ (30)}{567} = 54.8\ lbs.\ per\ sq.\ in.\ abs.$

Pressure increases from 30 lbs. per sq. in. to 54.8 lbs. per sq. in.
Volume is constant.
Temperature increases 468° F.
Intrinsic energy increases 400 B.t.u.
Heat content increases 562 B.t.u.

$Work = \displaystyle\int Pdv = 0.$

$_1Q_2 = 400\ B.t.u.\ supplied.$

Example 2.—The temperature of a quantity of air initially at $p_1 = 30$ lbs. per sq. in. abs., $V_1 = 35$ cu. ft., $T_1 = 567°$ F. abs., is increased to $1035°$ F. abs., while the pressure remains constant.

Find the change in each of the properties P, V, T, U, H, and also the heat exchange and the work done.

$Solution.$—$W = \dfrac{P_1 v_1}{RT_1} = \dfrac{30\ (144)\ (35)}{53.35\ (567)} = 5\ lbs.$

$\dfrac{V_2}{V_1} = \dfrac{T_2}{T_1},\quad V_2 = \dfrac{T_2 V_1}{T_1} = \dfrac{1035\ (35)}{567} = 63.9\ cu.\ ft.$

$T_2 - T_1 = 1035 - 567 = 468°\ F.$

$U_2 - U_1 = W(c_v)(T_2 - T_1) = 5\ (.171)\ (468) = 400\ B.t.u.$

$H_2 - H_1 = W(c_p)(T_2 - T_1) = 5\ (.24)\ (468) = 562\ B.t.u.$

$_1Q_2 = W(c_p)(T_2 - T_1) = 5\ (.24)\ (468) = 562\ B.t.u.$

(The result for $_1Q_2$ is positive, thus heat was *supplied to* the substance.)
Pressure is constant.
Volume increases by $63.9 - 35 = 28.9$ cu. ft.
Temperature increases by $1035 - 567 = 468°$ F.
Intrinsic energy increases by 400 B.t.u.
Heat content increases by 562 B.t.u. which is also the heat supplied in this case.

$Work = P(V_2 - V_1) = 30\ (144)\ (28.9) = 124,800\ ft.\text{-}lbs.$ This is positive, thus work is done *by* the gas.

IV–12. Isothermal Process.—The characteristic equation, $\dfrac{Pv}{T} = R$, becomes $pv = $ const. when the temperature is made constant for isothermal changes, thus the *pv relationship* becomes

$$(p_1v_1)_T = (p_2v_2)_T = \text{const.} \qquad \text{(IV–27)}$$

Since by Joule's Law the intrinsic energy of a perfect gas depends upon its temperature only, there will be *no change in intrinsic energy* during an isothermal change $(dE = 0)$ and the general equation may be written,

$$dQ = 0 + \frac{dW}{J} \quad \text{or} \quad {}_1Q_2 = \int_1^2 \frac{PdV}{J}, \qquad \text{(IV–28)}$$

that is, *the heat supplied* during an isothermal expansion is equal to the thermal equivalent of the external work done.

To evaluate the expression for external work in terms of the *pv* properties, it is necessary to substitute for P in equation (IV–28) its value in terms of v obtained from equation (IV–27),

$$P = \frac{\text{const.}}{v}.$$

Then

$$\int Pdv \text{ becomes const.} \int \frac{dv}{v} = \text{const.} \log_e\left(\frac{v_2}{v_1}\right) = Pv \log_e\left(\frac{v_2}{v_1}\right)$$

and the *expression for work* reduces to

$$W = PV \log_e\left(\frac{V_2}{V_1}\right). \qquad \text{(IV–29)}$$

For a compression process where the final volume is less than the initial, the value of the above will be negative, thus indicating that work has been done *on* the gas instead of *by* the gas as in an expansion.

Example.—Five pounds of air at $p_1 = 30$ lbs. per sq. in. abs., $V_1 = 35$ cu. ft., are compressed isothermally to $p_2 = 150$ lbs. per sq. in. abs.

Find: Heat supplied or rejected, work done, and change in the properties P, v, T, u, and h.

Solution.—$P_1V_1 = P_2V_2$, $\quad V_2 = \dfrac{P_1V_1}{P_2} = 30\,(35)/150 = 7$ cu. ft.

Work $= P_1V_1 \log_e V_2/V_1 = 30\,(144)\,(35)\,(\log_e \tfrac{1}{5}) = 30\,(144)\,(35)\,(-1.6094)$
$= -243,200$ ft.-lbs.

${}_1Q_2 = {}_1W_2/J = -243,200/778 = -313$ B.t.u.

Pressure increases to 150 lbs. per sq. in. abs.

Volume decreases to 7 cu. ft.
Temperature is constant.
Intrinsic energy is constant ($c_v dt = 0$).
Heat content is constant ($c_p dt = 0$).
Work $= -$ 243,200 ft.-lbs., therefore done *on* the gas.
Heat exchange $= -$ 313 B.t.u., therefore heat *rejected*.

IV–13.   Adiabatic Process.—For an adiabatic change no heat, as such, is supplied, $dq = 0$, and the PV relationship may be derived as follows. Differentiating the characteristic equation we have

$$Pdv + vdP = Rdt,$$

from which

$$dt = \frac{P}{R} dv + \frac{V}{R} dp.$$

The general energy equation is

$$dq = c_v dt + \frac{Pdv}{J}.$$

In this dq is now zero, and substituting the value of dt from (IV–30) we have

$$0 = \frac{c_v P}{R} dv + \frac{c_v v}{R} dP + \frac{Pdv}{J},$$

but, $R = \dfrac{Pv}{T}$, and substituting

$$0 = c_v T \frac{dv}{v} + c_v T \frac{dP}{P} + \frac{RT}{J} \frac{dv}{v},$$

further, $R/J = c_p - c_v$,

$$0 = c_v T \frac{dv}{v} + c_v T \frac{dP}{P} + c_p T \frac{dv}{v} - c_v T \frac{dv}{v},$$

cancelling and dividing by $c_v T$, we have

$$0 = \frac{dP}{P} + \frac{c_p}{c_v} \frac{dv}{v},$$

replacing the specific heat ratio $\dfrac{c_p}{c_v}$ by k, and integrating, gives

$$\text{const.} = \log_e P + k \log_e v,$$

clearing of logs we have

$$Pv^k = \text{const.,} \qquad\qquad\qquad \text{(IV–30)}$$

or $P_1v_1^k = P_2v_2^k = $ const., which is the pv relation for an adiabatic change for any perfect gas.

Returning now to the general energy equation, $dq = du + pdv$, which becomes for adiabatic action

$$0 = du + \frac{dw}{J} \quad \text{or} \quad 0 = c_v dt + \frac{dw}{J},$$

$$_1w_2 = -(u_2 - u_1) \quad \text{or} \quad -Jc_v(T_2 - T_1), \qquad \text{(IV-31)}$$

which simply states that in an adiabatic expansion the work is done at the expense of the intrinsic energy and substitutes the intrinsic energy change of the perfect gas for the general expression.

It is usually more convenient to deal with the properties p and v, and equation (4) may be transformed into these terms by algebraic manipulation as follows:

$$_1w_2 = -Jc_v(T_2 - T_1),$$

substituting pv for T,

$$_1w_2 = -\frac{J}{R}c_v(P_2v_2 - P_1v_1),$$

but $R/J = c_p - c_v$,

thus

$$_1w_2 = -\frac{c_v}{c_p - c_v}(P_2v_2 - P_1v_1),$$

or

$$_1w_2 = \frac{P_2v_2 - P_1v_1}{1 - k}. \qquad \text{(IV-32)}$$

Example.—Five pounds of air at $p_1 = 150$ lbs. per sq. in. abs., $V_1 = 7$ cu. ft., expand adiabatically to 30 lbs. per sq. in.

Find the work done, the heat exchange, and change in properties P, v, T, u, h.

Solution.—$T_1 = \dfrac{P_1V_1}{W(R)} = \dfrac{150\,(144)\,(7)}{(5)\,(53.35)} = 567°$ F. abs.

$$V_2 = V_1\left(\frac{p_1}{p_2}\right)^{1/k} = 7\left(\frac{150}{30}\right)^{\frac{1}{1.4}} = 22.12 \text{ cu. ft.}$$

* This may be transformed by combination with the characteristic equation ($Pv = RT$) to give relations between P and T and between V and T, as follows:

$$\frac{T_1}{T_2} = \left(\frac{V_2}{V_1}\right)^{k-1}; \quad \frac{T_1}{T_2} = \left(\frac{P_1}{P_2}\right)^{\frac{k-1}{k}}.$$

For the details of this Transformation see Art. 60.

$$T_2 = T_1\left(\frac{p_2}{p_1}\right)^{\frac{k-1}{k}} = 567\left(\frac{1}{5}\right)^{\frac{1.4-1}{1.4}} = 567\left(\frac{1}{5}\right)^{.286}$$

$$= 567\ (.631) = 358°\ \text{F. abs. or} -102°\ \text{F.}$$

$$U_2 - U_1 = W(c_v)(T_2 - T_1) = 5\ (.171)\ (358 - 567) = 5\ (.171)\ (-209)$$

$$= -178.6\ \text{B.t.u.}$$

$$H_2 - H_1 = W(c_p)(T_2 - T_1) = 5\ (.24)\ (-209) = -\ 251\ \text{B.t.u.}$$

$$\text{Work} = \frac{P_1V_1 - P_2V_2}{K - 1} = \frac{[150\ (7) - 30\ (22.12)]\ 144}{1.4 - 1}$$

$$= \frac{386\ (144)}{.4} = 139{,}000\ \text{ft.-lbs.} = J(U_2 - U_1).$$

$$_1Q_2 = 0.$$

Pressure decreases to 30 lbs. per sq. in. abs.
Volume increases to 22.12 cu. ft.
Temperature decreases by $567 - 358 = 209°$ F.
Intrinsic energy decreases 178.6 B.t.u.
Heat content decreases 251 B.t.u.

IV–14.   The General Case (Polytropic Processes).   The four preceding cases are but specialized forms of a general one stating the property relations as $pv^n = $ const.,* in which n may be assigned any value but does not vary when so assigned.   Both the property and energy relations for these special cases may be derived by modifications of the value of n in this parent equation which is commonly called the *polytropic.*†

Considering first the property relations, if n be assigned the value *zero*, $p_1v_1^n = p_2v_2^n = $ const., becomes

$$p_1 = p_2 = \text{const.,}$$

which is true for the *constant pressure* change.

When n is given the value of *unity*, the polytropic becomes

$$p_1v_1 = p_2v_2 = \text{const.,}$$

which is the property relation for the *isothermal* change.

Giving n the value of $c_p/c_v = k$, it becomes

$$p_1v_1^k = p_2v_2^k = \text{const.,}$$

which is the property relation for the *adiabatic* change.

---

* It should be noted that $pv^n = $ const. is but a generalization from the pv relations for the four common processes; it is not based on any thermodynamic reasoning.

† From the Greek, meaning many-form.

When n is made *infinity*, we have

$$p_1 v_1^\infty = p_2 v_2^\infty = \text{const.,}$$

or

$$p_1^{\frac{1}{\infty}} v_1 = p_2^{\frac{1}{\infty}} v_2 = \text{const.,}$$

or

$$v_1 = v_2 = \text{const.,}$$

which is true for the *constant volume* change.

The *work done* during a polytropic expansion is

$$_1W_2 = \int_1^2 P dv = \text{const.} \int_1^2 V^{-n} dv$$

$$= \frac{P_2 V_2 - P_1 V_1}{1 - n}. \tag{IV–33}$$

If the same values of n that were used to obtain the property relations just discussed be substituted successively in this expression, there will result expressions for work identical with those previously derived, except in the case of the isothermal change. For this the polytropic form becomes $0/0$, an indeterminate expression. Thus when,

$n = 0$, we have the constant pressure change and $w = P(v_2 - v_1)$,

$n = 1$, we have the isothermal change and $w = 0/0$,

$n = k$, we have the adiabatic change and $w = \dfrac{P_2 v_2 - P_1 v_1}{1 - k}$,

$n = \infty$, we have the constant volume change and $w = 0$.

For the isothermal case where the expression is indeterminate, we are forced to revert to the original method for deriving the expression for work, see Art. IV–12.

The various expressions for the *heat supplied*, q, can be derived by substituting the proper values for n in the expression for the general specific heat (Art. IV–15), and using the resulting value in the expression, $_1q_2 = c_n(T_2 - T_1)$.

The expressions for intrinsic energy and heat content are the same for all cases $c_v(T_2 - T_1)$ and $c_p(T_2 - T_1)$ respectively, and are independent of n.

Example.—A quantity of air is compressed, from $p_1 = 15$ lbs. per sq. in. abs., $V_1 = 65$ cu. ft., $t_1 = 66°$ F., according to the path $PV^{1.21} = C$, to $p_2 = 180$ lbs. per sq. in. abs.

Find the work done, the heat exchange, and the change in the properties P, v, T, u, h.

$$\text{Solution.}—W = \frac{P_1 V_1}{RT_1} = \frac{15\,(144)\,(65)}{53.35\,(526)} = 5 \text{ lbs.}$$

$$V_2^{1.21} = \frac{p_1 V_1^{1.21}}{p_2} = \frac{15\,(65)^{1.21}}{180} = 13, \quad V_2 = 8.34 \text{ cu. ft.}$$

$$T_2 = \frac{P_2 V_2}{WR} = \frac{180\,(144)\,(8.34)}{5\,(53.35)} = 810° \text{ F. abs.}$$

$$W = \frac{P_1 V_1 - P_2 V_2}{n-1} = \frac{[15\,(65) - 180\,(8.34)]\,144}{1.21 - 1} = \frac{(-526)\,(144)}{.21}$$

$$= -361,000 \text{ ft.-lbs.,}$$

or,

$$W = \frac{WR\,(T_1 - T_2)}{n-1} = \frac{5(53.35)(-284)}{.21} = -361,000 \text{ ft.-lbs.}$$

$$U_2 - U_1 = W \times (c_v)(T_2 - T_1) = 5\,(.171)\,(284) = 244 \text{ B.t.u.}$$

$$_1Q_2 = (U_2 - U_1) + \frac{_1W_2}{J} = 244 - \frac{361,000}{778} = -220 \text{ B.t.u.}$$

$$H_2 - H_1 = W(c_p)(T_2 - T_1) = 5\,(.24)\,(284) = 341 \text{ B.t.u.}$$

Work = 361,000 ft.-lbs. done *on* the gas.
Heat *rejected* = 220 B.t.u.
Pressure increases to 180 lbs. per sq. in. abs.
Volume decreases to 8.34 cu. ft.
Temperature increases to 810° F. abs., or 350° F.
Intrinsic energy increases 244 B.t.u.
Heat content increases 341 B.t.u.

IV–15. Specific Heat for Polytropic Processes. The amount of heat required to change the temperature of one pound of a perfect gas one degree, when the heating is done in any regular manner (provided only that the change conforms to the general equation $pv^n = \text{const.}$), is termed the general specific heat. It is useful in problems dealing with air compressors, internal combustion engines and other devices using gases as the working fluid.

An expression for this specific heat, for the general or polytropic change, may be derived as follows:

$$dq = du + \frac{Pdv}{J},$$

for any perfect gas this may be written

$$_1q_2 = c_v(T_2 - T_1) + \frac{P_2v_2 - P_1v_1}{J(1 - n)},$$

but, $PV = RT$,

$$_1q_2 = c_v(T_2 - T_1) + \frac{R}{J}\frac{(T_2 - T_1)}{(1 - n)}$$

and $R/J = c_p - c_v$; also $_1q_2 = c_n(T_2 - T_1)$, where c_n signifies the general specific heat.

Then

$$_1q_2 = \left[c_v + \frac{c_p - c_v}{1 - n} \right](T_2 - T_1)$$

or

$$c_n = c_v + \frac{c_p - c_v}{1 - n}$$

$$= c_v \left(1 + \frac{k - 1}{1 - n} \right)$$

$$c_n = c_v \left[\frac{k - n}{1 - n} \right] \qquad \text{(IV–34)}$$

As an illustration of its application, let it be assumed that the indicator diagram of an internal combustion engine is available. From this the value of n for the compression curve is found to be 1.35 and it is further known that the specific heat at constant volume for the gases in the cylinder is 0.17 and k has the value 1.4, then for such a compression the value of the general specific heat will be

$$c_n = 0.17 \left(\frac{1.4 - 1.35}{1 - 1.35} \right)$$

$$= -\,0.0243.$$

From the indicator diagram, $p_1 = 14.7$ lbs. per sq. in. abs. and $T_1 = 520°$ F. abs., the final volume is one-fourth of the volume at the beginning of compression. The final pressure will be

$$p_2 = p_1 \left(\frac{V_1}{V_2} \right)^{1.35} = 14.7 \times 4^{1.35},$$

$$p_2 = 95.6 \text{ lbs. sq. in.}$$

The corresponding temperature will be

$$T_2 = \frac{13{,}760 \times 3.275}{53.35} = 846° \text{ F. abs.}$$

The heat supplied during the compression process will be

$$c_n(T_2 - T_1) = -0.0243 \times 326$$
$$= -7.92 \text{ B.t.u.}$$

This means that 7.92 B.t.u. were *withdrawn* from every pound of gas during this compression by the cooling system.

IV–16. Other Polytropic Relations.—The polytropic equation, $pv^n = $ const., may be transformed by combination with the characteristic equation, $Pv = RT$, to give relations between p and T, and between T and v, as follows:

$$p_1 v_1{}^n = p_2 v_2{}^n = \text{const.,}$$
$$p_1 v_1 v_1{}^{n-1} = p_2 v_2 v_2{}^{n-1},$$

but $Pv = RT$ and substituting we have

$$RT_1 v_1{}^{n-1} = RT_2 v_2{}^{n-1}$$

$$T_1 v_1{}^{n-1} = T_2 v_2{}^{n-1} = \text{const.} \quad \text{or} \quad \frac{T_1}{T_2} = \left(\frac{v_2}{v_1}\right)^{n-1}. \qquad \text{(IV–35)}$$

In a similar manner the T and P relation may be derived, it is

$$p_1{}^{\frac{1}{n}} v_1 = p_2{}^{\frac{1}{n}} v_2,$$

$$p_1{}^{\frac{1}{n}-1} p_1 v_1 = p_2{}^{\frac{1}{n}-1} p_2 v_2,$$

$$p_1{}^{\frac{1-n}{n}} T_1 = p_2{}^{\frac{1-n}{n}} T_2.$$

As n is usually greater than unity a more convenient form which avoids the use of negative exponents is obtained by writing this as

$$\frac{T_1}{T_2} = \left(\frac{p_1}{p_2}\right)^{\frac{n-1}{n}}. \qquad \text{(IV–36)}$$

IV–17. Evaluation of Change in Entropy for Various Processes.—In addition to the need of predicting the heat supplied, the work done, and the change in intrinsic energy, it is also important that we be able to determine the change of entropy which a perfect gas experiences for various changes. These are obtained by manipulating the fundamental energy equation, $dq = du + dw/J$, to accept the special conditions and combining it with the equation, defining the change of entropy for a reversible process,

$$dS = \frac{dQ}{T}.$$

Thus for a reversible change at *constant volume* the change of entropy for a perfect gas will be

$$dS = \frac{dQ}{T} = \frac{c_v dt}{T} \times W.$$

Integrating,

$$S_2 - S_1 = c_v \log_e \frac{T_2}{T_1} \times W. \tag{IV-37}$$

Similarly the entropy change for a reversible *constant pressure* process is

$$S_2 - S_1 = c_p \log_e \frac{T_2}{T_1} \times W. \tag{IV-38}$$

The entropy change for a reversible *adiabatic* process is zero, since by definition dQ is zero for any adiabatic process and $dS = \frac{dQ}{T}$ for all reversible processes, thus, $dS = 0$ and there results the important fact that *for any reversible adiabatic change the entropy remains constant.* Such changes are frequently called Isentropic.

The entropy change for an *isothermal* process can be obtained by a slight manipulation of the general equation for the effects of adding heat as follows:

$$dQ = dU + \frac{dW}{J},$$

for an isothermal change $dU = 0$ and thus $dQ = \frac{dW}{J}$, the change of entropy is, by definition,

$$dS = \frac{dQ}{T}.$$

Therefore

$$dS = \frac{dW}{JT} \quad \text{and} \quad S_2 - S_1 = \frac{PV \log_e \frac{V_2}{V_1}}{TJ} \tag{IV-39}$$

$$= WAR \log_e \frac{V_2}{V_1}. \tag{IV-40}$$

For the general case covering polytropic changes we may go from state 1 to state 2 by way of an intermediate state x so selected that a heating at constant volume to x followed by a cooling at constant pressure will bring

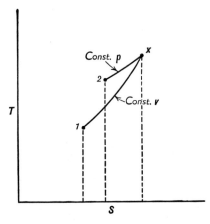

Fig. (IV–8).

the substance to state 2. For the change from 1 to x at constant volume, the change of entropy will be

$$\int_1^x dS = \int_1^x W c_v \frac{dt}{T}$$

and for the change from x to 2, which takes place at constant pressure, the change of entropy will be

$$\int_x^2 dS = \int_x^2 W c_p \frac{dT}{T}.$$

The entire change in going from 1 to 2 will be equal to the sum of the entropy changes of the individual steps, 1 to x, and x to 2.

$$s_x - s_1 = c_v \log_e \frac{T_x}{T_1} = c_v \log_e \frac{P_x}{P_1} \qquad \text{(since } V \text{ is Const.)},$$

$$s_2 - s_x = c_p \log_e \frac{T_2}{T_x} = c_p \log_e \frac{V_2}{V_x} \qquad \text{(since } P \text{ is Const.)}.$$

Adding these two,

$$s_2 - s_1 = c_v \log_e \frac{P_x}{P_1} + c_p \log_e \frac{V_2}{V_x}, \text{ but } P_x = P_2 \text{ and } V_x = V_1,$$

$$\therefore \quad s_2 - s_1 = c_v \log_e \frac{P_2}{P_1} + c_p \log_e \frac{V_2}{V_1}.* \qquad \text{(IV–41)}$$

This is the expression for the entropy change for any perfect gas when going from state 1 to state 2. Since entropy is a true property, a point function, it is independent of the path by which the change proceeds, so when evaluated by the above special paths it holds for any route, including the polytropic, $pv^n = $ const.

By substitution, the above equation may be transformed to use P and T or V and T as follows:

$$s_2 - s_1 = c_v \log_e \frac{T_2}{T_1} + \frac{R}{J} \log_e \frac{V_2}{V_1}, \qquad \text{(IV–42)}$$

$$s_2 - s_1 = c_p \log_e \frac{T_2}{T_1} + \frac{R}{J} \log_e \frac{P_1}{P_2}. \qquad \text{(IV–43)}$$

Example.—For each of the following changes of state for five pounds of air, determine the corresponding entropy change:

(a) Constant volume compression. $p_1 = 30$ lbs. per sq. in. abs., $V_1 = 35$ cu. ft., $T_1 = 567°$ F. abs., $p_2 = 54.8$ lbs. per sq. in. abs., $T_2 = 1035°$ F. abs.

Solution.—$S_2 - S_1 = W(c_v) \log_e T_2/T_1 = 5 (.171) \log_e 1035/567 = 5 (.171) (.6016) = 0.5135$ unit of entropy (increase).

---

* The entropy change for a perfect gas undergoing any sort of reversible change from state 1 to state 2, may also be obtained by substituting the value of the general specific heat c_n and integrating as follows:

$$c_n = c_v \left(\frac{k - n}{1 - n} \right)$$

$$\int_1^2 ds = \int_1^2 \frac{dq}{T} = \int_1^2 c_n \frac{dt}{T} = \int_1^2 c_v \left(\frac{k - n}{1 - n} \right) \frac{dt}{T}$$

$$= \int_1^2 \frac{c_p - nc_v}{1 - n} \frac{dt}{T}$$

$$s_2 - s_1 = \frac{1}{1 - n} \left[\int_1^2 c_p \frac{dt}{T} - n \int_1^2 c_v \frac{dt}{T} \right]$$

$$= \frac{1}{1 - n} \left[c_p \log_e \frac{T_2}{T_1} - nc_v \log_e \frac{T_2}{T_1} \right]$$

which reduces to

$$s_1 - s_2 = c_p \log_e \frac{v_2}{v_1} + c_v \log_e \frac{p_2}{p_1}.$$

(b) Expansion at constant pressure of 30 lbs. per sq. in. abs. $V_1 = 35$ cu. ft., $T_1 = 567°$ F. abs.; $V_2 = 63.9$ cu. ft., $T_2 = 1035°$ F. abs.

Solution.—$S_2 - S_1 = W(c_p) \log_e T_2/T_1 = 5 (.24) \log_e 1035/567 = 5 (.24) (.6016) = 0.72$ unit (increase).

(c) Isothermal compression. $p_1 = 30$ lbs. per sq. in. abs., $V_1 = 35$ cu. ft.; $p_2 = 150$ lbs. per sq. in. abs.

Solution.—$S_2 - S_1 = W(AR) \log_e p_1/p_2 = \dfrac{5 (53.35)}{778} \log_e 30/150 =$

$\dfrac{5 (53.35) (-1.0094)}{778} = - 0.552$ unit (decrease).

(d) Adiabatic (reversible) expansion. $p_1 = 150$ lbs. per sq. in. abs., $V_1 = 7$ cu. ft.; $p_2 = 30$ lbs. per sq. in. abs.

Solution.—For the reversible adiabatic there is no change in entropy.

(e) Compression according to $PV^{1.21} = C$. $p_1 = 15$ lbs. per sq. in. abs., $V_1 = 65$ cu. ft.; $p_2 = 180$ lbs. abs., $V_2 = 8.33$ cu. ft.

Solution.—

$$S_2 - S_1 = W\left(c_p \log_e \frac{V_2}{V_1} + c_v \log_e \frac{p_2}{p_1}\right) = 5 \left(.24 \log_e \frac{8.33}{65} + .171 \log_e \frac{180}{15}\right)$$

$$= 5 [(.24) (-2.054) + .171 (2.48)]$$

$$= 5 (-.4925 + .424) = 5 (-.0685) = - .3425 \text{ unit (decrease)}.$$

IV–18. Determination of Exponent for Polytropic Processes.—Actual expansions and compressions of air and the various gases treated as perfect are rarely exactly either isothermal or adiabatic but usually follow paths intermediate between these two which serve in a manner as limiting processes. If the changes are orderly, that is, without jerks or turbulence, or other irregular action, these actual changes can be represented usually by the equation of the polytropic,

$$p_1 v_1^n = p_2 v_2^n = \text{const.}$$

For such cases n can be determined readily from the curve of the actual indicator diagram if the equation is put in slightly different form,

$$\frac{p_1}{p_2} = \left(\frac{v_2}{v_1}\right)^n.$$

Taking the logs of both sides,

$$\log p_1 - \log p_2 = n(\log v_2 - \log v_1),$$

or

$$n = \frac{\log p_1 - \log p_2}{\log v_2 - \log v_1}.$$

Using this and substituting the values of p and v read for any two points on the curve n is readily solved for. For example, the indicator diagram from an air compressor (with zero clearance) is shown in Fig. (IV–9), readings from the compression curve give for point 1, $p = 80$ lbs. abs., $v = 0.35 \times$ stroke, and for point 2, $p = 25$ lbs. abs., $v = 0.9 \times$ stroke. The actual cylinder volumes are proportional to the stroke plus clearance for any piston position and it is more convenient to use them. Thus,

$$n = \frac{\log 80 - \log 25}{\log 0.9 - \log 0.35},$$

$$= \frac{1.90309 - 1.39794}{(9.95424 - 10) - (9.54407 - 10)}$$

$$= \frac{0.50515}{0.41017}, = 1.23.$$

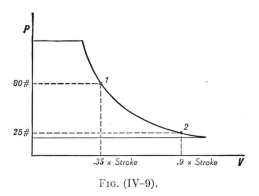

FIG. (IV–9).

To allow for clearance a line of zero volume should be erected spaced the amount of the clearance beyond the terminal position of the piston and the volumes measured from that.

IV–19. Intrinsic Energy and Heat Content of Perfect Gases.— Expressions for intrinsic energy and heat content in terms of specific heat and temperature are convenient, and, especially for perfect gases, are the most useful form for computing any change in these properties.

In general, as already noted (Art. IV–6), the change in intrinsic energy is

$$du = c_v dt,$$

or

$$u_2 - u_1 = \int_1^2 c_v dt.$$

Also the change in heat content has been shown to be (Art. IV–10),

$$dh = c_p dt,$$

or

$$h_2 - h_1 = \int_1^2 c_p dt.$$

For the perfect gas the specific heats are constant and these expressions become

$$u_2 - u_1 = c_v(T_2 - T_1) \qquad\qquad \text{(IV–44)}$$

and

$$h_2 - h_1 = c_p(T_2 - T_1), \qquad\qquad \text{(IV–45)}$$

providing the datum of Temp. measurement be taken as the absolute zero. This is the same as assuming that at absolute zero both the intrinsic energy and heat content are zero.

Thus the expression for the intrinsic energy for any state of a perfect gas is $u = c_v T$, and the expression for the heat content for any state is $h = c_p T$.

Example.—Find the intrinsic energy and heat content, based on absolute zero, of air at 80° F.

Solution.—Both properties are expressed in B.t.u. per lb. of the substance.

$$u = c_v T = .171 (80 + 460) = .171 (540) = 92.2 \text{ B.t.u.}$$
$$h = c_p T = .24 (540) = 129.6 \text{ B.t.u.}$$

IV–20. Throttling.—So far adiabatic expansions have been considered as always productive of useful work, i.e., the pushing out of a piston against an external resistance or the production of kinetic energy in the issuing jet, and in these cases heat energy leaves the substance in amount equivalent to the work done.

There are many cases in actual practice where a different sort of adiabatic expansion is encountered, where there is a drop from a condition of high pressure and temperature to one of lower pressure and temperature without any useful work being done and thus no energy going from the fluid in the form of external work, as, for example, when steam passes through a reducing valve or a partially opened throttle valve. Such a chaotic or turbulent flow through restricted openings with attendant pressure drop is called *throttling* or *wire drawing*. Such processes are essentially changes in which the total energy of the fluid undergoes no diminution or quantitative change but does undergo a degradation or qualitative change to a state of lower availability.

A throttling process may be defined as *an adiabatic expansion of a flowing fluid during which no useful work is done.* For such a process the heat content remains constant. This may be shown as follows: consider a tube of non-conducting material arranged as in Fig. (IV–10) with a disc having a small opening in it inserted at the termination of the small or

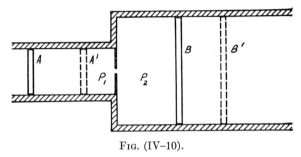

FIG. (IV–10).

high-pressure section. If the flow is continuous the total energy of the fluid approaching the orifice must equal the total energy it possesses as it passes along the tube after leaving the orifice. By total energy is meant not only the heat energy but the sum of all the energies possessed by the flowing fluid, there would be the kinetic energy of the flowing stream, the heat energy intrinsic to the fluid and the energy stored up in the form of the work done on the fluid to push it into place against the existing pressure. Hence the

$$\text{Total energy of approaching fluid} = KE_1 + U_1 + AP_1V_1,$$
$$\text{Total energy of leaving fluid} = KE_2 + U_2 + AP_2V_2.$$

If the sectional areas at A and B are proportional to the specific volumes before and after passing the orifice, the kinetic energies of the flowing stream approaching and leaving are equal ($KE_1 = KE_2$), and these terms can be dropped from further consideration. Furthermore, the heat equivalent of the kinetic energies due to the velocities usually encountered in pipes is small compared to the heat energies involved, and even if the areas of the pipes were the same, the corrective term to allow for the increase in the leaving velocity would be trivial and is rarely applied.

The work done *on* the fluid approaching the orifice and done *by* the fluid after passing through the constriction is in each case the product of the respective pressure and corresponding volume, as may be demonstrated by imagining phantom pistons at A and B. As the pressure at A is higher than at B the flow will be to the right and will be in the prime positions after a given weight of the fluid has passed through the orifice. The work done by A *on the substance* is P_1V_1 and the work done *by the substance* on B is P_2V_2.

As the energy totals for the approaching and leaving fluid must be equal we have

$$KE_1 + U_1 + AP_1V_1 = KE_2 + U_2 + AP_2V_2.$$

For the reason just mentioned, KE may be assumed equal to KE and $U + APV = H$ by definition, hence,

$$H_1 = H_2$$

or, *the heat content remains constant for a throttling operation.*

This fact that the heat content does not change during a throttling operation is very important. It is general and applies to any flowing fluid undergoing a frictional drop in pressure. It has been used to define heat content, i.e., as that property which remains constant during a throttling change.

IV–21. Joule's Law and Actual Gases.—Joule's Law as enunciated for the *perfect* gas was to the effect that no matter what change took place in the properties, so long as no energy had been supplied from or rejected to outside sources, the temperature remained constant. The intrinsic energy thus remaining constant was a function solely of the temperature, consisted entirely of sensible heat (*kinetic* molecular energy), and could be evaluated as $u = c_vT$.

In Joule's experiments for demonstrating this, the air flowed in an unresisted expansion from the high-pressure vessel to the low-pressure one, and the average temperature of the bath surrounding the entire apparatus remained apparently unchanged. Actually there had been, however, a slight drop in temperature (about .003° C.) but so slight that it could not be detected by this form of apparatus. Suspecting the existence of a cooling effect which had escaped detection, Joule, together with Wm. Thomson (Lord Kelvin), began a series of tests to further investigate it. They modified the earlier apparatus by replacing the stop-cock between the air vessels with a plug of porous material and arranged for a continuous flow. Air was supplied to the plug at constant pressure, the plug exerted a continuous throttling effect and lowered the pressure without the air doing any external work. Care was taken to make the process adiabatic and, with the pressures maintained constant, the throttling process itself could be carefully studied.

It was found that all the gases experimented with underwent *some* change of temperature during this "no work" expansion. For the so-called permanent gases it was extremely small, for those more readily liquefiable it was greater, while for that imaginary fluid, the perfect gas, it should have been zero because that, by definition, would conform exactly to the laws of both Boyle and Joule.

The change in temperature, usually a cooling, which any gas undergoes when passing through a throttled expansion, is now called the *Joule-Thomson Effect*, and its investigation has furnished much data concerning the properties of actual gases and vapors.

IV-22. Joule-Thomson Effect.—In the original experiments for investigating this effect, as made by Joule and Thomson, air was the medium

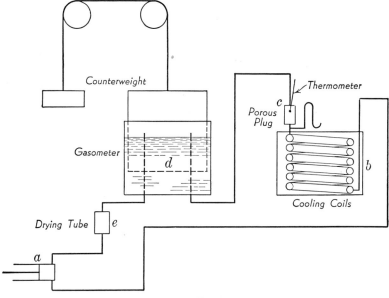

Fig. (IV-11).

used, later carbon dioxide and other gases were also studied. The modifications of the original Joule apparatus permitted the segregation of the throttling process and its study as a separate phenomenon. The apparatus used is shown diagrammatically in Fig. (IV-11) and consisted of an air compressor (*a*) supplying gas at a uniform pressure, and cooled to a constant temperature in the coil (b), to the throttling plug at (c). Immediately on leaving the plug its temperature was observed and the quantity of gas flowing was measured by the gasometer (d) from which it returned to the air compressor passing through the drying tube (e) on the way.

The experiments had these salient features, pressures were maintained constant on both the high-pressure and low-pressure sides, the flow through the plug was adiabatic, i.e., thermally isolated, and the temperatures of the flowing stream were very accurately measured before and after passing through the throttling plug. In its most successful form the plug itself consisted of a boxwood shell firmly stuffed with silk wool, the whole sur-

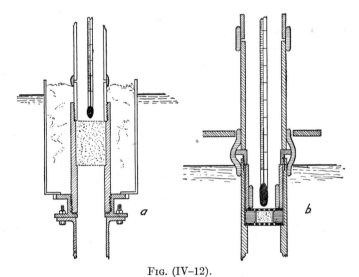

FIG. (IV–12).

rounded by cotton wool lightly packed in a metal cylinder which served as an insulating jacket. The details of this are shown at (a) of Fig. (IV–12). This type of plug, because of its large thermal capacity, was slow in reaching a condition of equilibrium and was superseded by one like (b) for the later experiments.

Without their stating it in just this form, the problem was one of finding whether the intrinsic energy possessed by a gas was solely of the kinetic form or partly kinetic and partly potential, corresponding to sensible heat and disgregation energies respectively.

The most general form of the energy equation is

$$dq = du + A\,dw, \qquad\qquad \text{(IV–46)}$$

separating the intrinsic energy, u, into its kinetic and potential subdivisions, u_k and u_p, it becomes

$$dq = du_k + du_p + Adw. \qquad \text{(IV–47)}$$

If no heat was supplied during the experiment and no external work done ($dq = 0$ and $dw = 0$), then the intrinsic energy change should remain constant ($du = 0$). As the *total* intrinsic energy *might* be of both kinetic and potential form and the kinetic form (du_k), or sensible heat, could be measured by a thermometer, then observations of the exit temperature would indicate whether the gas was perfect or not. If the temperature did not change ($dt = 0$) the gas was perfect; if it did change, then, while the *total* intrinsic energy had remained constant ($du = 0$), the kinetic part of it had changed and there must have been a converse effect on the potential or disgregation part since the *sum* still had to remain unchanged ($du_k + du_p = 0$).

With Joule's original apparatus the expansion was truly unresisted and the entire system underwent a change without change of *intrinsic energy*. In the porous plug experiment only the flow through the plug was under investigation. This was a pure throttling process, therefore, a process occurring at constant *heat content*. (See Art. (IV–20).) *

The cooling effect in the two cases is thus slightly different but for the perfect gas each would be zero.

The change in temperature per unit change in pressure for the *throttled* flow is called the Joule-Thomson Coefficient and has been determined for many gases. It may be written

$$\mu = \left(\frac{dt}{dp}\right)_h$$

and serves as an excellent criterion for measuring the departure of actual gases from the perfect gas. The smaller the Joule-Thomson Coefficient the less *imperfect* is the gas. It can be readily evaluated by throttling experiments and has been so determined for many gases and vapors. Such measurements are of great value for determining certain other properties of these gases† and are of particular service in commercial refrigeration and

---

* In Joule's original experiments the system underwent a *process* change and in the porous plug experiments there was a change in a continuously flowing medium. Irreversible adiabatic changes of the former type occur at constant *intrinsic energy* while irreversible adiabatic changes of the latter type occur at constant *heat content*.

† Throttling experiments on steam were used by Davis to accurately determine the heat content of saturated steam. *Proc. Am. Soc. Mech. Engrs.*, Vol. 30 (1908).

the production of extremely low temperatures necessary for liquefying gases.

For air this cooling effect amounts to about 3/100 of a degree F. (0.0313° F.) for every pound of throttled pressure drop when throttled from pressures of 80 lbs. per sq. inch to atmospheric conditions while for Carbon Dioxide under similar conditions it is over four times as great (0.143° F.), and for saturated steam at 20 lbs. per sq. inch pressure throttled to atmospheric conditions it is over one-half a degree (0.61° F.) per lb. drop; for Hydrogen at atmospheric pressure and temperature it is negative, i.e., a heating effect.

IV-23. Actual Gases and Their Divergence from " Perfect."—Thus far our efforts have been spent on the consideration of the characteristics and thermal changes of an admittedly hypothetical substance, the perfect gas, in order to thoroughly understand fundamental principles by illustrating their application to a substance of especially simple structure. It will now be interesting to see how closely actual gases conform to these perfect gas laws, especially those gases commonly entering into engineering work, and what corrective factors it will be necessary to apply to our earlier deductions when dealing with them.

Because, with their limited facilities, they were unable to liquefy, Oxygen, Nitrogen, Air and Hydrogen, these were classed by the early chemists as *permanent* gases, a name which still persists, but now quite without significance, as all have been liquefied and even solidified by modern methods. These are characteristic, however, of a group which at ordinary conditions of pressure and temperature are so far removed from the conditions necessary to effect a change of phase that their departure from perfect gas action is slight and no hesitation exists in treating them as perfect. For these the general characteristic equation, $Pv = \dfrac{1545}{M} T$, serves for all conditional relations and the general energy equation, $dq = du + \dfrac{dw}{J}$, simplified into the form, $dq = c_v dt + \dfrac{dw}{J}$ is sufficient for all energy relations. The limitations, however, should be carefully kept in mind, namely, that these have assumed constancy of specific heats and strict conformity to the laws of Boyle, Charles and Joule.

A substance may exist normally in three distinct states or phases, solid, liquid, and gaseous, and, in addition to these, in two transitional states which cover the periods during which the substance is changing from one to another of these normal phases. These transitional states are the processes of melting and of vaporization, occurring when the substance is changing from a solid to a liquid and from a liquid to a gas, respectively. All these states are differentiated one from another (provided the chemical structure retains its integrity) solely by the substance having progressively more and more intrinsic energy, i.e., by variations in molecular activity and molecular aggregation. To take, for example, a most familiar substance, water, it may exist as ice, liquid water, or superheated steam, corresponding respectively to the solid, liquid, and gaseous phases. These phases may be reached in succession by the continued addition of heat, and, furthermore, the substance in achieving them passes through the intermediate stages of melting and vaporization or boiling.

The actual changes in molecular arrangement which take place are somewhat as follows: with ice well below the freezing point the molecules are moving with translatory motion but of an oscillatory character about fixed centers. Here the mutually attracting forces are so strong that the relative position of one molecule with reference to its neighbors remains the same. The molecules wiggle but do not wander. As heat is added, the translatory velocity of the molecules, and therefore their kinetic energy, increases and is indicated by a rise in temperature. This is shown diagrammatically in a and b of Fig. (IV–13). Further addition of heat continues this process until the ice reaches the melting temperature, the transition to the liquid state then begins (b). At this point the molecular velocities have become so great that the attractive forces between the molecules no longer restrict them to relatively fixed positions and they are continually breaking away from one group and flying to another, thus wandering freely about. This change (b-c) requires additional energy to separate the molecules against their attractive bonds, but it all occurs without further increase of their translatory velocities, thus without increase of temperature. The molecules now move in orbits instead of oscillating, and when all have achieved this motion the ice is " melted " and the substance is in the liquid phase.

A further addition of heat will then speed up the molecules to still faster velocities, evidenced by a rising temperature which will continue until velocities are reached, which are so great that again the dynamic equilibrium of the entire group breaks down and a new state of aggregation begins to take place, (d), the molecules now breaking away from their orbital paths and traveling in paths that approach more nearly to straight lines. Just as in the earlier transitional process, melting, this transition from the liquid to the gaseous phase, vaporization, requires heat energy to tear apart or disgregate the existing molecular aggregation, and the process of vaporization (d, e) proceeds as fast as this energy is supplied but without

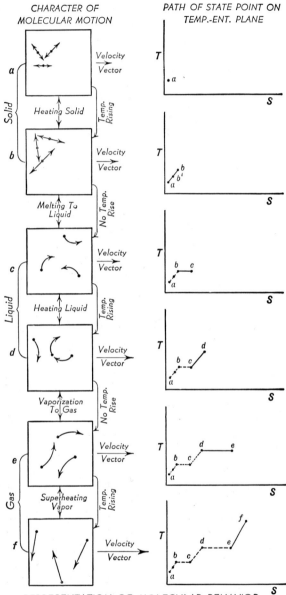

CHARACTER OF MOLECULAR MOTION

PATH OF STATE POINT ON TEMP.-ENT. PLANE

REPRESENTATION OF MOLECULAR BEHAVIOR
RESULTING FROM SUCCESSIVE HEAT ADDITIONS

FIG. (IV–13).

change in molecular velocities or temperature until the entire mass has changed state. When this is finished and the substance is entirely vaporized (*e*), then further addition of heat, with the pressure kept constant, will result in increased molecular velocities and increased temperature (*f*). This increase of temperature above that possessed during the vaporization period is called the *superheat*.

When well above the temperature of vaporization they continue indefinitely in paths that are practically straight lines unless intercepted by the walls of the containing vessel or collision with other molecules, and the substance is then in the gaseous state.

From this brief outline of the changes in molecular behavior corresponding to the changes of phase it is obvious that the only state which is at all similar to that of the perfect gas is the superheated vapor phase, and for this the greater the superheat the more closely will the action parallel that of the perfect gas. It is to be expected that vapors which are but slightly superheated will have molecular paths still feeling the influence of adjacent molecular attractions as the separation, while great, is not sufficient for the interattractions to be entirely negligible, and thus their paths must have some curvature. Strictly, it would not be until the gas were superheated an infinite amount that it would become truly perfect. In fact though, since we are dealing with intermolecular attractive forces which, like gravity, decrease very rapidly with increasing separation, the divergence rapidly decreases with increasing superheat, and vapors well removed from the saturation zone behave much like perfect gases.

IV-24. Critical Phenomena.—The changes mentioned in the preceding paragraph were considered as occurring with the pressure kept constant. The same changes could also be brought about by the continued addition of heat while the substance is kept at constant temperature. This implies that the original state is of great pressure and the substance is permitted to expand, but with just enough heat continually supplied to keep the temperature constant throughout the various processes. To illustrate, we may imagine a cylinder like that of the Carnot engine (Art. (V-6)), but filled with a liquid under great pressure and resting on a source of heat of infinite capacity and constant temperature. If the load on the piston be reduced the volume will increase slightly, the remaining load is pushed up a small distance and the energy for doing this work is supplied in the form of heat from the source, but without the temperature of either the source or the fluid changing (Isothermal Expansion). At first the fluid will remain a liquid, but when the pressure is reduced to that at which the liquid will begin to boil when at the temperature of the source, vaporization will begin.

This will continue at this pressure and temperature as heat is supplied from the source until the liquid is entirely vaporized. Further reduction of pressure then results in rapidly increasing volumes.

In practice, however, the experiments were carried out in the converse order, i.e., by isothermal compression instead of expansion and heat was removed in just sufficient amounts to keep the temperature constant throughout. Such an experiment is shown on the PV and TS planes in Fig. (IV–14). a–b represents the isothermal compression of a superheated

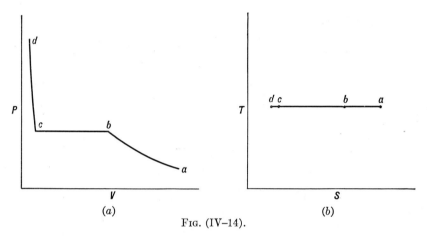

(a)   (b)

Fig. (IV–14).

vapor and approximates the rectangular hyperbola representative of the isothermal compression of the perfect gas. At b the substance begins to condense and this continues as fast as the heat is removed until at c it has been entirely liquefied. The curve from c to d represents the isothermal compression of the liquid and is characterized by the slight reduction in volume which accompanies even very large pressure increments.

Curves of this sort were actually determined experimentally by Andrews in a classical series of experiments published in 1869 and 1876.* Fig. (IV–15). It was noticed that on these isothermal curves that portion which represented the condensation process ($a - b$) grew less and less as isothermals of increasing temperature were plotted, and, furthermore, that above a certain temperature there were no abrupt changes in the curve from one end to the other.

If on the lower isothermals, where the changes of phase are well defined, a dotted contour line be drawn connecting the points of inflection between the superheated and vapor phases and another connecting those between

* *Phil. Trans.*, 1869, Part 11, pp. 575 and 1876; Part 11, p. 421.

the liquid and vapor phases, it will be seen that these bend toward each other and meet at the point k. This point is called the Critical Point. An isothermal T_4, Fig. (IV–15), just touching this critical point would be at a temperature called the Critical Temperature. It is sometimes defined as that temperature above which it is impossible to liquefy a gas by pressure alone, but the preceding statement is preferable as it does not rest on any subordinate conception as to exactly what state the molecular aggregation

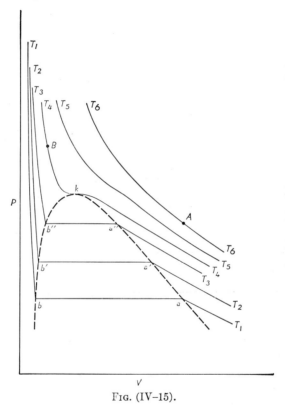

Fig. (IV–15).

must be in order to be classed as a liquid. The pressure at the Critical Point is called the Critical Pressure. Both the Critical Temperature and the Critical Pressure define limits above which the fluid cannot exist as a mixture part vapor and part liquid or, as will be defined later, as a saturated vapor.

In order to be liquefied a gas must be cooled below its critical temperature and be compressed to a pressure at least equal to the vapor pressure of the temperature of compression, or, conversely, be compressed to the critical pressure and cooled to any temperature below the critical temperature.

The diagram of Fig. (IV–15) may be translated also to the Temperature-Entropy coördinates and is shown in Fig. (IV–16). Here the isothermals are horizontal lines proceeding from right to left as the compression progresses and heat is removed. The dotted line, as before, indicates the limits of the vapor phase and is sometimes referred to as the *vapor dome.* In both of these figures the area under the dotted line represents the vapor phase of which the essential characteristic is that the liquid is at boiling temperature in contact with its vapor, and the entire mixture is *always at*

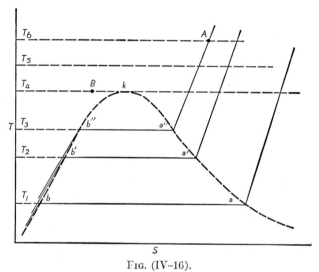

Fig. (IV–16).

this temperature. This temperature is of course different for different pressures but a given temperature is coincident with one and only one pressure. This rigid binding together of pressure with temperature is the outstanding characteristic of the true vapor phase.*

The dotted line ka is called the saturated vapor line and the other branch kb is called the saturated liquid line. For lines of constant pressure the state point is in the superheated vapor region when it is to the right of ka and is in the liquid region when to the left of kb. As long as this is not above the critical condition or crest of the vapor dome there is little

---

* When so existing the vapor is called a *saturated* vapor and the liquid a saturated liquid, another instance of thermodynamic misnomer as a more correct term would be, vapor (or liquid) *at boiling conditions.*

confusion in mentally picturing the state of the substance as a gas or as a liquid, according to whether it lies to the right or left of the vapor dome, but above the critical state there is a sort of no man's land in which an exact definition of phase becomes difficult.

It is obvious that points such as A would be considered as in the superheated vapor or gaseous phase and points like B would probably be considered in the liquid phase, but when it is realized that one can pass from the superheated vapor state of A to the highly compressed liquid state of B without going through the saturated vapor phase at all, it becomes difficult to say exactly when the transition occurred without an exact definition of what state of molecular activity and aggregation shall be called a liquid.

TABLE II
(Condensed from International Critical Tables)

Substance	Boiling Point (Atmospheric), °F.	Critical Temperature, °F.	Critical Pressure, Atmospheres
1. Air..........................	−317.6	−220.3	37.2
2. Helium.......................	−452.0	−450.2	2.26
3. Hydrogen.....................	−422.9	−399.8	12.8
4. Nitrogen.....................	−320.4	−232.8	33.5
5. Carbon monoxide (CO)..........	−313.6	−218.2	35.0
6. Oxygen......................	−297.2	−181.8	49.7
7. Argon.......................	−302.3	−188.3	48.0
8. Methane (CH_4)...............	−258.5	−116.5	45.8
9. Nitric oxide (NO).............	−239.8	−137.2	65.0
10. Ethylene (C_2H_4)............	−155.0	49.5	50.9
11. Carbon dioxide (CO_2).........	−109.3	88.0	73.0
12. Ethane (C_2H_6)...............	−127.5	89.8	48.8
13. Nitrous oxide (N_2O)...........	−129.1	97.7	71.7
14. Hydrogen sulfide (H_2S)........	− 74.9	212.7	88.9
15. Ammonia (NH_3)...............	− 28.0	270.3	111.5
16. Sulfur dioxide (SO_2)...........	14.0	315.0	77.7
17. Ether ($C_4H_{10}O$)...............	101.8	380.8	35.5
18. Alcohol, grain (CH_4O).........	147.3	464.0	78.7
19. Alcohol, wood (C_2H_6O)..........	173.0	469.6	63.1
20. Chloroform ($CHCl_3$).............	142.2	505.4	.....
21. Carbon disulfide (CS_2)...........	115.3	523.4	76.0
22. Benzene (C_6H_6)................	176.0	551.3	47.7
23. Water......................	212.0	705.4	217.7

Table II gives the critical data for a large number of common fluids. Those above the first heavy line are usually treated as perfect gases, those between that and the next heavy line are so treated only when in the highly superheated state, and those below the second heavy line are rarely considered as gases except occasionally for low pressures and high superheats. For these latter the properties for the liquid, vapor, and superheated vapor phase are usually tabulated from experimental observations and computations are based on these.

IV–25. Van der Waals' Equation.—No gas follows the perfect gas laws exactly and computations by the perfect gas characteristic equation give results always divergent from exactitude. Where the divergence is so slight as to be of no importance in the practical application under consideration the simplicity of the perfect gas equation warrants its use. There are increasing instances, however, where the need of a more accurate characteristic equation is felt. This is particularly true for very high pressures, especially if accompanied by high temperatures. Under these conditions both the size of the molecules and their proximity one to another need to be considered. Where, for the perfect gas, the volume occupied by the molecules themselves was zero, because they were considered as mathematical points possessing mass, actually they do occupy some space. As long as this space is but an extremely small proportion of the space occupied by the gas it may be neglected, but that which was a very small proportion at normal pressures may become quite an appreciable percentage when the gas is compressed to a much smaller volume, since the volume occupied by the molecules themselves remains the same. Furthermore, while in the low-pressure state the molecules were so remote from one another that it was entirely justifiable to neglect the mutual attractive forces existing between them and tending to divert them from straight-line paths, when the compression process has placed them much nearer together these attractive forces may have become sufficiently increased to also have an appreciable effect.

To correct for these influences there have been proposed many characteristic equations for the actual gas. Probably the best known of which is that proposed by Van der Waals which is as follows:

$$(p + a/v^2)(v - b) = RT$$

The second term in parentheses is supposed to represent the free volume left after deducting the volume of the molecules themselves represented by the constant b. The increase in the attractive forces tends to help keep the gas together and thus augments the pressure exerted from the outside. This is quantitatively evaluated by the corrective term a/v^2 in the first parenthetical expression. Values of the constants a and b are listed in the following table.

TABLE III

VAN DER WAALS' CONSTANTS

Calculated from Critical Data from International Critical Tables

	a	b
Air....................	344	.587
Helium.................	275	.379
Hydrogen..............	625	.425
Nitrogen..............	343	.617
Carbon monoxide........	373	.629
Oxygen.................	347	.509
Argon..................	344	.516
Methane...............	576	.682
Nitric oxide.............	353	.452
Ethylene...............	1141	.912
Carbon dioxide..........	918	.684
Ethane.................	1382	1.025
Nitrous oxide...........	970	.709
Hydrogen sulphide........	1141	.690
Ammonia...............	1070	.596
Sulphur dioxide..........	1730	.909
Ether..................	4460	2.165
Grain alcohol...........	2410	1.070
Wood alcohol...........	3065	1.342
Carbon disulphide........	2850	1.181
Benzene................	4810	1.932
Water.................	1398	.488

In using Van der Waals' Equation with the above constants, the pressure is in standard atmospheres, the volume is cu. ft. per mol. and $R = 0.729$.

IV–26. Other Characteristic Equations.—Beside the characteristic equation proposed by Van der Waals there are several others which have received considerable attention, notably those of Clausius, Dieterici and Keyes.*

* The equations of Clausius and Dieterici, as presented by Ewing in his "Thermodynamics for Engineers," are as follows:

Clausius,
$$p = \frac{RT}{v - b} - \frac{a'}{T(v - b')^2}.$$

Dieterici,
$$p = \frac{RTe^{\frac{-a}{RTv}}}{(v - b)}$$

where a, a', b and b' are constants for a given gas and e is the base of the Naperian system of logarithms (2.7183).

The equation of Keyes is the most recent and much work has been done in determining its constants for various gases. His equation has the general form of

$$p = \frac{RT}{v - \delta} - \frac{a'}{(v + b')^2},$$

where a' and b' are constants for any given gas and δ is of the form, $\log_{10} \delta = a - \dfrac{b}{v}$, involving the additional constants a and b.

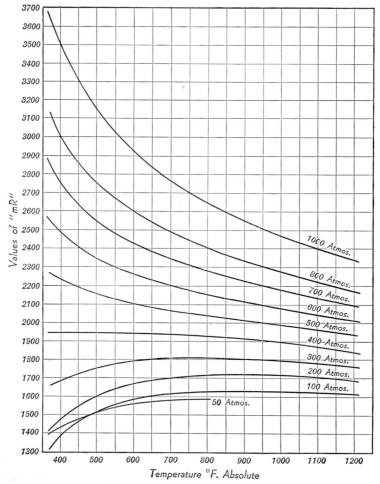

FIG. (IV–17). Universal Gas Constant (mR) at High Pressures for the Diatomic Gases; CO, O, N, Air. From Experimental Data on N and CO obtained by Bartlett and Associates, Journal of Am. Chem. Soc., 1928 and 1930.

For this equation the constants are as follows:

	R	a	b	a'	b'
Air.....................	2.8332	0.20113	0.296	1605.3	0.0880
Nitrogen...............	2.9286	0.24713	0.4623	1687.1	−0.136
Oxygen................	2.5641	0.14195	0.3026	1475.1	0.861

Units: p is in atmospheres, v is volume in cubic centimeters of one gram, and T is absolute temperature in degrees Centigrade.

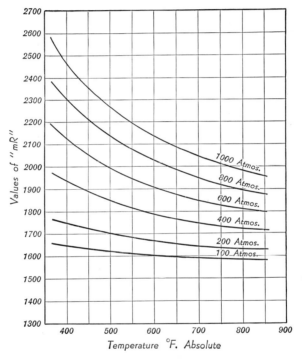

FIG. (IV–18). Universal Gas Constant (mR) for Helium. From Experimental Work of Wiebe, Gaddy and Heins, published in Journal of American Chem. Soc., 1931.

IV–27. Properties of Actual Gases When at High Pressures.—The foregoing characteristic equations are of interest largely because their logical or semi-logical derivation permits interpolation and possibly extrapolation, of experimental data. They are, however, inconvenient in form, and the calculation of properties by means of them is arduous. Direct experimental data covering a wide range of pressures and temperatures is now available for many of the common gases, and such data can be presented in the form of graphs evaluating the universal gas constant, MR, as used in the common form of the perfect gas equation, $PV = MRT$. Such graphs are more convenient to use and permit easy solutions of specific

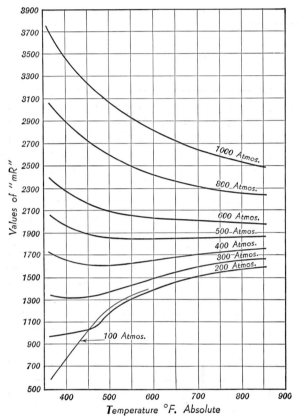

FIG. (IV-19). Universal Gas Constant (mR) for Methane (CH_4). From experimental work of Kralnes and Gaddy, published in Journal of American Chem. Soc., 1931.

volumes for those cases where pressure and temperatures are sufficiently remote from normal to require special attention.

Curves of this sort are given in Fig. (IV-17) for the common diatomic gases, Oxygen, Nitrogen, Carbon-monoxide, and Air, and in Figs. (IV-18) and (IV-19) for Helium and Methane.

CHAPTER V

THE SECOND LAW OF THERMODYNAMICS

V–1. Insufficiency of the First Law.—Our main interest centers in obtaining useful work from a supply of heat energy. The First Law establishes an evaluation between the two forms of energy, heat and work, but it says nothing concerning the facility with which the transformation of one to the other may be affected. Transformation of work to heat is easy, in fact, inevitable, and whenever one horsepower of work is dissipated into heat as in a Prony brake its equivalent, or 2544 B.t.u. per hour, appears. The converse, however, is not true. If, for example, to a mechanically perfect internal combustion engine we supplied 2544 B.t.u. per hour, the output could not by any possibility equal one horsepower even though there were no frictional losses in the engine and no heat transferred by conduction, radiation, etc.

Energy appears in various forms with widely differing potential values and one criterion for classification is the ease with which they may be converted into useful mechanical energy, or work. Those forms readily converted are classed as high-grade energies and those only capable of less complete conversion as lower grades. Electrical energy when converted to useful work in an electric motor is an illustration of high-grade energy while the heat energy evolved by mechanical friction is an example of low-grade energy. The first has a much greater availability for doing useful work than the second. Thus, in discussing any energy transformation, it is necessary to consider it from two points of view, the quantitative and the qualitative or directional.

The First Law of Thermodynamics states the quantitative equivalence of heat and mechanical energy while the Second Law of Thermodynamics was formulated to avoid absurd conceptions of what might be expected in the way of useful returns from heat-work transformations. It is stated in many forms but the following, due to Clausius, will serve our present purpose. *It is impossible for a self-acting machine, unaided by any external agency, to convey heat from one body to another at a higher temperature.* This is equivalent to saying that no heat engine can transform *all* the heat supplied to it into work. It is a negation and as such is incapable of direct proof, thus differing from the First Law which is a statement of an experimental fact.

Just as the First Law was a specialized form of the general law of the *conservation* of energy, the Second Law is a specialized form of the general law of the *degradation* of energy which, as enunciated by Lord Kelvin, stated that " the result of any natural (unassisted) change or transformation of energy is to leave the energy in its final form less available for doing useful work."

Up to the present the discussion of the transformation of heat into work and, conversely, has been purely quantitative and without regard as to whether it may be affected either way with equal ease. We have found the property relations and the energy relations for various states and changes of the perfect gas and for these have needed in most cases only the First Law.

Mechanical and electrical energies are both types of high-grade energy, they are capable of mutual transformation theoretically without loss and actually with but small losses and both are completely convertible into heat. The converse transformation of heat into electrical or mechanical energy is not so readily carried out and never is a complete conversion even approximated. Thus the First Law, while true, is not the *whole* truth.

It is a matter of universal experience that " heat cannot of itself pass from a colder to a hotter body " (Clausius) obviously then, heat which is at a high temperature should be more available for doing mechanical work than heat which is at a lower temperature.

Example.—A heat engine is supplied with 190,800 B.t.u. per hr. Is it possible for the engine to develop 75 Hp. throughout the hour?

Solution.—Heat equivalent of the output = 75 (2544) = 190,800 B.t.u. per hr. According to the Second Law, all of the heat supplied to an engine cannot be transformed into work. Therefore, this performance is not possible.

V–2. Various Statements of the Second Law. *Peabody.*—All reversible engines working between the same source of heat and refrigerator have the same efficiency.

The efficiency of a reversible engine is independent of the working substance.

A self-acting machine cannot convey heat from one body to another at higher temperature.

Noyes and Sherrill.—A process whose final result is only a transformation of a quantity of heat into work is an impossibility.

Reeve.—Energy tends ever, so long as it undergoes no transformation, to gravitate to a lower degree of intensity. This tendency ceases only with transformation. The energy of a mass-system can never regain intensity except by two methods: (1) by a contribution of energy from some external mass-system, or (2) by undergoing a double energy-transformation, into some other energy-form and back again.

He stated the above as a general law of energetics and adds that it is intolerable to use one set of laws for mechanics, another for heat, a third for chemical action and a fourth for electricity, when all four of these sorts of the same energy are at work in nearly every engine room in the country.

Clausius.—" It is impossible for a self-acting machine unaided by any external agency to convey heat from one body to another at higher temperature." Also, " Heat cannot of itself pass from a colder to a hotter body."

Lord Kelvin.—It is impossible by means of inanimate material agency to derive mechanical effect from any portion of matter by cooling it below the temperature of surrounding objects. Kelvin also gives a more general statement in his enunciation of the law of degradation of energy which he states as follows: There is " a Universal tendency in Nature to the dissipation of Mechanical Energy."

Planck.—It is impossible to construct an engine which will work in a complete cycle and produce no effect except the raising of a weight and the cooling of a heat reservoir.

Peabody says the mathematical expression of the Second Law is $\dfrac{dQ}{T} = 0$, for a reversible cycle.

V–3. Availability.—The amount of energy available from any transformation can be determined only when the initial and final states are clearly specified. In thermodynamics the initial state is usually clearly defined but what may be defined for the final state in order to estimate the available energy justly, is not so obvious. A mechanical analogy may emphasize this point. If we consider a boulder perched on the edge of a high cliff a short distance from the seashore, its potential energy consists of its weight multiplied by its elevation. But the elevation may be measured to the ground at the cliff's base, to the mean sea level or even to the center of the earth and dependent upon the selection of the datum plane would be the magnitude of the arithmetical result. One might say that the first gave the amount actually available, the second the amount theoretically available and the third a quantity conceivably available but utterly impossible of attainment, for even if a hole were dug clear into the center of the earth the work of removing it should be debited against the account and the net energy realized could not exceed that reckoned to sea level.

All heat engines operate on cycles which are similar, in that they receive heat from some source at high temperature, transform part of it into work and deliver the remainder to a sink at lower temperature, usually termed the refrigerator. For an internal combustion engine the source would be the heat of combustion of the charge in the cylinder and the sink, or refrigerator, the atmosphere to which the exhaust is delivered. For a steam engine, the boiler and condenser are source and refrigerator respectively. The difference between the heat energy received from the source and the heat energy which, under ideal conditions, must be delivered to the refrigerator is termed the *available* heat energy. It is usually reckoned per pound of working fluid and may be different for different cycles. Cycles exist for which the working limits consist of pressures, or volumes, or temperatures. Carnot clearly showed, however, that the absolute maximum of available energy and correspondingly the absolute minimum of unavailable energy for any conceivable heat engine exists when the cycle limits are temperatures. Strictly speaking, therefore, the available and unavailable energies should be fixed only by the most favorable cycle, the Carnot, actually, however, loose thinking has permitted the use of these terms as pertaining to the particular cycle under discussion.

V–4. Reversible Processes.—For *any* transformation the question of whether it has been accomplished without loss or not can be answered most surely by reversing the change and seeing whether the original status is completely recovered. For example, if it is desired to convert a banknote into pennies, the exchange will have been a perfect one, i.e., without losses, provided the process may be reversed and the banknote regained by presentation of the pennies. Thus we have, as already pointed out in Article 32, that any heat-work transformation in order to be considered perfect must be completely reversible. Just as perfection is never achieved in actual things, so reversible processes are never found in actual heat engines, but such processes are readily imaginable and furnish proper criteria for measuring the perfection of actual conversions.

Imagine a non-conducting cylinder (*a*) filled with a perfect gas at high pressure and fitted with a frictionless piston as shown in Fig. V–1. Outside the cylinder is a curved surface up which the ball (*b*) is pushed as the piston moves outward. The slope of this curved surface is made such that for every position of the piston the horizontal component of the weight of the ball just balances the pressure exerted on the piston by the gas in the cylinder. Thus as the piston moves outward and the gas pressure becomes successively less and less, the decreasing curvature of the surface up which the ball is pushed causes a corresponding reduction in the resistance offered. The system is, therefore, in complete balance at every position of the piston and, neglecting friction, will remain at rest in any position or, if started, will continue in motion until stopped by some outside force, just as a perfect billiard ball on a perfect table would roll indefinitely until stopped and then if started back would travel the reverse path again without losses. If the piston were at the extreme left and were started toward the right, the gas would undergo adiabatic expansion, its

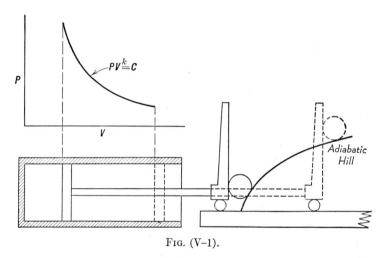

FIG. (V–1).

intrinsic energy would be used in doing the external work of raising the weight of the ball and there would be a direct conversion of heat energy into work. If the piston were stopped at the extreme right of its travel and the ball started rolling to the left by an infinitesimal force, the ball would continue to roll, the piston would be returned to its original position and there would be a reconversion of the potential energy of the ball into heat energy (intrinsic energy) of the gas. The original states of all members would be recovered, the process would be a reversible one, therefore a perfect one, and all the heat energy available between the initial and final states would be converted into work. Thus an adiabatic expansion of a perfect gas doing external work in an orderly manner is a reversible process. Had there been impact, shock or turbulence, there would have been degradation of energy and the process would have been irreversible, thus imperfect.

Another reversible process is the isothermal expansion which occurs when the source of heat is at the same temperature as the working medium. To illustrate, consider the cylinder of the foregoing case modified by the substitution of a *bottom* of perfectly conducting material in place of the bottom of non-conducting material. Place in contact with this, on the outside, a source of heat of infinite capacity, i.e., one which is capable of giving up heat but whose temperature never changes. The curved surface up which the ball is forced will have a different shape than before as it should be so built that the horizontal component of the weight of the ball

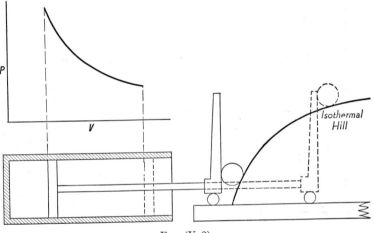

Fig. (V–2).

will offset the various pressures experienced in the isothermal expansion instead of the adiabatic expansion of the previous case. Starting with the piston at the extreme left, a slight movement to the right would tend to lower the temperature of the gas but the moment this occurred heat would flow in from the source and recover the original temperature. Thus heat energy is continually supplied from the source as the piston moving to the right pushes the ball up the incline. Like the preceding case, the entire system is always in equilibrium, work is done at the expense of the heat supplied and the process is reversible. A reversal of the direction of the motion of the piston results in an isothermal compression which squeezes out heat into the source in an amount just equal to the work which has been done by the ball in descending the curved surface.

Other reversible processes are constant pressure heating and constant volume heating when the heating unit is at the *same temperature as the working fluid* at all times. This involves a variation in the temperature of the source.

Conduction of heat across a temperature gradient, radiation, turbulence, shock, or friction of any sort cannot enter into any reversible process. All such are not states of equilbrium but processes which are *proceeding to* such a state and which will persist with continued energy degradation until a state of equilibrium is finally reached.

Reversible expansion implies that the action proceed leisurely without internal turbulence or friction of the fluid or any losses whereby kinetic energy is degraded into heat. Throttling such as described in the Joule experiment (Art. IV–22) is a completely irreversible process. Here the kinetic energy engendered in the jet leaving the high-pressure chamber is completely frittered back into heat.

A direct transfer of heat to or from a substance is reversible only when the temperature of the substance and the source of heat are the same, then heat may flow from one to the other in either direction at will. If there is a temperature difference the gradient thus existing is an impassable barrier to reversed action unless assisted by some external agency.

V–5. The Work of Sadi Carnot.—As soon as it was recognized that mechanical work could be obtained from heat there followed inevitably the question, can a tangible machine be conceived which will be a perfect device for obtaining work from heat and, if so, will all the heat supplied do work or will it be impossible even with such a perfect machine to obtain 100 per cent conversion of the heat supplied.

These questions were answered by a young French engineer (28 yrs. old), named Nicolas Leonard Sadi Carnot in a masterly paper* published in 1824 in which he first proposed a cycle proper for such an ideal engine and then developed an expression for its efficiency. Carnot's paper is a most beautiful piece of deductive reasoning. It is independent of the substance used for the motive fluid and is based on no assumptions as to the nature of heat. When he presented it, the kinetic theory had not found acceptance nor had the First Law been enunciated. Carnot, however, was not in sympathy with the Caloric Theory and certain of his expressions lead one to the belief that he suspected that heat was a form of energy.

* "Reflexions sur la puissance motrice du feu et sur les machines propre a developper cette puissance." An excellent translation of this by R. A. Thurston, together with an article by Lord Kelvin on Carnot's Theory, is published by John Wiley & Sons under the title of "Reflections on the Motive Power of Heat."

Perhaps the best statement of his thesis is contained in Carnot's own words, " to examine the principle (law) of the production of motion (or work) by heat in all its generality, it must be conceived independently of any mechanism, or any particular agent; it is necessary to establish proofs applicable not only to steam engines, but also to other heat engines, irrespective of the working substance and the manner in which it acts."

His line of reasoning was about as follows, " heat cannot perform work except when it passes from a higher to a lower temperature level," therefore, there must be a temperature difference between the source of heat and the receiver for the rejected heat. Further, if the engine is to be perfect in its heat-work relations, then it must operate by means of a series of processes, each of which shall be perfect. The criterion of thermodynamic perfection is reversibility, therefore, all the processes must be reversible. A series of such processes combined to form a closed cycle will permit the engine to operate in a continuous manner.*

A graph of such a cycle would result from the cutting of two isothermal lines at different temperatures by two adiabatic lines at two different entropies. There would be four events to such a cycle, isothermal expansion, adiabatic expansion, isothermal compression and adiabatic compression.

V–6. Carnot Engine.—Carnot himself never suggested a complete mechanism for an engine to operate on the cycle he proposed.

He simply specified a cylindrical vessel provided with a movable diaphragm or piston and two bodies—kept each at constant temperature —one temperature being higher than the other. Lord Kelvin, twenty-five years later (1849), impressed by the simplicity and the fundamental importance of Carnot's conceptions, re-presented them in slightly modified form before the Edinburgh Royal Society. He made specific mention of certain conditions obviously implied by Carnot and showed a frictionless non-conducting piston reciprocating in a non-conducting cylinder, the latter, fitted with a head of perfectly conducting material to which could be applied at will any one of three devices, (1) a non-conducting plate,†

---

* A cycle is simply a series of events and a closed cycle is a series of events or processes which returns the working substance to its original state.

† The non-conducting plate is not mentioned by Carnot nor does the word reversible occur, yet both are implied in his description of the processes occurring in the cylinder. Carnot worked at a time when the Caloric Theory of heat was the accepted explanation of heat effects. He did not, however, accept this and though his engine and cycle were equally good, whether heat were considered matter or energy, some of his notes presenting his own hypothesis of heat are startling when we recall that they were made over twenty years before Joule's work on the mechanical equivalent of heat appeared. Note for example, "Heat is simply motive power or rather motion which has changed

(2) a source of heat always remaining at the temperature, T_1, and (3) a receiver for heat also of infinite capacity but at a lower temperature, T_2, than the source.

Such a device, when the end was covered with the non-conducting plate, permitted adiabatic action of the substance within the cylinder and when the end was put in contact with either source of heat or the receiver of heat, permitted isothermal action of the working substance. In such a cylinder, then, it would be possible to obtain at will reversible adiabatic

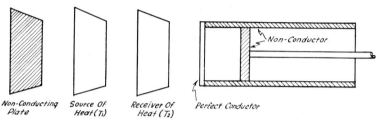

Non-Conducting Plate   Source Of Heat (T_1)   Receiver Of Heat (T_2)   Perfect Conductor

FIG. (V-3).

or isothermal expansion or compression which were the processes of which Carnot's cycle was composed.

The cylinder and piston of the preceding articles is, in effect, this device and the curved surface along which the ball is propelled is only a device for keeping the piston in constant balance with the pressure of the expanding gas. A slight amplification of this combination permits the visualization of a complete mechanism operating as a Carnot engine, i.e., a heat engine operating on the Carnot cycle. Fig. (V-4) illustrates such a device. Instead of the simple curved surface of Art. (V-4), the ball is now propelled up a compound surface giving first, isothermal expansion, then adiabatic expansion. During these two processes the ball was filled with water which had entered at the low level. When the ball reaches the top of the adiabatic hill the water is emptied into the high level and the ball, now much lighter, returns, pushing the piston ahead of it and compressing the gas, first isothermally, then adiabatically.

form. It is a movement among the particles of bodies. Wherever there is destruction of motive power there is, at the same time, production of heat in quantity exactly proportional to the quantity of motive power destroyed. Reciprocally, wherever there is destruction of heat there is production of motive power."

Apparently Carnot was diplomatic and rather than get into a controversy concerning the nature of heat he was willing to use the orthodox caloric theory in the presentation of his perfect heat engine, especially as he had in his premises entirely sidestepped any assumptions concerning the *nature* of heat.

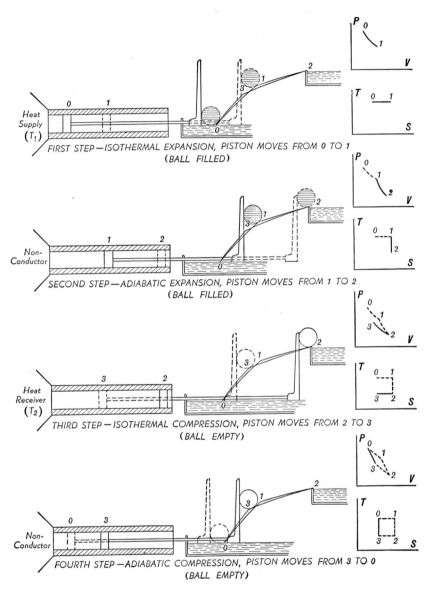

FIRST STEP—ISOTHERMAL EXPANSION, PISTON MOVES FROM 0 TO 1
(BALL FILLED)

SECOND STEP—ADIABATIC EXPANSION, PISTON MOVES FROM 1 TO 2
(BALL FILLED)

THIRD STEP—ISOTHERMAL COMPRESSION, PISTON MOVES FROM 2 TO 3
(BALL EMPTY)

FOURTH STEP—ADIABATIC COMPRESSION, PISTON MOVES FROM 3 TO 0
(BALL EMPTY)

FIG. (V-4).

In Fig. (V–4) the complete cycle is traced step by step, the successive positions of the piston are shown and the corresponding graphs plotted on both the PV and the TS planes. The full line shows, in each case, the process under consideration. Consider the piston in equilibrium at the position 0 and the source of heat, at T_1, applied at the cylinder head. Imagine the application of an infinitesimal force toward the right. The piston will start to move outward, but instantly the temperature will tend to fall and, therefore, heat will at once flow in to the gas from the source. The whole is in balance and frictionless, thus the motion will continue until stopped. Let it continue until the position 1 is reached. During this process, heat has been supplied, work has been done in raising the ball filled with water, and the whole operation is depicted in Part 1 of Fig. (V–4).

Next consider the non-conducting stand replacing the source of heat at the end of the cylinder. The gas is now thermally isolated, also the hill up which the ball is to travel is altered to the adiabatic form. The piston may now proceed still in perfect balance, and the gas expanding adiabatically will cause the filled ball to travel to the position 2, thus work has been done at the expense of the intrinsic energy of the gas, and consequently its energy and temperature have been reduced. Let this continue intil the temperature has fallen to T_2, the temperature of the heat-receiving stand.

When the gas has reached this temperature, let the heat receiver (at T_2) be placed across the end of the cylinder and the ball, now emptied of water, and therefore much lighter, started downward along the isothermal slope. The piston will start to move to the left, the temperature will start to rise and immediately heat will flow from the gas to the receiver. Let this process continue from 2 to 3. During this isothermal compression, heat has been removed from the gas equivalent to the work done on the gas. This isothermal compression continues until the volume is reduced in the same proportion that it was increased during the isothermal expansion, i.e., $V_2/V_3 = V_1/V_0$.

If, after reaching position 3, the cylinder has the non-conducting stand replaced, an adiabatic compression will follow as the empty ball travels along the path $3 - 0$ designed for that purpose. This will bring the gas back to its original state and the cycle is closed. The engine will then be ready to repeat the cycle and thus continually perform useful work at an *absolutely minimum* expenditure of heat.

V–7. Efficiency of the Carnot Cycle.—The complete cycle is shown in Fig. (V–5). The general expression for the efficiency of any heat engine (equation III–7) is

$$e = \frac{Q_{\text{sup.}} - Q_{\text{rej.}}}{Q_{\text{sup.}}}$$

By inspection of the TS graph, $Q_{sup.}$ is obviously the area $0'\ 0\ 1\ 1'$. This is a rectangle whose area is $0'\ 0 \times 0'\ 1'$, but $0'\ 0 = T_1$ and $0'\ 1' = S_1 - S_0$, therefore

$$Q_{sup.} = T_1(S_1 - S_0).$$

Similarly,

$$Q_{rej.} = T_2(S_2 - S_3),$$

but as the changes were adiabatic,

$$S_0 = S_3 \quad \text{and} \quad S_1 = S_2$$

thus,

$$Q_{rej.} = T_2(S_1 - S_0).$$

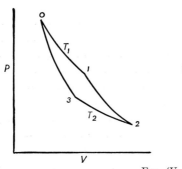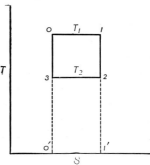

Fig. (V–5).

The expression for efficiency then becomes,

$$e = \frac{T_1(S_1 - S_0) - T_2(S_1 - S_0)}{T_1(S_1 - S_0)},$$

$$e = \frac{T_1 - T_2}{T_1}.$$

Example.—A Carnot engine is supplied with 15,000 B.t.u. at a temperature of 2040° F. The exhaust temperature is 100° F.

Find: (a) Heat rejected; (b) Heat transformed into work; and (c) The efficiency.

Solution.—(Reference to Fig. V–5.)

(a) $Q_{rej.} = Q_{sup.} \left(\dfrac{T_2}{T_1}\right) = 15,000 \left(\dfrac{100 + 460}{2040 + 460}\right) = 15,000\ (560/2500)$

$$= 3360 \text{ B.t.u.}$$

(b) $AW = Q_{sup.} - Q_{rej.} = 15,000 - 3360 = 11,640$ B.t.u.

(c) $e = \dfrac{AW}{Q_{sup.}} = 11,640/15,000 = 0.776$

or, $e = \dfrac{T_1 - T_2}{T_1} = \dfrac{2500 - 560}{2500} = 0.776.$

V–8. Carnot's Law.—While the cycle just discussed has been shown using a perfect gas as the working fluid, the conclusions are independent of the working substance and the cycle could be drawn considering any fluid for the medium. The graph on the PV plane would be different for different substances, but the graph on TS plane would always be a rectangle. Obviously for this to have any area (therefore any useful work), there must exist a temperature difference and, though not arriving at it in this way, Carnot stated the expression for efficiency as a function of the temperature and the temperature difference.

$$Eff. = \text{funct. } t, \, dt.$$

He called attention to the fact that this does not depend in any way upon the properties of the working substance, but solely upon the *reversibility of the processes*, the temperature at which heat is supplied and a *temperature difference*. In his day the conception of Absolute Temperature had not received acceptance and the function of temperature represented by ft was called Carnot's Function, a term much used in the early works on thermodynamics. He summarized the action of the perfect heat engine in a statement known as *Carnot's Law* which states in effect that *the efficiency of a perfect engine does not depend upon the nature of the working substance, but does depend upon the temperatures of the source of heat and refrigerator.*

* Carnot does not use the term *efficiency*; he does, however, discuss "the quantity of motive power produced by ... unity of heat from the temperature $t + dt$, to the temperature t," calling this du. He states (Appendix B),

$$du = f't, \, dt.$$

Obviously du corresponds to our definition of efficiency applied to a cycle of infinitesimal temperature difference, $A/dW \div dQ$.

For finite temperature difference his expression may then be written,

$$\text{eff.} = \text{function } t(t_1 - t_2).$$

If now function t be given the form $1/T$, we have

$$\text{eff.} = \frac{T_1 - T_2}{T_1}.$$

This form for Carnot's function was first proposed by Lord Kelvin (Math. and Phys. Papers, Vol. I, pp. 393, 457) in conjunction with Joule at the time they proposed an absolute scale of temperature (the Kelvin scale) 1854.

See Art. V–14 for discussion of the Kelvin Scale.

† Translated from his paper, "Réflexions sur la puissance motrice de feu" (Paris, Bachelier, 1824), it reads, "The motive power of heat is independent of the agents employed to realize it; its quantity is fixed solely by the temperatures of the bodies between which is effected, finally, the transfer of the caloric." Substitute *useful work* for *motive power*, call *caloric*, *heat* and we get the same conception as given above; since for equal quantities of heat supplied, the efficiencies will be directly proportional to the useful works accomplished.

If Carnot's Function be given the form, $ft = \dfrac{1}{T}$, the expression for efficiency becomes that derived in the preceding article, namely,

$$\text{Eff.} = \frac{T_1 - T_2}{T_1}.$$

The efficiency is thus a function of the difference in temperature (of the source and the refrigerator) and the temperature of the source, or the drop in temperature and the high temperature.

V–9. Entropy.—The definition of change of entropy previously given, namely, the integral of $dq \div T$ for any reversible change, is the simplest and most concise definition that can be given. It is strictly correct as far as it goes. It is insufficient, however, in that it holds for reversible processes only, nothing is said about the entropy change during an irreversible process, and the vast majority of actual processes are irreversible. All such are inevitably accompanied by increases in the entropy of the substance under consideration and it is well, therefore, to have a more comprehensive conception and definition of change of entropy.

For any amount of heat supplied to a body the Carnot efficiency shows the amount that is conceivably transformable into work, i.e., the part available for doing useful work or the available energy.*

$$\text{Avail. Energy} = Q_{\text{sup.}} \times \text{Eff.}$$

$$= Q_{\text{sup.}} \times \left(1 - \frac{T_2}{T_1}\right),$$

where T_1 is the temperature at which heat is supplied and T_2 the lowest temperature at which it can be rejected, or the lowest available temperature. This maximum amount of work is always less than the mechanical equivalent of the heat supplied because it is impossible to expand to absolute zero.

Similarly, the part which must be rejected, as heat thus the unavailable energy is

$$\text{Unavail. Energy} = Q_{\text{sup.}} \left(\frac{T_2}{T_1}\right).$$

This is true when heat comes to the body from some outside source, but there are many cases where heat appears in the substance from other than a direct supply at temperature T_1. It may be supplied by work being done upon the substance, work which is transformed into heat as fast as performed as when water is stirred with a paddle, where the mechanical

* Called by Kelvin its "motivity."

energy delivered is used in overcoming the frictional resistance of the fluid. Whenever frictional resistances are overcome, work is required and reappears ultimately as heat. If energy for this is not available from some outside source it must be supplied from the store of available energy. For example, during a throttling process the available energy is first utilized in producing high velocities in the issuing streamlets. These issue in all directions (turbulence) and spend their individual kinetic energies in bucking each other and overcoming internal friction, thereby transforming their individual kinetic energies of flow back into molecular kinetic energy or heat. Denoting the heat supplied, due to the work of overcoming frictional resistance by Q_f, the increment of unavailable energy for such a process will be the unavailable energy in the heat so added, or,

$$Q_f \frac{T_2}{T_1}.$$

The temperature at which heat is supplied may vary and for infinitesimal increments, T_1 must be replaced by T. The minimum temperature at which heat can be rejected, however, remains the same for each portion of heat added and thus T_2 is constant for a given problem and may be written as $T_{\text{Min.}}$ for all cases. Assuming homogeneous material and equilibrium of temperature throughout the substance, the total increment of unavailable energy will be

$$\int_1^2 dU_{\text{Unav.}} = \int_1^2 dQ \frac{T_{\text{Min.}}}{T} + \int_1^2 dQ_f \frac{T_{\text{Min.}}}{T}.$$

This may be rewritten as

$$\int_1^2 \frac{dU_{\text{Unav.}}}{T_{\text{Min.}}} = \int_1^2 \frac{dQ}{T} + \int_1^2 \frac{dQ_f}{T}.$$

When integrated this expression gives the change of entropy and it is perhaps simpler and more comprehensive to define entropy from the left-hand member of this equation, thus, for any change

$$\int_1^2 \frac{dU_{\text{Unav.}}}{T_{\text{Min.}}} = S_2 - S_1 = \int_1^2 \frac{dQ}{T} + \int_1^2 \frac{dQ_f}{T}.$$

or, *The increase of entropy is the ratio of the increase of unavailable energy to the lowest available temperature.*

One advantage of this definition is the obvious utility of entropy as a measure of *unavailability*. When no heat is added from external sources (adiabatic process), yet through internal friction (an irreversible process), some energy is transformed into heat (Q_f), the unavailable energy has increased and the entropy has inevitably increased by a corresponding amount.

This also permits a simple presentation of a very important law. *The increase in unavailable energy accompanying any self-proceeding change is always equal to the increase in entropy multiplied by the lowest available temperature.* (See end of Art. V–3.)

For non-adiabatic changes, i.e., changes where heat as such is supplied or rejected, any change in the entropy indicates a corresponding change in the unavailable energy of the system, but while in the case of the adiabatic changes the increase in the unavailable energy was equal to the decrease in the available energy, this is no longer true for the non-adiabatic changes. For these the increase in entropy, while still indicating an increase in the unavailable energy, no longer implies a corresponding decrease in the available energy, since the addition of heat as such has *increased both* the available and the unavailable energies.

Our earlier definition of change of entropy as $\int \dfrac{dQ}{T}$, for a reversible process, if amplified to include the heat resulting from internal irreversible processes, becomes the equivalent of the above definition and the definition may be stated as follows. The change of entropy is equal to the sum of the $\int \dfrac{dQ}{T} + \int \dfrac{dQ_f}{T}$ where Q is the heat received in a reversible manner from some external source and Q_f is the heat appearing in the substance from internal irreversible operations.

Of more importance, however, than an academic definition of entropy is the correct understanding of its distinctive traits and its use in thermodynamic computations.

Entropy is a true property,* a function of state only and therefore a perfect differential. It is correct to write

$$\int_{1}^{2} dS = S_2 - S_1.$$

---

* Defining entropy change as the ratio of the change in unavailable energy to the lowest available temperature, it obviously partakes of the same characteristics as energy since the lowest available temperature is constant for any process or cycle, thus it is a true property.

For any closed cycle the substance returns periodically to its original state, thus the entropy in its final state is identical with that of its original state and the net change for the cycle is zero. Entropy like energy is additive, i.e., $S_{Total} = S_A + S_B + S_C$, etc., where the members on the right-hand side of the equation represent the entropies of a series of bodies, A, B, C, etc. Entropy is dependent upon the mass, that is, the entropy of two pounds of a substance at a given state is twice as great as that of one pound.

Many attempts have been made to present conceptions of entropy, which would have some physical significance, though with but meager success. The term was but a name coined to cover a certain mathematical function, the manipulation of which led to interesting and important conclusions. As has been pointed out, it furnishes excellent data as to the availability or rather the unavailability of heat energy for transformation into useful work and may be considered in a way as playing the part of one type of factor of which the complex quantity, energy, is composed.

Energy is essentially a compound quantity of two elements assembled, not as a sum, but as a product. These are recognizable when dealing with it in the form of work, as force multiplied by distance, or as pressure multiplied by increment of volume. Similarly, potential energy is the product of weight and elevation and kinetic energy, of mass and one-half velocity squared. Of these pairs, we may say that one factor in each case expresses the concentration or intensity and the other the distribution or extensity of the energy quantity.

Carrying this analogy further, we may write for the heat supplied,

$$dQ = TdS,$$

in which it might be suggested that temperature represented the intensity factor and entropy the extensity or distribution factor when discussing a certain amount of heat energy supplied to some substance. Obviously, here an increase in the entropy would be at the expense of the intensity factor, temperature, if the value of dQ were to remain unchanged. A decrease in the intensity factor, therefore, increase in the entropy factor, indicates a decrease in availability.

The unit of entropy is without a name,* and numerical quantities expressing differences of entropy are quoted simply in units of entropy. The unit used in American engineering practice uses the B.t.u. and the absolute temperature on the Fahrenheit scale for the component quan-

* It was proposed to call the unit a Rank, after Rankine, but this is rarely used.

tities. Thus the entropy change, due to adding 500 B.t.u. at a constant temperature of 300° F., is 500 ÷ 760 = 0.658 unit of entropy.

Example 1.—During the adiabatic expansion of a gas to a temperature of 500° F. abs., the entropy increased 0.75 unit.

What was the loss of available energy during the process, and to what was it due?

Solution.—Decrease in availability = $(S_1 - S_2)(T_2)$ = 0.75 (500) = 375 B.t.u. The increase in entropy was due to a part of the kinetic energy of flow, resulting from available heat, being retransformed into heat through internal friction or friction within the fluid.

Example 2.—If, in an expansion with the entropy increasing 0.7 unit, an increase in entropy of 0.3 unit is due to the addition of heat from an outside source, by how much does the internal friction increase the entropy?

Solution.—$dS = dQ/T + dQ_f/T$ $\int dS = \int dQ/T + \int dQ_f/T = 0.7$

$\int dQ_f/T = 0.7 - 0.3 = 0.4$ unit of entropy.

V–10. Entropy as a Coördinate.—Because entropy is a true property it may be used as a coördinate for expressing the changes a substance undergoes. When used in conjunction with absolute temperature for the other coördinate, the graph showing a change from one state to another has the added value that the area between it and the entropy coördinate axis represents the heat required for the change, provided the process has been a reversible one, i.e., without the fluid undergoing impact, friction or conduction, as discussed in Art. III–14.

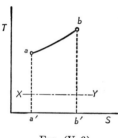

FIG. (V–6).

$$ _1\text{Area}_2 = \int_1^2 T\,dS, \text{ also } _1Q_2 = \int_1^2 T\,dS; \text{ therefore, } _1\text{Area}_2 = {}_1Q_2. $$

For example, if heat be added to a certain substance and it passes from state (a) to state (b) along the path (ab), the heat so added can be represented by the area *a′ a b b′* as shown in Fig. V–6. This will always be true as long as the change is a reversible one.

When the scales of the coördinate axes are known, the area may be measured in square inches and multiplied by the scale factor to obtain the B.t.u. directly. If the area of Fig. V–6 were 0.75 square inch and the scales for temperature and entropy were 1 in. = 500° F. and 1 in. = 0.2 unit of entropy, respectively, one square inch would represent 500 × 0.2 = 100 B.t.u. and the area *a′ a b b′* would represent 100 × 0.75 = 75 B.t.u.

If a line be drawn corresponding to the lowest temperature to which a heat engine could work, such as x–y, the area above this will represent the heat *available* for doing work and the area below it will represent the *unavailable* heat or the heat which must be rejected to the refrigerator.

Example.—A gas expands isothermally, at a temperature of 240° F., with an increase in entropy of 1.2 units.

Sketch on T–S coördinates and find the heat supplied during the process.

Solution.—$_1Q_2 = T(S_2 - S_1) = (240 + 460) (1.2) = 700 (1.2) = 840$ B.t.u.

V–11. Entropy and Availability.—Let us consider that a definite amount of heat is added with the temperature remaining constant; such a process will be represented by the line a–b of Fig. (V–8). If, as before, the line x–y represents the minimum temperature to which the engine can operate, the area lying below it represents energy unavailable for transformation into useful work, and this is a definite fraction of the total that has been supplied. If now the same amount of heat be supplied, but at a temperature lower than formerly, represented by c–d, the area $a'\,c\,d$ d' will be the same as $a'\,a\,b\,b'$, but obviously the portion above the line x–y is less than formerly

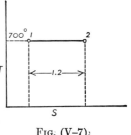

Fig. (V–7).

and the unavailable portion, which is represented by the area below the line x–y, is a larger fraction of the total supplied. Thus the acquisition of heat which has taken place with the greater increment of entropy has

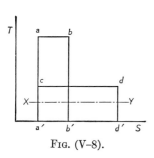

Fig. (V–8).

been that which has been supplied with the greater percentage of unavailable, or the smaller percentage of available, energy. It is universally true that, considering a given quantity of heat supplied, reversibly to any body, the process which produces the largest increase of entropy has supplied the heat in the least available form.

The entropy of a body may be increased in two ways, non-adiabatically or adiabatically; it may be increased by the *addition of heat* to the body or it may be increased by *transformations of the energy already contained in the body*. In the first case, the entropy has increased simply because we have added more heat and, therefore, that ingredient of heat, known as entropy. The question of availability does not enter in except as to the manner by which the heat is supplied as already discussed. In the second case, energy within the body may undergo transformations of many sorts and wherever and whenever these occur in practice they are inevitably accompanied by an increase of entropy of the system provided the change has been what is known as a self-proceeding one, i.e., without external assistance. For example, a body of gas contained in a reservoir in a state of extreme turbulence will come into a state of rest and equilibrium by the kinetic energy of the streamlets in the whirling mass being transformed into heat of friction and the entropy of the entire mass will have increased, although no energy has been communicated to the gas from any outside source. It is an irreversible process, and while dQ of equation V–1 is zero, dQ_f has a value equal to the heat equivalent of the kinetic energy of the infinitesimal streamlets. Summarized into a law it has been stated as, *In any self-proceeding change the entropy of an isolated system always tends toward a maximum.*

Care should be taken not to confuse changes of entropy which may be due to the simple addition or subtraction of heat (non-adiabatic changes), thus increasing or decreasing the total energy and entropy of the substance by direct addition or subtraction, with the increase which occurs as the result of internal changes only (adiabatic changes), wherein the total energy of the substance is simply rearranged and possibly transformed, but remains constant in quantity. Any irreversible *adiabatic* change is accompanied by an *increase* of entropy and, conversely, if any adiabatic change be accompanied by an increase of entropy it is an irreversible operation. For such the availability is decreased. For a reversible adiabatic change the entropy remains constant.

There should be borne in mind also the distinction between *unavailable* and *waste* energies. By waste we mean something which could be put to useful purpose but which was not and has been discarded. Of the total heat supplied to any heat engine only part of it, as stated by the Second Law, can do work, and that portion is called the *available* energy. That other portion which must pass off as heat, because of the lower limit specified for the working range of the cycle, is *unavailable* energy. This is true regardless of whether the limit be set by nature, as the average temperature of the earth's surface (about 60° F.), or by our own desires at a higher temperature for some specific problem. In ideal engines all the available energy is transformed into work but in actual engines not all the available energy goes into work, certain of it is lost for the doing of work by the imperfections of the mechanism, friction, throttling, radiation, etc. This part which is lost is called *wasted* energy. For reversible adiabatic changes there is no waste; for irreversible adiabatic changes the loss in availability is equal to the gain in unavailable energy, i.e., the product of the entropy change by the lowest available temperature.

To a certain extent, entropy as applied to heat energy is analogous to stability as a descriptive term for mechanical structures in that any changes which proceed of themselves inevitably result in new arrangements of greater stability. When a house falls down the same amount of material may be there but it is in a less elevated and a more stable state. In a way entropy corresponds to the stability of the heat energy, the greater the stability the less the availability.

Generalizing, it has been said that, *the energy of the universe remains constant but the entropy of the universe tends toward a maximum.*

Example 1.—One pound of a gas possessing kinetic energy (from both translational and vortex motion) of 3890 ft.-lbs., is brought to rest at a final temperature of 80° F.

Neglecting the rise in temperature during the transformation from kinetic energy to heat, find the increase in entropy due to this self-proceeding, and irreversible, change.*

Solution.—The kinetic energy will ultimately be transformed to $\dfrac{3890}{778} =$ 5 B.t.u. of heat.

$$S_2 - S_1 = \int dQ_f/T = \frac{5}{80 + 460} = \frac{5}{540} = .00926 \text{ unit.}$$

Example 2.—A certain actual engine delivers a Hp.-hr. for every 20,000 B.t.u. supplied. The temperature at which heat is received is 700° F., and at which it is rejected is 100° F.

Based on Carnot's cycle, find: (a) the heat available; and (b) the wasted heat, both per 20,000 B.t.u. supplied.

Solution.—

(a) $Q_{av.} = Q_{sup.} \left(\dfrac{T_1 - T_2}{T_1}\right) = 20,000 \left(\dfrac{1160 - 560}{1160}\right) = 20,000\,(600/1160)$
$= 10,350$ B.t.u.

(b) Wasted heat $= Q_{av.} - AW = 10,350 - 2544 = 7806$ B.t.u.

V–12.   Absolute Zero of Temperature.—The definition of temperature given earlier, that it is a gage or measure of the sensible heat (which in turn

---

* Properly speaking, the temperature rise would have to be taken into consideration by a summation of the infinitesimal increase in entropy for each increment of temperature rise during the transformation.

was defined as the translatory kinetic energy of the molecules) implies that if the body were cooled to such an extent that the molecules became stationary, the body then would have no sensible heat and would have been reduced to an absolute zero of temperature.*

Another inkling that temperature is a true property and capable of being measured on some absolute scale is obtained from the physical behavior of the permanent gases which approximate the action of a perfect gas at ordinary conditions of temperature and pressure. Air, for example, at constant pressure decreases in volume about one four hundred and sixtieth (1/460) of its volume at 0° F. for each degree of reduction on the Fahrenheit scale. If this rate were maintained the volume would become zero at a temperature 460° below the zero of the Fahrenheit scale. Early experiments along this line gave graphs similar to those shown in Fig. IV–2 where each line represents the cooling of a different gas at constant pressure. Analysis of such a graph led to the conclusion that the focal point of all these lines extrapolated represented a zero of temperature that was a true zero and independent of scale. Speculation as to the state of matter which would exist at this point of zero volume of the perfect gas is profitless, bound up as it is in all the hypotheses assumed for the structure of the perfect gas. The important fact is to note that the common scales for measuring temperature are purely arbitrary, that temperature is a true property and that it is capable of being expressed in various units but on an *absolute* scale.

The best data on the determination of the value of this important point, the absolute zero, place it at 459.69° below the zero of the Fahrenheit scale and 273.16° below the zero of the Centigrade scale. Conversion of common temperatures to absolute are accomplished by the following elementary relations.

$$T = t + 459.69° \text{ (Fahrenheit scale)},$$

$$T = t + 273.16° \text{ (Centigrade scale)}.$$

V–13. Scales of Temperature. If a definite interval of temperature, such as that defined by the melting of ice and the boiling of water at some fixed pressure, be divided into an equal number of parts, an arbitrary scale for the measurement of temperature is thereby established. If 180 subdivisions are used we have the Fahrenheit scale and if 100 subdivisions are

* Such a state cannot be reached actually though temperatures closely approaching it have been achieved; for example, the gas helium has been liquefied at 450° below zero on the Fahrenheit scale, and even lower temperatures have been reached.

used, the Centigrade scale. Obviously, there may be as many scales as we care to make subdivisions. The commonest way of measuring temperature variations is by noting the expansion or contraction of some fluid used as the measuring agent. If all substances underwent uniform volumetric changes per degree of temperature change throughout the range of temperature usually encountered it would be immaterial what substance were used in the thermometer, for all would be ideal and give identical readings on their respective scales. Unfortunately no fluid behaves in this manner, all vary from point to point and it is only those with minimum variation that are at all suitable. The ones most commonly used are mercury and alcohol of the liquids and air, nitrogen and hydrogen, of the gases. Measurements of equal increments of temperature will thus differ slightly, depending on the agent used and the scale of the fluid is compounded with the arbitrary Fahrenheit or Centigrade scale, so that for accuracy it is necessary, when quoting temperatures, to state the measuring fluid, such as, 250° C. (Hydrogen Thermometer).*

V–14. Kelvin's Absolute Scale of Temperature.—A scale of temperature absolutely uniform and independent of any substance was proposed in 1848 by Lord Kelvin † (Sir Wm. Thompson). Its fundamental idea was that temperature intervals should be taken proportional to the energy decrements (or increments) which any body underwent, instead of proportional to the volumetric decrements (or increments) of some thermometric fluid. It was thus the substitution of a direct *energy* conception for the indirect *volume* conception of temperature.

As the Carnot engine transforms *all* the energy lying between two temperatures into work and rejects the remaining heat energy at the lower temperature, it would be quite conceivable for this rejected heat to be taken by a similar engine, passed through a similar cycle and the portion not transformed into work passed on, in turn, to still another. If the condition were imposed that each of these cycles should produce equal amounts of work, there would result a series of temperatures representing equal decrements in the heat energy originally supplied. Moreover, these cycles would continue successively until *all* the heat energy originally supplied were used up, finally reaching an absolute zero of the intrinsic

---

* Corrections for the scale of the mercury thermometer vary from about 1/10 of one degree at 50° C. to nearly 2° at 300° C. and for the hydrogen thermometer from 1/4 at −200° C. to 4/100 of a degree at 450° C. Circular No. 8 issued by the U. S. Bureau of Standards gives excellent information concerning corrections and precautions to be observed for fluid thermometers.

† "On an Absolute Thermometric Scale," Vol. I, Art. XXXIX, p. 100, Mathematical and Physical Papers; also Vol. I, Art. XLIX, Part II, p. 393.

energy of the substance and thus an absolute zero of temperature. The above is the gist of the argument which was actually presented about as follows.

Using the PV coördinates, Fig. V–9, draw two adiabatics for a perfect gas. These will extend indefinitely to the right, always approaching the V axis. For the temperature 100° C. draw the isothermal line 1–1' and since this has less slope than the adiabatic it will cross them both. Next draw another isothermal, but for the temperature 0° C. represented by the curve 2–2'. We now have the cycle of a Carnot engine working between

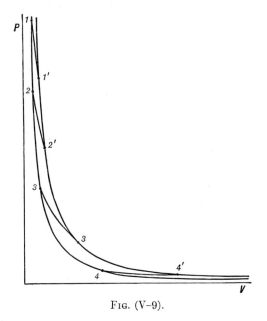

Fig. (V–9).

the temperatures of boiling water and melting ice. If another isothermal be drawn at 3–3', so located that the *work of its cycle* is exactly equal to that of the preceding, the isothermal 3–3' would determine a temperature which was as far below freezing as the first temperature was above it, but on a scale which truly measured equal temperature decrements. In a similar manner, another isothermal, 4–4', could be drawn, cutting off another equal decrement of heat and corresponding to −200° C.

The remaining area is the figure bounded by the isothermal 4–4', and the two adiabatics which extend on to infinity. Its area can be computed, for though the adiabatic curves themselves are infinite in length, the area between each and the V axis is finite and can be computed readily.*

When so figured the remaining area is found to be $\dfrac{731}{1000}$ of each of the three equal areas previously discussed. There is, therefore, a point 2.731 times the original interval below the freezing-point isothermal at which all the heat energy of the substance will have been used and the absolute zero of temperature will have been reached. Moreover, it will be impossible to go beyond this point since the assumption of a fictitious temperature lower than this results in an efficiency greater than unity,

$$\text{Eff.}_c = \frac{T_1 - (-T_2)}{T_1} = \frac{T_1 + T_2}{T_1} > 1.0,$$

which is impossible.

While the above discussion has dealt with a perfect gas as the operating medium in order to be specific, the Carnot cycle is independent of the substance and the same scale of temperature could be conceived by specifying some original temperature interval at which heat shall be supplied and rejected and requiring the later decrements of temperature to be such that equal amounts of work are performed by each consecutive cycle as shown in the adjacent Fig. V-10 using the T-S coördinates.

As a result, we have a scale of temperature dependent only upon the fundamental assumptions of thermodynamics and the basic units of mass and length. It is called the Kelvin, or Thermodynamic scale of temperature, and temperatures on it are usually indicated by the letter K. after the figures

Fig. (V-10).

* The area under the adiabatic extending from 4 to infinity is

$$\int_{v_4}^{\alpha} p\,dv = \frac{1}{1-k}(p_\alpha v_\alpha - p_4 v_4) = \frac{p_4 v_4}{k-1},$$

and similarly the area under the adiabatic from $4'$ is $\dfrac{p_{4'} v_{4'}}{k-1}$. The net area of the figure $4 - 4'$ to infinity is

$$A = \int_4^{4'} p\,dv + \int_{4'}^{\alpha} p\,dv - \int_4^{\alpha} p\,dv = p_4 v_4 \log_e \frac{v_{4'}}{v_4} + \frac{p_{4'} v_{4'} - p_4 v_4}{k-1} = p_4 v_4 \log_e \frac{v_{4'}}{v_4}.$$

as the letters C. and F. are used to denote the Centigrade and Fahrenheit scales respectively.*

It has become customary to accept the nomenclature "Kelvin scale" or "degrees Kelvin" as applying to the absolute temperature reckoned in Centigrade degrees and "Rankine scale" or "degrees Rankine" as applying to the absolute temperature reckoned in Fahrenheit degrees.

Thus: Absolute temperature, $^{\circ}K$ = Temperature, $^{\circ}C$ + 273.2
or   Absolute temperature, $^{\circ}R$ = Temperature, $^{\circ}F$ + 459.7

In accordance with the foregoing, the definition of temperature proposed by Lord Kelvin is: " If any substance whatever, subjected to a perfectly reversible cycle of operations, takes in heat only in a locality kept at a uniform temperature, and emits heat only in another locality kept at a uniform temperature, the temperatures of these localities are proportional to the quantities of heat taken in or emitted at them in a complete cycle of operations." †

V–15. Useful Heat.—The Carnot engine is a *perfect* heat engine. It transforms *all* of the heat energy, *between the limits prescribed for its receipt and rejection,* into work. This is, however, very different from saying that it transforms ALL the heat supplied to it into work, for that is something it most certainly does *not* do.

A bank may require that its depositors maintain a certain balance in order to be permitted checking accounts. If the bank requires a minimum

---

* The accompanying table gives the comparison between the Kelvin scale and the best constant-pressure type gas thermometers.

CORRECTIONS TO READINGS OF CONSTANT PRESSURE (100 CM.) GAS THERMOMETERS TO OBTAIN CORRECT TEMPERATURES ON THE THERMODYNAMIC OR KELVIN ABSOLUTE SCALE

$$T_{\text{k.}} = T_{\text{Gas Th.}} + \text{Correction}$$

Temperature, Degrees Centigrade	Correction for Thermometers Using		
	Helium	Hydrogen	Nitrogen
− 200	+0.13°	+0.26°	....
− 100	+0.04°	+0.03°	+0.40°
0	0.00	0.00	0.00
+ 100	+0.00	0.00	0.00
+ 200	+0.01°	+0.02°	+0.11°
+ 450	+0.10°	+0.04°	+0.50°
+1000	+0.30°	....	+1.70°

Abstracted from Smithsonian Physical Tables.
† *Ibid.*, p. 394.

balance of 100 dollars and a depositor has 1000 dollars there, his useful or available capital will be but 900 dollars. Similarly, if we impose the conditions on a heat engine that it shall receive its heat at 600° F. and shall reject its heat at 100° F., we have specified the range over which it shall operate and whether those limits have been settled voluntarily on our part or by conditions over which we have no control, our consideration of the engine's performance must be limited to its action within that range. Independent of the quantity supplied all the heat energy lying below 100° F. must be rejected by the terms of our original agreement before the working fluid can receive a new supply and again start on its cycle. Actually the lowest temperature to which any heat engine can work is the temperature of the bodies by which it is surrounded and to which it delivers its rejected heat, a limit fixed by nature as the average temperature of the earth's surface, roughly 60° F. All the heat energy existing at that or any lower temperature is unavailable for useful work.

The Carnot cycle efficiency tells what portion of the whole heat supplied is useful or available for work.

$$\frac{W}{J} = Q_{\text{useful}} = \frac{Q_1(T_1 - T_2)}{T_1},$$

where Q_1 is the heat supplied, T_2 is the lowest available temperature and W the work done by the engine. The heat which must be rejected and which is unavailable for doing useful work is

$$Q_{\text{unavailable}} = Q_1 - Q_{\text{useful}} = Q_1\frac{T_2}{T_1}.$$

Moreover, this is the absolute minimum that can be rejected, any departure from the ideal conditions specified for the Carnot cycle would require a greater amount of heat to be rejected, therefore a larger value of $Q_{\text{unavailable}}$. Conversely any increase in the unavailable heat would signify a departure from maximum efficiency.

The question is sometimes asked, if the Carnot Cycle is the cycle of a *perfect* engine why is not its *efficiency* 100 per cent. The answer may be given from two viewpoints, one, if efficiency may be considered as the ratio of possible output to a given input, the quantities used for numerator and denominator should be the *useful work done* and the *available* energy put in, then, truly enough, efficiency would be 100 per cent, for the Carnot engine transforms *all* of the *available* energy into useful work. The other would be that if the lower limit were not fixed by nature at about 60° F. and the engine could continue to operate to the absolute zero of temperature, then again its efficiency would be 100 per cent, but the lower limit is always fixed at some other temperature than absolute zero and thus even the Carnot engine is not transforming all the heat supplied into useful work and this through no fault of its own but due to the limitations imposed upon its operating range.

CHAPTER VI

ENGINES USING GASES FOR WORKING FLUID

VI-1. Technical Applications of Perfect Gas Relations.—There are many engineering devices in which the fluid acting, or acted upon, may be treated as a perfect gas and the relations just discussed used directly for the solution of problems connected with their performance and design.

The principal groups are, Compressors, Air Engines, Refrigerating Machines (using air as the working fluid), Hot-air Engines, and Internal Combustion Engines. Broadly speaking, Compressors take their charge at constant pressure and after squeezing it to a higher pressure (doing work on it), deliver this higher pressure, to the receiver where it is stored for future use. Conversely, Air Engines, after accepting a charge of constant pressure, *expand* it to a lower pressure and work is done *by* the working fluid. Air Refrigeration Machines allow compressed air to expand behind a piston in a cylinder, thus doing work and lowering its intrinsic energy and temperature, and the cooled air is then circulated to refrigerate the desired space. In Hot-air Engines a constant quantity of air in a cylinder is alternately heated and cooled by external means. The energy so supplied forces the piston out, work is done and the piston returned to its original position by the excess energy stored in the mechanism. In Internal Combustion Engines, of which the common automobile engine is a good example, the working substance is heated by direct combustion within the cylinder itself. The chief thermodynamic difference between these last two lies in the manner in which the heat energy is supplied to the working substance, in the former by a source external to the cylinder and in the latter by burning or explosion within the cylinder.

For all of the above, the working substance may be considered a gas whose departure from the behavior of a *perfect gas* is so slight that its performance can be predicted with sufficient accuracy for most practical purposes from the equations deduced for perfect gases.

VI-2. Air Compressors.—Air compressors constitute a large portion of all compressors which handle gases, as distinguished from vapors, and the problems met with in these are typical of those encountered in all gas-compression work. Classified mechanically they are of the reciprocating

141

or rotary type with single- or multi-stages depending on whether the entire compression is accomplished in a single process or in a series of successive steps.

Reciprocating compressors that deliver air at low pressures (from 10 to 30 lbs. per sq. in.) are commonly called blowing engines, they are usually large slow-speed single-stage machines. For higher pressures they retain the name of compressors and for pressures not exceeding 80 pounds per square inch are usually single-stage units. An important application of compressed air is to the driving of pneumatic tools, most of which require an air pressure at the throttle of 90 lbs. per sq. in. This means a maintained pressure in the storage tank of from 100 lbs. to 120 lbs. per sq. in. and for such pressures two-stage compression is customary. For pressures up to 1000 lbs. per sq. in., such as are used for the injection air of Diesel engines, three stages are used. Even higher pressures are common commercially as, from 2000 lbs. to 3000 lbs., which is necessary in liquefying air and the permanent gases and 5000 lbs. per sq. in. is required for compressing the air charges of naval torpedoes. For such pressures four and five stages are necessary.

Various cylinder arrangements are resorted to and the accompanying sketch (Fig. VI–1) shows some of the most common. When pairs of cylinders are used, if they are placed end to end, the arrangement is called "tandem," and if abreast of each other, "duplex" or "twin." Air compressors are both single-acting and double-acting, i.e., they deliver air throughout one or both strokes of the piston, and their size is customarily rated in cubic feet of *Free Air* per minute. By *Free Air* is meant air at the atmospheric conditions existing just outside the compressor cylinder, it is air in the condition in which it first starts its journey into the suction pipe*.

Mainly for mechanical reasons, but partly for thermodynamic gain, it is customary to cool the cylinders of compressors, usually by water jacketing. This cooling is necessary from the mechanical point of view in order to maintain a temperature of the cylinder walls sufficiently low to permit the oil film remaining on the surface for lubrication purposes. From the thermodynamic aspect, cooling during the compression reduces the amount of work which has to be done by the compressor. In compressors operating at high rates of revolution, cylinder cooling has but little

---

* Strictly, the moisture content of the atmosphere should be taken account of as a cubic foot of moist air weighs less than a cubic foot of dry air at the same atmospheric pressure and temperature. Thus free air conditions would be the pressure corresponding to the partial pressure of the dry air and the temperature of the mixture or regular atmosphere temperature. Unless special refinement is desirable it is usual to consider air 14.7 lbs. and 68° F. as free air conditions at sea level.

effect thermodynamically, due to the slowness of the heat transfer from the gas to the cylinder walls.

A. Horizontal, Single Stage, One Cylinder, Single Acting or Double Acting.

B. Horizontal, Single Stage, Tandem, Single Acting or Double Acting.

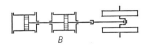

C. Horizontal, Single Stage, Duplex, Single Acting or Double Acting.

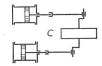

D. Horizontal, Two Stage, Duplex, Single Acting or Double Acting.

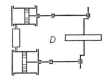

E. Horizontal, Two Stage, Tandem, Single Acting or Double Acting.

F. Angle, Two Stage, Two Cylinder, Single Acting or Double Acting.

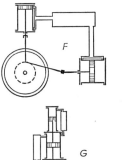

G. Vertical, Three Stage, Three Cylinder, Single Acting or Double Acting.

FIG. (VI–1).

VI–3. Cycles, Mechanical and Thermodynamic.—As previously defined a cycle is a series of events, if the series periodically returns the item under consideration to its initial status we term the cycle a closed cycle. Obviously, these statements are general and there is possible a large number of types of cycles dependent upon the character of the events in which we are interested, such as thermodynamic or mechanical, and the item whose performance we are following, such as the working fluid or the piston in the cylinder.

Two types of cycle, however, are of major interest, one, that dealing with the thermodynamic changes which a fixed quantity of the working fluid undergoes, and the other detailing the repetitive performance of some particular mechanism. To illustrate, if considering a steam-power plant, the thermodynamic cycle would be the history of one pound of water as it receives its heat in the boiler followed by its later thermodynamic adventures as it passes from the boiler through the engine, condenser, feed-pump, etc., back to the boiler. Strictly the entire plant is the heat engine and the cycle is as shown in Fig. VI–2.

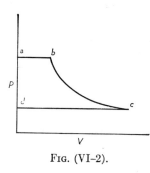

Fig. (VI–2).

However, it frequently happens that our interest centers upon just one unit of the several devices that constitute the complete power plant, usually the steam engine itself. If this is to be studied, the thermodynamic cycle cannot be used as all the thermal processes have not taken place here, thus consideration is restricted to the mechanical events repetitively occurring in this unit. Such a cycle is strictly a mechanical cycle. It can also be represented on the *PV* coördinates by Fig. VI–2, but the significance of the lines is entirely different. For the thermodynamic cycle the line *a–b* represents the receipt of heat by the water in the boiler and the change from liquid to vapor. For the mechanical cycle this line (*a–b*) represents the movement of the piston from admission to cut-off with corresponding induction of steam. Similarly, the line *c–d* represents for the thermodynamic cycle the rejection of heat at constant pressure corresponding to the liquefying of the steam in the condenser, but for the mechanical cycle it simply represents the ejection of steam at exhaust pressure as the piston moves from *c* back to *d*. The expansion line *b–c* has the same significance in both cases as this thermodynamic change occurs in the cylinder as the piston is moving from *b* to *c*, but the cycles taken as a whole represent two entirely different things. One presents the true thermodynamic picture of what occurs in the complete heat engine and the other gives the restricted picture of the pressure-volume relations which hold for one isolated mechanical part.

VI–4. Single-stage Compressor Without Clearance.—Let a, b, c, d, Fig. (VI–3) represent the mechanical cycle of a single-stage air compressor without clearance.

The line $a\,b$ represents the drawing in of a unit weight of air, at constant pressure $p_1\,b\,c$, its compression to the higher pressure, p_2 and $c\,d$, the forcing out of the compressed air at the pressure p_2. The character of the compression line $b\,c$ depends upon the amount of heat removed from the air during the process. If no heat is removed it is an adiabatic compression. On the other hand, if the heat is removed just as fast as the work of compression generates it, the temperature thus remaining constant, it is an isothermal compression. Between these two limiting conditions

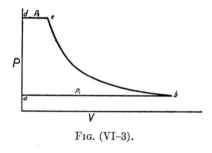

Fig. (VI–3).

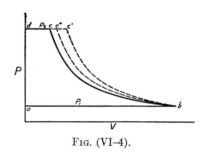

Fig. (VI–4).

there may lie any number of compression lines corresponding to different amounts of heat withdrawn, but all of the polytropic form pv^n = Const., the exponent n varying from k (1.4 for air) of the adiabatic to 1.0 for the isothermal, as discussed on pp. 81, 82.

VI–5. Optimum Cycle for Compressors.—Obviously, as the isothermal has the least slope, the area of the mechanical cycle and, therefore, the work of the compressor will be least for isothermal compression and the optimum cycle for compressor performance comprises this feature together with lines of constant pressure for suction and discharge.

The compression line in actual machines lies between the two limiting ones just mentioned and conforms to the polytropic for a perfect gas, PV^n = Const. The value of n is usually about 1.3 and the compression line (b–c'' of Fig. VI–4) lies between the adiabatic (b–c') for which $n = k = 1.4$, and the isothermal (b–c) for which $n = 1.0$. The value as determined from an actual indicator diagram may also be affected by leakage past the piston though this should be negligible in a compressor in good mechanical condition.

VI–6. Work of the Cycle.—The net work of the cycle will be the sum of the works of the individual steps. Consider a unit weight as drawn in at b and then compressed *isothermally* from the absolute pressure (per square foot) P_1 to P_2. The volume of one pound at b will be the specific volume (v_1) of the entering air.

$$W_{\text{cycle}} = {_a}W_b + {_b}W_c + {_c}W_d + {_d}W_a$$

$$= P_1(v_b - v_a) + P_1v_b \log_e \frac{v_c}{v_b} + P_2(v_d - v_c) + 0,$$

but v_a and v_d equal zero, thus

$$W_{\text{cycle}} = P_1v_b + P_1v_b \log_e \frac{v_c}{v_b} - P_2v_c.$$

Since v_b is the specific volume for the initial condition v_c will be the specific volume for the final condition, and we may write $v_b = v_1 \quad v_c = v_2$. Then, the expression for work of the cycle becomes

$$W_{\text{cycle}} = P_1v_1 + P_2v_2 \log_e \frac{v_2}{v_1} - P_2v_2.$$

Since the compression is isothermal

$$P_1V_1 = P_2V_2 \quad \text{and} \quad W_{\text{cycle}} = P_1v_1 \log_e \frac{v_2}{v_1}. \qquad \text{(VI–1)}$$

As v_2 is smaller than v_1 the evaluation of this will be negative, thus indicating that work is done *on* the air, not *by* the air.

W_1 is in ft.-lbs., P_1 is pounds per sq. ft., and v the specific volume in cubic feet. Since compression ranges are usually stated in pounds per square inch the following form of (VI–1) may be more convenient,

$$W_{\text{cycle}} = -\,144\ p_1v_1 \log_e \frac{p_2}{p_1},$$

where p_1 and p_2 are the absolute pressures in pounds per square inch. Equation (VI–1) gives the work in foot-pounds for drawing in, compressing isothermally and delivering one pound of any perfect gas. Sometimes the work per cubic foot of entering air (free air) is more convenient, in which case the work obtained from equation (VI–1) should be divided by the specific volume of the free air.

If the compression line be other than an isothermal, it may be represented by the exponential equation $PV^n = $ Const., for such cases, the work of the cycle for compressing one pound will be

$$P_1v_1 + \int_{v_1}^{v_2} Pdv - P_2v_2$$

$$W_{cycle} = P_1v_1 - P_2v_2 + \text{const} \int_{v_1}^{v_2} \frac{dv}{v^n}.$$

Since $\dfrac{\text{const }(v_2^{1-n} - v_1^{1-n})}{1-n}$ becomes $\dfrac{P_2v_2 - P_1v_1}{1-n}$,

$$W_{cycle} = P_1v_1 - P_2v_2 + \frac{P_2v_2 - P_1v_1}{1-n}$$

$$= \frac{n}{1-n}(P_2v_2 - P_1v_1), \tag{VI-2}$$

or

$$W_{cycle} = \frac{n}{n-1}(P_1v_1 - P_2v_2). \tag{VI-2 a}$$

This can be manipulated algebraically to give the following expression involving the ratio of the compression pressures which sometimes is more convenient.

$$W_{cycle} = 144 \frac{n}{n-1} p_1v_1 \left[1 - \left(\frac{p_2}{p_1}\right)^{\frac{n-1}{n}} \right] \tag{VI-3}$$

In this, the initial and final pressure p_1 and p_2 are expressed in pounds per square inch (absolute). Also as $Pv = RT$. Equation (VI-2) may be written

$$W_{cycle} = \frac{n}{1-n} R(T_2 - T_1). \tag{VI-4}$$

Example.—A single stage air compressor compresses 1500 cu. ft. of free air per minute to 90 lbs. per sq. in. abs. according to $PV^{1.3}$ const. Atmospheric conditions are 14.7 lbs. abs. and 70° F.

Find: (a) The power necessary to compress for the ideal compressor cycle; (b) The actual power necessary; (c) The power that would be required for adiabatic compression. (Neglect clearance and mechanical friction.)

Solution.—(*a*) The ideal cycle uses isothermal compression, and

$$W_{cycle} = P_1 V_1 \log_e \frac{P_1}{P_2} = 14.7\ (144)\ (1500) \log_e \frac{14.7}{90}$$

$$= 3,176,000\ (-1.812) = -\ 5,750,000 \text{ ft.-lbs.}$$

$$\text{Hp.} = \frac{-5,750,000}{33,000} = -\ 174.1 \text{ Hp.}$$

(*b*) $V_2^n = \dfrac{P_1 V_1^n}{P_2} = \dfrac{14.7\ (1500)^{1.3}}{90} = \dfrac{14.7\ (13,500)}{90} = 2203$

$$V_2 = 372 \text{ cu. ft.}$$

$$W_{cycle} = \frac{n}{n-1} (P_1 V_1 - P_2 V_2) = \frac{1.3}{.3} (144)\ (14.7 \times 1500 - 90 \times 372)$$

$$= -\ 7,140,000 \text{ ft.-lbs. per min.}$$

$$\text{Hp.} = \frac{-7,140,000}{33,000} = -\ 216.7 \text{ Hp.}$$

(*c*) $V_2^k = \dfrac{P_1 V_1^k}{P_2} = \dfrac{14.7\ (1500)^{1.4}}{90} = \dfrac{14.7\ (27,900)}{90} = 4560$

$$V_2 = 410.7 \text{ cu. ft.}$$

$$W_{cycle} = \frac{k}{k-1} (P_1 V_1 - P_2 V_2) = \frac{1.4}{.4} 144\ [14.7\ (1500) - 90\ (410.7)]$$

$$= -\ 7,520,000 \text{ ft.-lbs. per min.}$$

$$\text{Hp.} = \frac{-7,520,000}{33,000} = -\ 228 \text{ Hp.}$$

VI–7. Volumetric Efficiency.—Volumetric Efficiency is a term frequently met with in compressor work. It is an arbitrary term and means, strictly, the ratio of the volume of air actually delivered (when reduced to the temperature and pressure of the intake) to the piston displacement.*

$$\text{True Vol. Eff.} = \text{Eff.}_v = \frac{\text{Cubic Feet free air delivered}}{\text{Cubic Feet of Piston Displacement}}.$$

The most important factor influencing Volumetric Efficiency is clearance. Clearance is the volume of the cylinder minus the volume of the piston displacement. Where clearance is present, and there is always

---

* An alternative definition of volumetric efficiency is a ratio of the *weight* of air actually discharged to the *weight* of free air represented by the piston displacement for the same unit of time.

some, the air entrapped at the end of the stroke reëxpands as the piston moves outward, thus maintaining a pressure on the inlet valves. This prevents their opening until the piston has moved far enough to reduce this back pressure below the inlet pressure, when the valves can open and a new charge be drawn in for the rest of the stroke. This effect is shown in Fig. (VI–5).

The cycle for no clearance is, as before, *a b c d* in which case the stroke of the piston is equal to *Ob'*. If there is clearance the piston does not travel the entire length of the cylinder. Let *e' b'* represent the stroke and *o b'* the entire length of the cylinder. Then after compression the high-pressure air will be discharged by the piston's movement from *c* to *e*. On the return stroke from *e* to *f* the air entrapped in the clearance space is exerting a pressure on the piston in excess of *P*, thus keeping the inlet

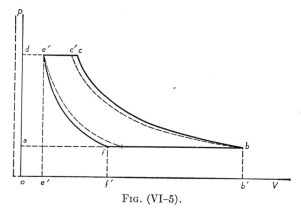

Fig. (VI–5).

valves closed until *f* is reached. From *f* to *b* the piston draws in its new charge.

Assuming the temperature to remain constant, the line *f b*, or *f' b'* of Fig. (VI–5) represents the volume of air actually drawn in and the ratio of this to the piston displacement *e'b'* represents the volumetric efficiency. Hence,

$$\text{Eff.}_v \text{ (diagram)} = \frac{f'b'}{e'b'}.$$

This ratio when taken from the indicator diagram of an actual compressor cylinder is sometimes called the *"Apparent Volumetric Efficiency."* It is an approximation to the true volumetric efficiency.

Increasing the clearance reduces both the amount of air discharged and the amount taken in as it moves the point *c* of the diagram, Fig. (VI–5) to the left and the point f to the right. Hence, as the piston displacement remains constant, increasing the clearance reduces the amount of air taken in each stroke and thus the volumetric efficiency.

It will be interesting to show how sensitive the volumetric efficiency is to changes in clearance. Assuming a clearance * of 5 per cent of the piston displacement $\left(\dfrac{oe'}{e'b'} = .05\right)$, the volumetric efficiency for the ideal cycle (isothermal compression) can then be found for any compression range. Assuming a pressure ratio $\dfrac{P_2}{P_1}$ of 6, $P_cV_c = P_bV_b$ and $P_eV_e = P_fV_f$, then, $V_e = \frac{1}{6}V_b$ and $V_f = 6V_e$. Let the piston displacement Vol. e' b' be considered unity. Then,

$$V_b - V_e = 1.0,$$

$$V_e = .05 \quad V_b = 1.05$$

and

$$V_f = 6V_e = .30.$$

$$\text{Vol. Eff.} = \frac{V_b - V_f}{V_b - V_e} = \frac{1.05 - .30}{1.0} = 75\%.$$

If for the same ratio of pressures the clearance is increased successively to 10, 15, and 20 per cent, Fig. (VI-6), a, b, c, the volumetric efficiencies become 50 per cent, 25 per cent and zero respectively. In this last case, no air is drawn in or discharged, the piston simply compressing and re-expanding a constant quantity of air. This limiting maximum of clearance corresponding to zero discharge for any isothermal compression range is given by the following relation, $1 + cl = cl\dfrac{P_2}{P_1}$, which reduces to

$$1 \div \left(\frac{P_2}{P_1} - 1\right).$$

Actually clearances are made the smallest possible (about 1 per cent for large machines). For high pressures, special precautions must be taken to have the clearances the minimum. If a pressure ratio (isothermal) of $\dfrac{P_2}{P_1}$

---

* Clearance is always expressed as a percentage of the *piston displacement*, not of the cylinder volume.

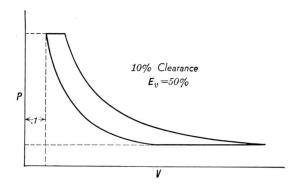

FIG. (VI–6a).

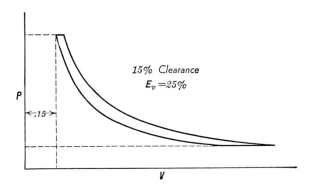

FIG. (VI–6b).

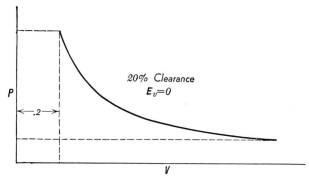

FIG. (VI–6c).

of 101 were possible in a single cylinder, a clearance of 1 per cent would give zero delivery.

It may be well to emphasize that volumetric efficiency is not a thermal efficiency in any sense and is purely a capacity term, the comparison of the *actual* with the *possible* intake.

Volumetric efficiency is also affected by leakage past the valves and pistons, by throttling of the intake and by the heating of the indrawn charge. The effect of leaky valves and piston rings is to lower the compression line on the actual diagram below that corresponding to no leakage, as bc' of Fig. (VI–5). Throttling during the intake causes the suction line to fall below the ideal constant-pressure line and causes the pressure at the beginning of compression to be less than b. Heating during the intake has no effect on pressure but does affect the specific volume at b and thus the weight drawn in.

In attempting to determine the true volumetric efficiency from the indicator diagram all of the foregoing effects must be allowed for.

Provided the expansion line of the clearance air has the same exponent as the compression line, there is a simple expression for the effect of clearance on the diagram volumetric efficiency. Let the size of the clearance volume be one $\dfrac{1}{m}$ part of the piston displacement. Then the expression for volumetric efficiency $\dfrac{f'b'}{e'b'}$ (Fig. VI–5) can be derived as follows:

$$V_b = V_{b'} = 1 + \frac{1}{m},$$

$$V_e = V_{e'} = \frac{1}{m} \quad \text{and} \quad V_f = V_{f'} = \frac{1}{m}\left(\frac{P_2}{P_1}\right)^{\frac{1}{n}}$$

$$\text{Vol. Eff.} = \frac{f'b'}{e'b'} = \frac{V_{b'} - V_{f'}}{V_{b'} - V_{e'}} = \frac{1 + \dfrac{1}{m} - \dfrac{1}{m}\left(\dfrac{P_2}{P_1}\right)^{\frac{1}{n}}}{1 + \dfrac{1}{m} - \dfrac{1}{m}}$$

$$\text{Vol. Eff.}^* = 1 - \frac{1}{m}\left(\frac{P_2}{P_1}\right)^{\frac{1}{n}} + \frac{1}{m}.$$

If in the above, the volumetric efficiency is made equal to zero we get directly either the clearance which will give zero discharge for any assigned

* This volumetric efficiency includes effect of clearance only; it does not take cognizance of leakage, throttling, or heating. These cause actual volumetric efficiencies, obtained by measuring the actual quantity of air delivered, to be materially less.

compression ratio, or the compression ratio giving zero discharge for any assigned clearance.   If isothermal compression is dealt with, n becomes 1.0.

Example.—Air is to be compressed from 14.7 lbs. abs., 70° F., to 100 lbs. abs. in a single stage compressor.   Clearance = 4%.   The pressure and temperature at the end of the suction stroke (Point b in Fig. 5) are 13.5 lbs. abs., and 90° F. respectively.   Seven per cent of the air drawn in (by weight) is lost by leakage (piston and valve) before being delivered. n = 1.3.
What is the volumetric efficiency?

Solution.—Vol. Eff. = $\dfrac{\text{Wt. of air actually discharged}}{\text{Wt. of free air equivalent to piston displacement}}$.

Assuming a piston displacement equivalent to volume of one pound of outside air,

$$\text{P.D.} = \frac{wRT}{P} = \frac{(1)\ (53.35)\ (530)}{14.7\ (144)} = 13.35 \text{ cu. ft.}$$

Considering effect of clearance alone, the volume drawn in (of 13.35 cu. ft. of free air) = $13.35\left[1 - .04\left(\dfrac{100}{14.7}\right)^{\frac{1}{1.3}} + .04 \right]$ = 10.48 cu. ft.   But this 10.48 cu. ft. is now at a pressure of 13.5 lbs. and a temperature of 90°.   The weight actually drawn in is, therefore,

$$\frac{PV}{RT} = \frac{144\ (13.5)\ (10.48)}{53.35\ (550)} = 0.695 \text{ lb.}$$

Of this .695 lb. drawn in, 93 per cent is discharged, the remainder being lost by leakage.   The weight discharged = .93 (.695) = .646 lb.   The piston displacement has been such that, with a mechanically perfect machine, without clearance, one pound of air would have been discharged.   Therefore,

$$\text{Volumetric efficiency} = \frac{.646}{1.000} = .646 \text{ or } 64.6 \text{ per cent.}$$

VI–8.   Efficiency of Compression.—As isothermal compression requires the least work, it is selected as the standard by which the performance of actual compressors may be judged.   The ratio of the work of the cycle for isothermal compression to the work actually expended in compressing the same amount is called the *Efficiency of Compression.*

If, on the indicator diagram of an actual compressor, a diagram be plotted for isothermal compression of the same amount of free air the ratio of the areas of these two diagrams will give the arbitrary quantity called Efficiency of Compression.   Efficiencies of Compression usually range from 65 per cent to 85 per cent.

Example.—For the example in Art. VI–6 compute the efficiency of compression for the actual case (n = 1.3).

Solution.—Work of ideal cycle 5,750,000 ft.-lbs.

Work of actual cycle 7,140,000 ft.-lbs.

$$\text{Eff. of compression } \frac{5,750,000}{7,140,000} = 0.806 \text{ or } 80.6 \text{ per cent.}$$

VI–9. Effect of Clearance on the Work per Pound of Air Delivered.—Neglecting losses, the air trapped in the clearance space gives back all the work that has been done upon it, when it re-expands as the piston moves away from the head. The expansion range is the same as that through which it has just been compressed and thus the work *per pound* returned to the piston will be the same as the work *per pound* spent in compressing it.

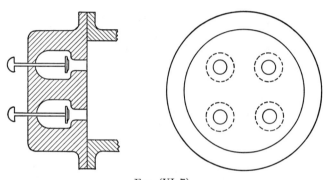

Fɪɢ. (VI–7).

The only difference is that there are not as many pounds pushing back as were originally ahead of the piston, and thus the *total* work returned is less than that originally spent upon it. Thus, *increasing the clearance has no effect*, theoretically, *upon the work per pound of air delivered*. It has, however, as we have just seen, an enormous effect upon the quantity delivered.

This fact, that neglecting mechanical losses, increasing the clearance volume simply decreases the output of the cylinder and does not affect the work done per pound of air delivered is made the basis of an ingenious system of regulating air compressors. There are in the cylinder cover several pockets which can be thrown into or out of communication with the cylinder at will. The governor is arranged to maintain the speed of the compressor constant and the output is varied to meet the needs by opening up one or more of these clearance pockets as needed. Thus while the compressor runs at constant speed the load and output is varied automatically by the variation of the clearance volume.

VI-10. Desirability of Cooling During Compression.—Since the equivalent of the work of compression will appear as heat in the compressed gas unless it be withdrawn, some sort of cooling during the compression process is highly desirable. If complete cooling could be accomplished much less work would be required, as has already been pointed out in the example of page 148. For that case adiabatic compression required nearly 228 Hp. while isothermal compression needed but 174 Hp., a saving of 20 per cent. The amount of work saved can be shown by comparing the idealized indicator diagrams, it is shown by the shaded area in Fig. (VI-8). The line $b\,c'$ represents adiabatic compression and bc the isothermal compression. In actual operation neither of these is attainable and the line bc'' may be considered as representing an actual compression consistent with the cooling actually accomplished by the cylinder jackets or other cooling devices.

It should be borne in mind that the diagrams of Fig. (VI-8) represent the mechanical cycle but not the thermodynamic cycle, as the substance

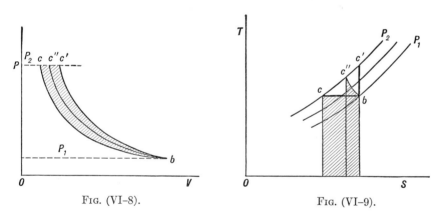

Fig. (VI-8).   Fig. (VI-9).

does not periodically return to its original state except through some external expanding device, such as an air engine or nozzle. The suction and discharge are without change of state and the lines of the diagram representing them simply show varying quantity at constant pressure. Moreover, on the TS plane it is possible to picturize *only* the compression process. This is shown in Fig. (VI-9), and, as before, bc' represents adiabatic compression, bc isothermal compression and bc'' actual compression.

The shaded area represents the amount of heat removed during the compression and for the problem in hand this amounted to 7400 B.t.u. per minute.

VI–11. Difficulty of Cooling in Single Stage.—The removal of heat from a gas undergoing compression is difficult, largely because the small temperature difference between the gas and the cooling agent, coupled with the small superficial area of the containing cylinder, cause only a *slow* transfer of heat. Attempts have been made by circulating water through a jacket around the outside of the cylinder, and even by spraying water into the cylinder. Neither of these is effective, particularly if rapid or high compression is desired.

The only effective way is to compress part way, pass the partially compressed air through a cooling device (called an *intercooler*), then to compress the rest of the way, or through other stages and intercoolers, to the final pressure. The cooling of air-compressor cylinders and heads by water jackets serves principally to facilitate lubrication, though a slight amount of heat is carried off. The only effective cooling is by multi-staging and intercoolers.

VI–12. Effect of Moisture.—Moisture in the air in the quantities encountered under the ordinary atmospheric conditions has but an insignificant effect upon the compression process. If anything, it slightly lowers the value of the exponent n of the compression line, $pv^n = $ Const., due to the fact that the specific heat of the water vapor is larger than that of dry air. The weight of water vapor, however, is so small compared with the weight of the air, even in a saturated mixture, that this effect is negligible. For example, a cubic foot of saturated mixture at 60° F. and 14.7 lb. weighs .0768 lb., and, of this, the weight of the water vapor is .0008 lb., thus constituting but about one per cent of the weight of the mixture. Even when water is sprayed into the cylinder during the compression process, as is sometimes done, it does not materially reduce the work of compression unless the compression is slow and the spray very fine.

The incoming air is always cooler than the cylinder walls, as these have retained approximately the temperature of the charge just compressed and delivered, and, as a result, heat is given to the incoming air. At the end of compression the air is at a higher temperature (due to the work of compression) than the cylinder walls, and heat then repasses from the air back to the cylinder walls. Moisture in the air increases this interchange of heat.

VI–13. Compounding and Multi-Staging.—If compression is carried out in two stages it is usually referred to as compound, and if more, as three stage, four stage, etc. Compounding and multi-staging are resorted to

principally to permit intercooling between stages, it also makes it possible
to reduce the clearance.   How intercooling affects the work of compression is best shown by comparing the diagrams of a single-stage compressor

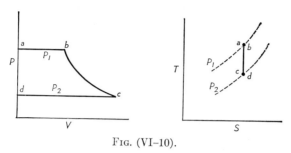

Fig. (VI–10).

with the combined diagram of a multi-stage compressor working between
the same initial and final pressures.   See Fig. (VI–13).

First consider the case of no clearance.   For the single-stage compressor
the actual line (following the law PV^n = Const.) would be $b\,c$ and the

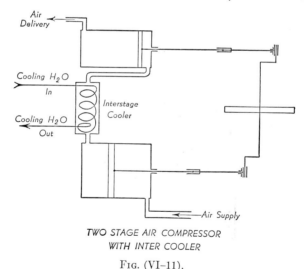

TWO STAGE AIR COMPRESSOR
WITH INTER COOLER

Fig. (VI–11).

isothermal line is shown by $b\,c'$.   The area $b\,c\,c'$ represents the additional
work, over that of isothermal compression, that must be done.   If instead
of the compression being carried out all in one cylinder, or stage, it was
carried out in three successive steps and between each the air was circulated through a cooling device (intercooler), and brought back to the

initial temperature, the combined diagram would resemble the full-line diagram of Fig. (VI–13). If the compression line in each stage had the same value of n as in the simple compressor, the combined diagram would be the same as if the simple diagram were cut horizontally at P' and P'', and the sections slid over till the beginning of each compression line landed on the ideal, isothermal, curve, $b\ c$.

Obviously, a much nearer approach to ideal conditions can be had by this device, as the excess area of the irregular diagram over that of the isothermal is much less than the excess of the simple diagram ($a\ b\ c\ d$) over the isothermal $a\ b\ c'\ d$. Thus multi-staging, when combined with inter-cooling, reduces the work of compression.

Clearance is also favorably affected by compounding mainly because the minimum clearance for a small cylinder is a much smaller absolute quantity than for a large cylinder. Therefore, the clearance in the high-pressure stage of a multi-stage compressor being smaller in cubic feet than in the corresponding single-stage compressor, the volumetric efficiency is improved and the weight of air delivered will be greater.

All of the foregoing is on the assumption that the air delivered is at the final pressure, and, ultimately, before being used, at the temperature at which it was drawn in. This is the usual condition as compressors deliver to a central storage reservoir from which the air is drawn as needed, and the time between leaving the compressor and going to the using unit generally is sufficient for the cooling to take place. If, however, the air is to be used at once and very near the compressor, there is little advantage in cooling during compression as the excess heat in the air can be made to do work in the air engine where it is used.

The theoretical power savings obtainable by multi-stage compression (with $n = 1.3$) over single-stage compression are as listed below.

TABLE IV

$\dfrac{P_2}{P_1}$	Saving in Power Over Single-stage Compression ($n = 1.3$)	
	2-Stage	3-Stage
	Per Cent	Per Cent
4	8	10
6	10	13
8	12	15
10	13	17
12	14	19
14	15	20

In multi-stage compressions the intermediate pressures for the various stages depend upon the volumes assigned to the individual cylinders.

It is important to determine what the intermediate pressures shall be to ensure the minimum area for the combined diagram, therefore, the least work of compression.

Example.—1000 cu. ft. of air per minute are to be compressed from 14.7 lbs. per sq. in. abs., 70° F. to 150 lbs. abs. by: (a) Single-stage compression, $n = 1.3$; (b) Two-stage compression, intercooling to 70° F. at 47 lbs. abs., $n = 1.3$.

Find the work and power required in each case, and the saving in power due to intercooling.

$$\text{Solution.}\text{—}(a) \quad V_2{}^{1.3} = \frac{14.7 \ (1000)^{1.3}}{150} = 778.$$

$$\log V_2 = \frac{\log 778}{1.3} = 2.225. \qquad V_2 = 168 \text{ cu. ft. per min.}$$

$$W_{\text{cycle}} = \left(\frac{1.3}{.3}\right)(144)\ [14.7\ (1000) - 150\ (168)] = 624\ (10,500)$$

$$= 6,550,000 \text{ ft.-lbs. per min.}$$

$$\text{Hp.} = \frac{6,550,000}{33,000} = 198.5 \text{ Hp.}$$

(b) First Stage: $V_2'^{(1.3)} = \dfrac{14.7\ (1000)^{1.3}}{47} = 2483. \quad V_2' = 408.6 \text{ cu. ft. per min.}$

$$W_{\text{cycle}} = 624\ [14.7\ (1000) - 47\ (408)] = 2,808,000 \text{ lbs. per min.}$$

Second Stage: $V' = 1000 \left(\dfrac{14.7}{47}\right) = 313 \text{ cu. ft. per min.}$

$$V_2{}^{1.3} = \frac{47\ (313)^{1.3}}{150} = 546. \qquad V_2 = 128 \text{ cu. ft. per min.}$$

$$W_{\text{cycle}} = 624\ [47\ (313) - 150\ (128)] = 2,808,000 \text{ lbs. per min.}$$

Total work $= 2,808,000 + 2,808,000 = 5,616,000$ lbs. per min.

$$\text{Hp.} = \frac{5,616,000}{33,000} = 170 \text{ Hp.}$$

Saving $= 198.5 - 170 = 28.5$ Hp.

VI–14. Best Intermediate Pressures for Multi-stage Compression.— Let the diagram, Fig. (VI–12), represent the combined diagram of a two-stage compressor without clearance or friction, but with the air cooled to its initial temperature between the stages. The problem is to so locate the intermediate pressure p' that the area of the resulting diagram for the entire compressor shall be a minimum. This will occur when the area of the diagram for the first stage is equal to the area of that for the second stage. Then each stage will be doing equal work and the total work will be a minimum.

By geometrical similitude, when these areas are equal the corresponding areas on the isothermal diagram are equal. We can thus work from the isothermal diagram.

Calling the initial and final pressures p_1 and p_2, and the intermediate

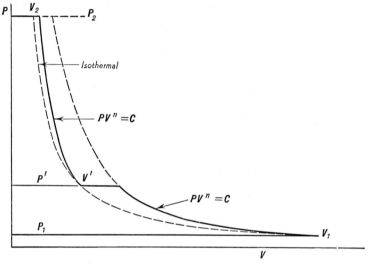

Fig. (VI–12).

pressure p' with the corresponding isothermal volumes $v_1 v_2$ and v', the area of the lower part of the isothermal diagram (first stage) is,

$$P'V' \log_e p_1/p'$$

and of the upper part (the second stage),

$$P_2 V_2 \log_e p'/p_2.$$

Equating these,

$$P_1 V_1 \log_e p_1/p' = P_2 V_2 \log_e p'/p_2.$$

Since the compression is isothermal,

$$P_1 V_1 = P_2 V_2.$$

Cancelling from both sides of the equation, we have,

$$\frac{p_1}{p'} = \frac{p'}{p_2}$$

and

$$p' = \sqrt{p_1 p_2}.$$

This same expression would have been obtained had the compression been assumed to be polytropic, but the algebraic work in deriving it is less simple.

Example.—Air is to be compressed from 14 lbs. per sq. in. abs. to 250 lbs. abs.
Determine the approximate intercooler pressure or pressures for (a) Two-stage compression; (b) Three-stage compression.

Solution.—

$$(a) \quad p' = \sqrt{p_1 p_2} = \sqrt{14\,(250)} = 59.2 \text{ lbs. abs.}$$

$$(b) \quad p' = \sqrt[3]{p_1{}^2 p_2} = \sqrt[3]{14^2\,(250)} = 36.6 \text{ lbs. abs.}$$

$$p'' = \sqrt[3]{p_1 p_2{}^2} = \sqrt[3]{14\,(250)^2} = 95.6 \text{ lbs. abs.}$$

Similarly, for a three-stage compressor, Fig. (VI–13), if we call the first

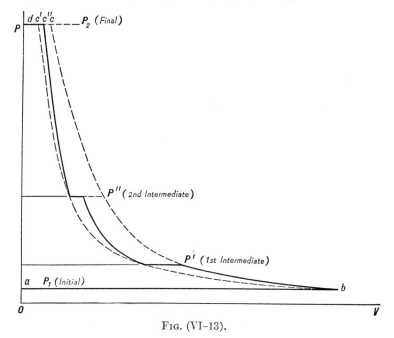

FIG. (VI–13).

intermediate pressure, p', and the second intermediate pressure, p'', equating the areas of the isothermal diagram, gives,

$$P_1 V_1 \log_e \frac{p_1}{p'} = P'V' \log_e \frac{p'}{p''} = P_2 V_2 \log_e \frac{p''}{p_2}.$$

From which, since,

$$p_1 v_1 = p'v' = p''v'' = p_2 v_2,$$

$$\log_e \frac{p_1}{p'} = \log_e \frac{p'}{p''} = \log_e \frac{p''}{p_2}$$

and

$$\frac{p''}{p_2} = \frac{p'}{p''} = \frac{p_1}{p'},$$

also,

$$(p')^2 = p_1 p'',$$

$$(p'')^2 = p'p_2,$$

which gives,

$$p' = \sqrt[3]{p_1^2 p_2},$$

$$p'' = \sqrt[3]{p_1 p_2^2}.$$

Similarly, for any number of stages.*

VI–15. Minimum Work for Multi-Stage Compression.—Having determined the intermediate pressures such that minimum work is performed, the expression for the total work of the complete compression follows directly by summing the individual stages; it is, for the compound compressor, *twice* the work of the first stage and for the three stage, *three times* the work of the first stage.

The work of the first stage was, for the compound compressor:

$$W_1 = \frac{n}{n-1} P_1 V_1 \left[1 - \left(\frac{p'}{p_1}\right)^{\frac{n-1}{n}} \right].$$

For two stages it will be,

$$W_{\text{total}} = \frac{2n}{n-1} P_1 V_1 \left[1 - \left(\frac{p'}{p_1}\right)^{\frac{n-1}{n}} \right],$$

but

$$p' = \sqrt{p_1 p_2},$$

* The above expressions may also be derived by taking sum of the areas of the actual diagrams, thus obtaining the total work of compressor; then differentiating with respect to an intermediate pressure and placing this differential expression equal to zero thus imposing the condition of minimum work. The algebra, however, is rather cumbersome. For this other method see Peabody's Thermodynamics of Heat Engineering pp. 367 and 368.

therefore,

$$W_{total} = \frac{2n}{n-1} P_1 V_1 \left[1 - \left(\frac{p_2}{p_1}\right)^{\frac{n-1}{2n}}\right],$$

and, similarly, for the three-stage compressor,

$$W_{total} = \frac{3n}{n-1} P_1 V_1 \left[1 - \left(\frac{p_2}{p_1}\right)^{\frac{n-1}{3n}}\right].$$

Example.—Determine the work of compression by: (a) Two-stage; (b) Three-stage compression for 1000 cu. ft. of free air from 14 lbs. per sq. in. abs., 70° F. to 250 lbs. abs. $n = 1.3$.

Solution.—

(a) $W = \dfrac{2n}{n-1} (P_1 V_1) \left[1 - \left(\dfrac{P_2}{P_1}\right)^{\frac{n-1}{2n}}\right]$

$= \dfrac{2(1.3)(14)(144)(1000)}{1.3 - 1} \left[1 - \left(\dfrac{250}{14}\right)^{\frac{.3}{2.6}}\right]$

$= 17{,}460{,}000 \ (1 - 1.394) = 6{,}880{,}000 \text{ ft.-lbs.}$

(b) $W = \dfrac{3n}{n-1} (P_1 V_1) \left[1 - \left(\dfrac{P_2}{P_1}\right)^{\frac{n-1}{3n}}\right]$

$= \dfrac{3(1.3)(14)(144)(1000)}{.3} \left[1 - \left(\dfrac{250}{14}\right)^{\frac{.3}{3.9}}\right]$

$= 26{,}250{,}000 \ (1 - 1.248) = 6{,}500{,}000 \text{ ft.-lbs.}$

VI–16. Air Engines.—In the broad sense of the term *air engines* should include all engines in which the working fluid is air or at least a gaseous mixture whose behavior and characteristics are much the same as air. This embraces the types commonly designated as Compressed Air Engines (pneumatic tools), Hot-air Engines and Internal Combustion Engines. The last two are obviously heat engines; as heat (Q_1) is supplied to the working fluid which in turn does work (W) and then rejects heat (Q_2). With compressed-air engines, however, the source of heat and refrigerator are not so obvious and the classification as heat engines is not so apparent. For these the motivating agency is the store of high-pressure air from which they draw and the previous history of this store of energy is of interest in discussing performance characteristics. For convenience, the analysis may be narrowed to include only the performance in the cylinder of the compressed air engine itself.

Considering Hot-air Engines and Internal Combustion Engines, the chief distinction between them lies in the manner of supplying the heat to the charge of air forming the impulsive unit. If the heat is supplied from some combustion outside the cylinder the device is termed a Hot-air Engine, if from combustion within the cylinder, it is an Internal Combustion Engine. In fact, this latter name was coined in the early days

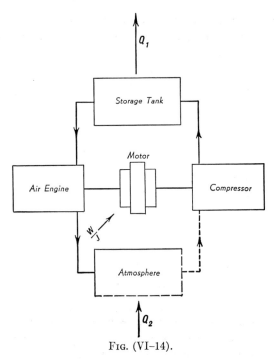

Fig. (VI–14).

when there was still a competition between these two types for popular favor in order to distinguish it from the Hot-air or, as then called, External Combustion Engines.

VI–17. Compressed Air (or Pneumatic) Engines.—Engines using air that has been previously compressed for their motive fluid are actually but reversed air compressors. Probably it would be more correct to say that air compressors are reversed air engines, save that our greater familiarity with the former tempts us to use it for the basis of comparison.

The use of compressed air as the motive fluid for the production of power is usually restricted to those cases where special considerations such as need for ventilation, portability, or convenience outweigh the need for thermal economy, for their thermal efficiency is and always must be poor.   Compressed air systems are made up of a compressor and an expander, in the former, work is done on the air and considerable energy is disposed of as heat at high temperature which is dissipated to the atmosphere, work is supplied and heat is given off.   In the expander cylinder, heat is required to produce the expansion and do the work, and this comes from the intrinsic energy of the high-pressure air.   We have then for the complete unit, the first member giving up heat at a high temperature, while the last member is taking on heat at a lower temperature with corre-

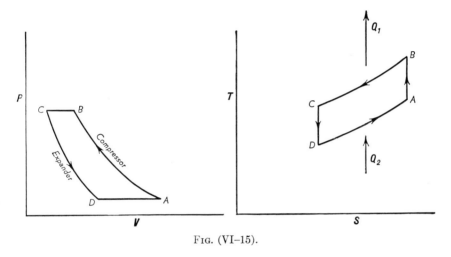

Fig. (VI–15).

sponding loss in efficiency.   Of course, if both compression and expansion were strictly isothermal, there would be no loss in the availability of the energy, but in practice the processes are never isothermal.

Treating the whole plant as a unit, the essential organs are, compressor, storage tank, and expander.   These are shown diagrammatically in Fig. (VI–14).   Tracing the progress of a unit of air around this plant, the cycle is shown on the P–V and T–S planes in Fig. (VI–15).   Here A–B indicates the compression, B–C the cooling in the storage tank, C–D the expansion in the cylinder of the air engine and D–A the warming of the expanded air back up to the original temperature at the constant pressure of the atmosphere.

For such an arrangement, the heat Q_2 passes from the atmosphere into the cold exhaust raising it to atmospheric temperature. The compressor then compresses and delivers to the storage tank. The air enters this tank at the high temperature of the compressor but gradually cools as it remains in storage until the heat Q_1 is given up to the atmosphere and the air has recovered its original temperature. Next it passes to the air engine, expands, doing work and exhausts at low temperature to the atmosphere. In the compressor and expander cylinders, work is done on the air and by the air respectively and only the difference between these must be supplied by some external agency. This additional energy supplied is the W/J of the simple heat engine concept considering the entire plant. The entire plant is, in effect, a heat engine reversed, taking in Q_2 at low temperature from the atmosphere, requiring the work W/J and delivering the heat Q_1 to the atmosphere at a higher temperature. If consideration be restricted to the processes occurring in the cylinder only of either the compressor or expander, then recourse must be had to the mechanical cycle for each particular unit.

The mechanical cycle of the compressed-air engine is practically that of the air compressor reversed, see Fig. (VI–10), in which $a\,b$ represents the admission of air at pressure p_1. At b, cut-off occurs, followed by adiabatic expansion to the final pressure p_2, at c, after which the air is exhausted at constant pressure. The line a–b thus shows progressively the volume corresponding to the weight of air taken into the cylinder. However, throughout the process the state or characteristic properties of the air remain constant. Only the mass of air varies, and variation of mass cannot be shown on a temperature-entropy diagram as this deals primarily with variations in characteristic properties. If it were of interest to show the mechanical cycle in the T–S plane, a–b would be shown as a point and c–d as another point. The process of adiabatic expansion, b–c, would be shown by the line connecting these points. However, such picturization renders very little aid and usually the mechanical cycle is shown only for the PV coördinates. The expressions for work and efficiency follow directly from those evolved for the air compressor.

$$\text{Work} = \frac{n}{1-n}\,(P_2V_2 - P_1V_1).$$

$$\text{Eff. of Power Transmission} = \frac{\text{Work of Expansion Cycle}}{\text{Work of Compression Cycle}}.$$

The cylinder in which the air expands and does work is, however, only one element of the complete mechanism and a proper consideration of the compressed air engine should include the air compressor, the transmission lines and storage reservoir, and the cycle should cover the complete travel of the air from Free air back to Free air again. The diagram for such a cycle, including losses, is shown in Fig. (VI–16).

Air is taken into the compressor at atmospheric pressure P_1 and is compressed adiabatically to P_2 (A–B). At B, assuming no loss, it is discharged into the receiver at P_2 and T_2 where it cools, by dissipation of heat to the atmosphere (B–C) till it is practically at atmospheric temperature, C. Through the pipe line to the expansion cylinder there is a loss of pressure at nearly constant temperature (C–D) (an irreversible process, throttling) until it enters the expansion cylinder and expands adiabatically

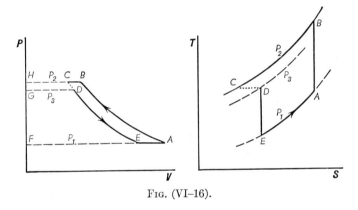

Fig. (VI–16).

to the initial pressure P_1 (D–E). The exhaust air at condition E next absorbs heat returning at constant pressure to the original condition at A.

The work of the compressor is shown by the area ABHF on the PV diagram and that of the working or expansion cylinder by DEFG. The first represents the work done on the air and the second work done by the air. The difference between these or the area ABCHGDE on the PV plane, is the work which is thrown away as heat diffused to the atmosphere and is the toll exacted for power generation by this method. In actual practice with good mechanical equipment this may amount to 50 per cent or more of the compressor power.

On the PV plane the cycle of events is shown by ABCDE with CD dotted to represent the irreversible change of the throttling through the pipes connecting the compressor to the expander. On this plane there can be shown also the indicator diagrams for the compressor and expander cylinders. On the TS plane, however, the thermodynamic cycle only can be shown as the *lines* on the *PV* plane representing, suction (*FA*), delivery (*BH*), supply (*GD*), and exhaust (*EF*), become *points* at *A*, *B*, *D*, and *E*, respectively, since during these events the *state* of the air remains constant, the amount of air under consideration being the only variable.

Example.—An air engine takes air at 250 lbs. abs. and 100° F. from the three-stage compressor in Example (previous). Assume complete expansion to 14 lbs. abs. and $n = 1.35$.

Find: (*a*) Work done per 1000 cu. ft. of free air; (*b*) Efficiency of power transmission.

Solution.—

(*a*) Wt. of air $= \dfrac{14\,(144)\,(1000)}{(53.35)\,(530)} = 71.4$ lbs.

$$V_3 = \frac{(71.4)\,(53.35)\,(560)}{250\,(144)} = 59.2 \text{ cu. ft.}$$

$$V_4{}^{1.35} = \frac{250\,(59.2)^{1.35}}{14} = 4405$$

$$\log V_4 = \frac{\log\,4405}{1.35} = 2.7$$

$$V_4 = 508 \text{ cu. ft.}$$

$$W = \frac{1.35}{.35}\,(144)\,[250\,(59.2) - 14\,(508)]$$

$$= 556\,(7680) = 4{,}270{,}000 \text{ ft.-lbs.}$$

(*b*) Eff. of Power Transmission $= \dfrac{4{,}270{,}000}{6{,}500{,}000} = 0.657$ or 65.7 per cent.

VI–18. Power, and Air Consumption.—The power to be expected from a compressed-air engine or the size a projected cylinder should have in order to produce a required power depends upon the average pressure effective for pushing the piston (Mean Effective Pressure (M.E.P.)), attained in the cylinder. This in turn is affected by the initial pressure, the back pressure and the expansion ratio. (The expansion ratio, *r*, is the ratio of the volume at the end of the expansion stroke to the volume at cut-off.) By assuming the expansion to follow a geometrical curve it is possible to construct a geometrical diagram which does not differ too radically from the actual mechanical cycle and for which the M.E.P. may be readily computed. Applying to this a factor to allow for actual variations, the value of the *Probable M.E.P.* can be predicted. This is the value that should be obtained from the actual indicator diagram of the engine in operation. For *convenience* the expansion line of this idealized diagram is assumed to be a rectangular hyperbola, $PV = $ Const., nothing is assumed as to character of the expansion, only that this simplest of curves does not differ too widely from an expansion line as taken from actual diagrams.

In Fig. (VI–17) the full-line diagram represents such an idealized

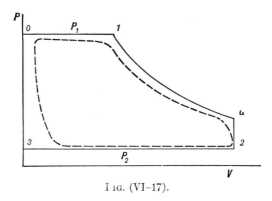

I IG. (VI–17).

diagram, P_1 and P_2 being the pressures of the supply and the exhaust. For such a diagram the area under the admission line is P_1V_1, that under the expansion line is $P_1V_1 \log_e \dfrac{V_2}{V_1}$, the area under the exhaust line is P_2V_2. Assembling these the net area of the diagram becomes,

$$P_1V_1 + P_1V_1 \log_e \frac{V_2}{V_1} - P_2V_2 \quad \text{or}$$

if we represent the volumetric expansion ratio from cut-off to release (called the Expansion Ratio) by r, the area of the diagram is

$$\text{Area} = P_1V_1 + P_1V_1 \log_e r - P_2V_2.$$

Dividing by the length of the diagram (V_2) to get the Mean Effective Pressure, we have,

$$M.E.P. = P_1\left(\frac{1 + \log_e r}{r}\right) - P_2.$$

Since P_1 and P_2 are in pounds per square foot, this M.E.P. is in the same units. Values of the term in parentheses for various expansion ratios are listed in Table V.

TABLE V

r (Expansion Ratio)	$\dfrac{1 + \log_e r}{r}$	r	$\dfrac{1 + \log_e r}{r}$	r	$\dfrac{1 + \log_e r}{r}$
50	0.09825	20	0.1998	4.00	0.5965
48	.10150	18	.2161	3.63	.6308
46	.10498	16	.2358	3.33	.6615
44	.10875	15	.2472	3.00	.6993
42	.11282	14	.2599	2.86	.7171
40	.11724	13.33	.2690	2.66	.7440
38	.12206	13	.2472	2.50	.7664
36	.12734	12	.2904	2.22	.8095
34	.13314	11	.3089	2.00	.8465
32	.13957	10	.3303	1.82	.8786
30	.14673	9	.3552	1.66	.9066
28	.15474	8	.3849	1.60	.9187
26	.16380	7	.4210	1.54	.9292
25	.16877	6.66	.4347	1.48	.9405
24	.17411	6.00	.4653	1.43	.950
23	.17982	5.71	.4807	1.33	.965
22	.18598	5.00	.5218	1.25	.978
21	.19260	4.44	.5608	1.18	.989

The ratio of the area of the diagram taken from an actual engine to this idealized diagram is called the Diagram Factor or Card Factor, it is also the ratio of the M.E.P. of the actual and idealized cards and is much used for predicting the probable indicator diagrams of reciprocating engines, both air and steam for assigned initial and back pressures and expansion ratios.

Under favorable conditions the value of this factor ranges from .80 to .90.

Sometimes it is preferred to plot or compute the probable diagram by a step-by-step process, making allowances for the drop in pressure during admission, plotting the expansion line with its probable value of the exponent n, allowing for the building up of pressure during exhaust due to the restriction of the ports, plotting the compression line and terminating the diagram at the assumed clearance volume. When carefully done this probably results in a more accurate prediction of performance but generally the gain does not warrant the added labor over the first method.

The air consumption of any particular compressed-air engine can be calculated from the probable indicator diagram knowing the volume pressure and temperature at cut-off or release and the volume pressure and temperature at compression. The only correction that needs to be applied is for the leakage past the piston which should be very small.

The temperature at the end of expansion may be found from

$$T_2 = T_1(P_2/P_1)^{\frac{n-1}{n}},$$

or

$$T_2 = T_1(V_1/V_2)^{n-1}.$$

The air consumption for various types of actual compressed-air engines is usually quoted in cubic feet of free air per minute. A builder's quotation for the performance of compressed-air hoisting engines of moderate size using air at 60 lbs. pressure is 12.7 cu. ft. free air per Brake horse power per minute which corresponds to about 60 lbs. per horse power per hour.

VI–19. Calculation of Cylinder Dimensions for a Compressed-Air Engine.—To illustrate the application of the above paragraph let it be required to determine the proper dimensions for an engine using compressed air which shall develop 100 indicated horse power at 150 r.p.m. The air being supplied at 90 lbs. pressure gage, and at 70° F.

For this case, $P_1 = (90 + 14.7)\ 144$ and $P_2 = 14.7 \times 144$. Assuming cut-off at one-quarter stroke the number of expansions (r) is 4 and the *theoretical* Mean Effective Pressure (p. 169) is

$$\text{Th. M.E.P.} = \frac{104.7}{4}\ (1 + \log_e 4) - 14.7$$

$$= 47.6 \text{ lbs. per sq. in.}$$

Taking a card factor of .85 the *Probable* Mean Effective Pressure is,

Prob. M.E.P. $= 47.6 \times .85 = 40.5$ lbs. per sq. in.

$$\text{Horse Power} = \frac{2PLAN}{33,000},$$

$$100 = \frac{2 \times 144 \times 40.5 \times LA \times 150}{33,000},$$

from which LA (which is the Piston Displacement) is,

$$LA = \text{Piston Disp.} = 1.89 \text{ cu. ft.}$$

If a ratio of Stroke to Diameter of 1.5 be accepted, then Piston Disp.

$$LA = 1.5D \, \frac{\pi D^2}{4} = 1.18D^3$$

and

$$D^3 = 1.89 \div 1.18 = 1.6.$$

Diam. = 1.17 ft. or a little over 14 ins.

and the stroke is $1.5 \times 14 = 21$ ins.

VI–20. Compounding and Reheating.—Compressed-air engines may be compounded when the pressure range is great and if the air is reheated between stages the compounding results in an improved economy. An arrangement of this sort has been used for compressed-air locomotives, used largely in mines and for the handling of explosives. In these the air is supplied at about 200 lbs. pressure and, after expanding through the first stage, is reheated by the surrounding atmosphere to nearly its original temperature and then expanded further in the second stage. This reheating results in an improvement of efficiency of about 50 per cent and is effected by a device similar to the intercooler.

In those units, such as the pneumatic hand tools, in which the air is admitted at full pressure for the entire stroke, there is practically no temperature drop in the cylinder since there is no expansion, but there is a slight drop in temperature due to the expansion that takes place in the exhaust passages. Such engines are rarely compounded.

VI–21. Restricted Field of Compressed Air Engines.—So far the discussion has been confined to air engines that have been practically reversed air-compressors, that is, they have been engines using air *mechanically* compressed to high pressure as their motive fluid. Moreover, this high-pressure air has been considered as practically at the temperature of the atmosphere. As already pointed out they are all, however, heat engines, but heat engines of poor thermal efficiency because of the extra link in the chain of conversion of heat into work introduced by the mechanical compressor.

There are, however, many extremely useful tools in this general classification, such as, compressed-air locomotives, hoisting engines, turbines, and the host of pneumatic hand tools, hammers, drills, hoists, and jacks but their use is warranted by other considerations than coal-pile cost, another name for thermal efficiency.

For instance, coal mine locomotives are frequently of the compressed-air type but mainly because the ventilation problem is a difficult one and could not be made to bear the extra burden of foul exhausts.   Pneumatic hand tools are an indispensable adjunct of modern construction but it is because of their portability and compactness.

VI–22. Hot-Air Engines.—To avoid the mechanical compressor and have the necessary high initial pressure obtained directly by heat, much work and some very clear thermodynamic thinking was done in the early development of the hot-air engine.   It is worthwhile to know of the principal ones actually built and operated even though they are today obsolete. Moreover, they afford another excellent opportunity of illustrating the application of the simple perfect gas laws to the prediction of performance of actual or proposed engines.

With the object of producing a practicable mechanism which should approximate reversible processes in all of its events (and thus approach the Carnot cycle efficiency), Robert Stirling, in 1827, designed an engine which operated successfully and with good economy.   His basic idea was

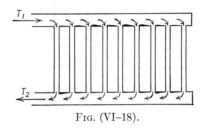

Fig. (VI–18).

to replace the two adiabatic operations of the Carnot cycle with two equivalent reversible processes by which the working fluid should alternately be placed in the high and low temperature states (T_1 and T_2) suitable for the receipt and rejection of the heat doing the useful work.   The equivalent process consisted of the temporary laying aside of sufficient heat to effect the temperature drop and the later restoration of this heat to effect the temperature rise.   Such a process can be made effective by use of a regenerative heater and in the idealized case is a completely reversible process.   Moreover, it can be carried out with either the volume or the pressure remaining constant.

Imagine a nest of long tubes (Fig. VI–18) through which air could flow and which had an infinite capacity for absorbing and restoring heat. If a volume of air flowed through this nest it would enter at T_1, and leave at a lower temperature T_2, the heat having been stored in the tubes.   If the direction of flow now be reversed and the same mass of air sent back through, the air would emerge at the original point at the original temperature. Furthermore, the transfer of heat would have been made reversibly both going and coming, as the tubes would be operating with temperatures gradually varying throughout their length from T_1 to T_2 but the air flowing through would be at the same temperature as the tube throughout. Thus, the actual transfer of heat at each individual point along the tube would be effected, not across a temperature gradient, but isothermally and thus reversibly. Such a device, which in a way simply borrows heat and later returns it, is called a *regenerator*. It was such a device that Stirling used to produce two operations which should take the place of the Carnot adiabatics and yet should be reversible. This alternate storing and restoring, or borrowing and returning of heat in place of the adiabatic expansion and the compression permits the working substance to pass reversibly from T_1 to T_2 and back from T_2 to T_1. It permits the working substance to drop to T_2 before giving up its heat to the refrigerator and brings it back to T_1 before it receives its charge of heat from the source thus discharging its heat at the lowest possible temperature and receiving all its heat at the highest possible temperature which are criteria of maximum efficiency.

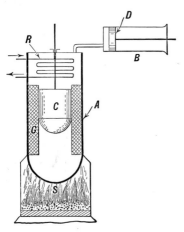

FIG. (VI–19).

When the adiabatics of the Carnot cycle are replaced by *constant volume* regenerative heating and cooling, there results the Stirling cycle and when replaced by *constant pressure* regenerative heating and cooling, there results the Ericsson cycle. This latter is named after John Ericsson, inventor and builder of the "Monitor" of Civil War fame, who also built several engines which operated successfully on this cycle.

A diagrammatic sketch of the mechanical arrangement of the Stirling engine is shown in Fig. VI–19.

The essential characteristics are a gridwork (G) of large thermal capacity to provide the regenerative heat transfers and two cylinders A and B. Cylinder A is of large size and its function simply is to retain the air while it is receiving heat from the source or rejecting heat to the refrigerator. Cylinder B is much smaller and is the working cylinder. The piston (C) in the larger cylinder is a member serving only to displace the air alternately from end to end of the cylinder and thus bring it in successive contacts with the source of heat (S) (the furnace), and the refrigerator (R) (the cooling coils). The movement of the displacer piston (C) occurs when the working piston is at the end of its stroke which is approximately 90° out of phase with the working piston (D).

Consider the mechanism to be in the position shown in the figure. The air below the displacer piston is heated and the piston (D) of the working cylinder is pushed out, doing work equivalent to the heat which has been isothermally supplied. At the end of the stroke of the working piston the displacer piston (C) is moved to the bottom of its stroke thus putting the main body of air in contact with the cooling coils (R) which constitute the refrigerator. The working piston (D) then returns compressing the air around the refrigerator coils (R) which withdraw the heat at such a rate that the compression is isothermal. The displacer piston then rises to its original position and the cycle is repeated.

A comparison of these three cycles between the same temperature limits and assuming identical conditions at the beginning of the isothermal compression stroke, is shown in Fig. (VI–20). These are for one pound of working fluid (air), receiving equal quantities of heat at the same temperature.

It is apparent that the efficiencies of all are the same and for the same heat supplied at the same temperature, the areas of the PV diagrams must be equal. The Stirling and the Carnot have the same maximum volumes, therefore, the piston displacement, though the Stirling is subjected to lower maximum pressure and, therefore should be a lighter engine. The Ericsson has the largest piston displacement, but all are tremendously massive affairs. One of Ericsson's designs which was actually built for the U. S. Navy had a cylinder 14 feet diameter and developed 300 I.Hp. when running at nine revolutions per minute.

They were not a commercial success, largely on account of the rapid deterioration of the heating surfaces. Moreover, it is true in general that it is impossible to get a large amount of heat *quickly* into the working fluid by any sort of external heating. This means that engines of this sort are necessarily bulky and slow, with correspondingly high weights per horsepower even though of high thermal efficiency. Engines of small size, however, are still built which operate substantially on this cycle and are used for light duty pumping engines.

One other early hot-air engine of interest is that proposed by Joule and diagrammatically shown in Fig. (VI–21).

Two large capacity chambers A and B are connected with a pair of cylinders M and N by a valve arrangement, as shown in Fig. (VI–21). M is the compressing cylinder and N the working cylinder. B is filled with low-pressure cold air (at T_2) and A is filled with high-pressure heated air

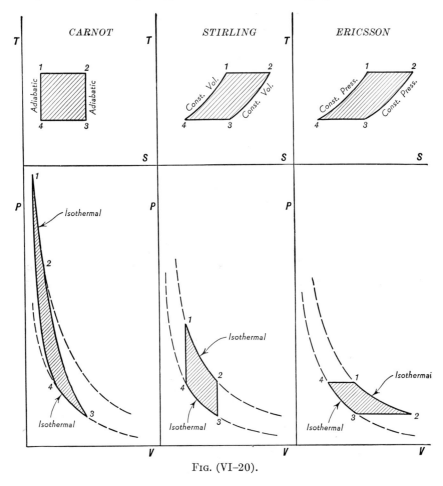

FIG. (VI–20).

(at T_1). M takes a charge of the low-pressure cold air from B, compresses it adiabatically to the pressure of A and delivers it into A. Here it is heated at approximately constant pressure to T_1. At the same time an equal quantity of the hot air passes from A to the working cylinder N, the valve then closes and the air expands adiabatically to the pressure of B

and is delivered on the return stroke.   It is cooled by the circulation of
water to T_2 at constant pressure.   The operation of the compression cylin-

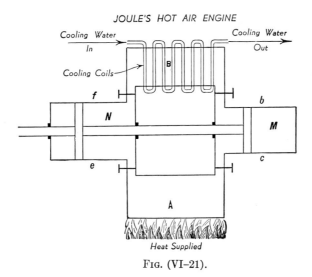

JOULE'S HOT AIR ENGINE

FIG. (VI–21).

der (M) is shown on the PV coördinates by $a\,b\,c\,d$, Fig. (VI–22), and that
of the expansion or working cylinder (N) by $d\,e\,f\,a$.   The net diagram is

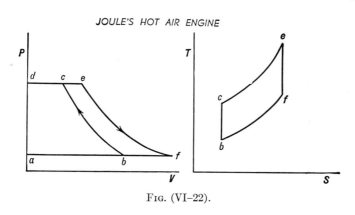

JOULE'S HOT AIR ENGINE

FIG. (VI–22).

$c\,e\,f\,b$ and this is shown on the temperature-entropy coördinates in Fig.
(VI–22).

Since the volume of the chambers A and B is large compared with the
cylinder M and N, the pressure in them remains practically constant and

the net cycle becomes (1) constant pressure heating, (2) adiabatic expansion, (3) constant pressure cooling, and (4) adiabatic compression.

The heat supplied is $c_p(T_e - T_c)$, and that rejected is $c_p(T_f - T_b)$, and the efficiency then is

$$\text{eff.} = \frac{c_p(T_e - T_c) - c_p(T_f - T_b)}{c_p(T_e - T_c)}$$

$$= 1 - \frac{T_f - T_b}{T_e - T_c},$$

but since the expansion and compression take place between the same pressures and are both adiabatic,

$$\frac{T_c}{T_b} = \frac{T_e}{T_f},$$

compounding

$$\frac{T_e - T_c}{T_f - T_b} = \frac{T_c}{T_b}$$

and

$$\text{eff.} = 1 - \frac{T_b}{T_c} = \frac{T_c - T_b}{T_c} \quad \text{or} \quad 1 - \frac{T_f}{T_e} = \frac{T_e - T_f}{T_e}.$$

It should be noted that this heating at constant pressure (ce) and the cooling at constant pressure (fb) are not reversible operations, as the temperature of the air changes (from T_c to T_e while T_1 remains constant) the cycle is therefore not reversible, and the efficiency must be less than that of the Carnot cycle $\dfrac{(T_1 - T_2)}{T_1}$, which modified for this case would be $\dfrac{T_e - T_b}{T_e}$. This could also be deduced from the fact that all of the heat is not added at the highest temperature (T_e) and discharged at the lowest temperature (T_b).

In place of a cool chamber B with its cooling coils to absorb the heat rejected, the engine may exhaust directly to the atmosphere and draw in a new charge already cooled for each suction stroke but the cycle is not affected.

Joule's original idea was for the hot chamber A to be heated by a furnace external to it, but the cycle is not affected if the heat be supplied by combustion within the cylinder. So modified, as will be seen later, this cycle becomes one of the basic cycles for internal combustion engines.

Note also that if this engine be operated reversed in a thermal sense, it will serve as a heat pump or refrigerating machine.   See Fig. (VI–23).

In case (a) *heat* is *supplied* and some delivered as work and the rest as heat at the lower temperature T_2.   In case (b), with the process *reversed* if work is supplied to run the engine, heat will be taken from T_2, augmented by the work done on it, and the total delivered at the higher temperature T_1.   This will be discussed more fully under the head of refrigeration.

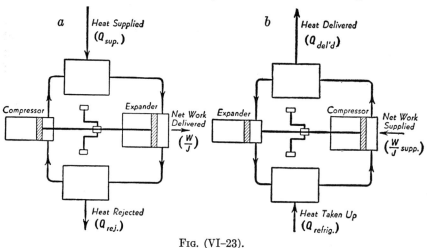

Fig. (VI–23).

VI–23.   Internal Combustion Engines.—As its name implies, this group embraces all those engines transforming heat energy into work, in which the heat energy is supplied to the working fluid by combustion within the working cylinder itself.   Fundamentally, this would seem to be a most desirable manner of heating the working substance, since it avoids completely the losses and degradation of energy inevitably accompanying any compound process of getting heat into the motive fluid, such as, from the flame to the container and from the container to the working fluid.   However, there are disadvantages tending to offset this, the principal of which is our inability to utilize the heat at the high temperature at which it is supplied.

VI–24.   Classification by Cycles.—Consideration of internal combustion engines falls naturally into two general groups, one identified by the number of piston strokes required to complete the cycle (sometimes called the mechanical or operative cycle), and the other by the thermodynamic characteristics of the processes of which the cycle is composed.   The former comprises the two-stroke and the four-stroke cycle, usually called two-cycle and four-cycle and is of interest from a mechanical viewpoint; the latter embraces the various thermodynamic cycles. These are usually called after their originators, or according to the manner in which the combustion takes place, as, for example, the Otto or Constant Volume Cycle. The thermodynamic cycle is practically unaffected whether the events be carried out in two or four strokes, and the same discussion applies to both.

VI–25. The Four-Stroke Cycle.—Using the cycle of the common gasoline engine for illustration, the first or suction stroke draws the charge consisting of a mixture of fuel and air into the cylinder through the inlet valve. This is compressed on the second or compression stroke, and, at the end of this, ignition occurs. The resulting explosion and expansion of the charge forces the piston out on the third or power stroke. Both inlet and exhaust valves are closed during this stroke. On the fourth stroke the exhaust valve opens and the piston pushes out the products of combustion and "scavenges" the cylinder.

These mechanical operations are shown in Fig. (VI–24). Adjacent to each operation is shown the thermodynamic graph of the process on both the PV and the TS planes. In this cycle there is thus one working or power stroke in four strokes, or two revolutions, and the formula for the I. Hp. for a single cyclinder, single-acting, four-cycle, engine becomes,

$$\text{I. Hp.} = \frac{PLAN}{2 \times 33,000}$$

where the letters have their customary significance.

VI–26. The Two-Stroke Cycle.—To avoid the non-power producing stroke, Dugald Clerk in 1881 brought out an engine which completed its mechanical cycle in two strokes, thus giving an explosion every revolution. This is called the two-stroke cycle, and engines operating on it, two-cycle engines. The events for an engine of the same thermodynamic cycle as that of the preceding paragraph, but operating as a two-cycle engine, are shown both mechanically and thermodynamically in Fig. (VI–25).

At the beginning of the working stroke the compressed fuel charge is ignited and the expansion of the gases forces the piston out. Just before reaching the end of its stroke the piston uncovers exhaust ports (or exhaust valves open) and releases the burned gases. A bit farther on, yet still before the end of the stroke, the piston uncovers other ports (or admission valves open) through which enters the new charge of air and fuel. This charge has been compressed previously to a pressure sufficient to quickly

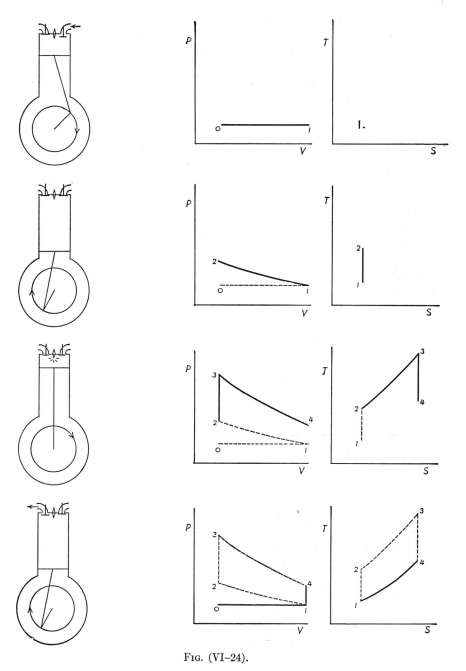

FIG. (VI–24).

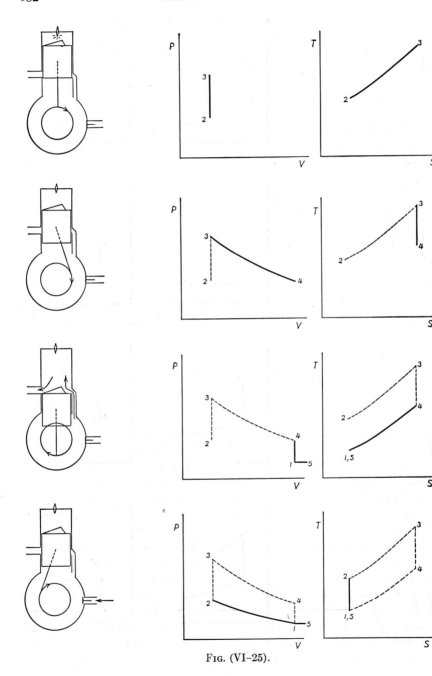

Fig. (VI–25).

force it into the cylinder, and as it enters it blows before it the spent gases of the previous charge, thus scavenging the cylinder. This operation of scavenging the cylinder and renewing the charge occupies the rest of the outward and the first part of the inward strokes, up to the point where the inlet ports (or valves) are closed. Next the exhaust ports are closed and then the piston has before it a fresh charge ready to be compressed and ignited. This description takes more time than the event, for it all takes place quickly, and nearly at the end of the outward stroke. The resultant diagram differs from that of the four-cycle principally in the omission of the lines of suction and exhaust, and the difference in the end of the diagram, due to the exhaust occurring earlier. This is shown in Fig. (VI–26).

For each the exhaust occurs at 4 with consequent drop to the admission pressure, 1, but, while this occurs at the end of the stroke (and diagram) for

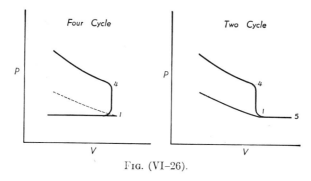

Fɪɢ. (VI–26).

the four-stroke cycle, it occurs about 20 per cent before the end of the stroke for the two-stroke cycle. Except for this variation at the end of the diagram both cycles have identical thermodynamic aspects.

The majority of internal combustion engines operate on the four-stroke cycle though the two-stroke cycle is widely used for small gasoline engines and occasionally for very large gas engines. In the Diesel field the honors are about even.

VI–27. **The Thermodynamic Cycles.**—Quite distinct from the mechanical peculiarities requiring four or two strokes to complete the series of events termed the cycle, internal combustion engines may effect the transformation of heat energy into mechanical work by a large variety of thermal processes, for example, the working stroke may consist of an adiabatic isothermal, or constant pressure expansion or combinations of these and the combustion may be arranged to take place at constant volume, constant pressure, or constant temperature and similarly for the event during which heat is rejected. What then determines the selection of the best cycle? Answer, practicability and thermal efficiency.

Of the great number of cycles that have been advocated or used there are four that are of particular interest, the Otto, the Joule or Brayton, the Carnot, and the Diesel. Of these the first three may be called *symmetrical* in that the addition and rejection of heat occur under similar conditions.

VI–28. The Otto or Constant Volume Cycle.—In this cycle there is an adiabatic compression followed by a heating at constant volume followed by an adiabatic expansion followed by a cooling at constant volume which returns the working substances to their original condition. There are thus

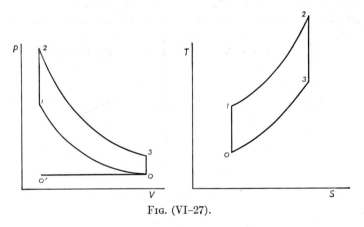

FIG. (VI–27).

four events, compression, combustion, expansion and cooling, taking place in two strokes of the piston and the cycle is the same whether the engine operates on the two- or four-stroke mechanical cycle since the lines representing suction and discharge merge into a single horizontal line at the lower part of the diagram.

It is customary to consider this and the other ideal cycles as the result of operations on a unit weight of working substance, such as air, passing through these various events, in which case it is possible to show characteristics both on the PV and TS planes. Actually, there is a transfer of gas into the cylinder and out from it, but such processes cannot be shown on the TS diagram and the conception is simplified if we consider a unit weight of the fluid as constantly retained in the cylinder and successively compressed, heated, expanded, and cooled. It is also customary to assume for all of these ideal cycles that the so-intended events take place instantaneously. Thus the compression and expansion lines are adiabatic and the supply and rejection of heat occur at constant volume, or pressure, or temperature, as the case may be.

In accordance with the above, graphs of the ideal Otto Cycle are as shown in Fig. (VI–27). Zero to 1 represents adiabatic compression of the working charge in the cylinder, 1 to 2 represents the heating at constant volume which follows the ignition of this charge, 2 is the maximum temperature and pressure reached during the combustion and 2 to 3 represents the adiabatic expansion of the hot gases pushing the piston out and doing work during the working stroke, 3 to 0 represents the cooling of the gases at constant volume at the termination of the stroke. In the actual engine there is a transfer of working substance from the cylinder to the atmosphere followed by a cooling at constant pressure in the atmosphere, but it can be shown that the heat withdrawn from the working charge during these actual processes is practically the same as the heat that would be withdrawn were the substance cooled at constant volume, a simplifying assumption.

1. Compression Stroke (0–1).   Adiabatic Compression from V_0 to V_1

$$\text{Work done} = {}_0W_1 = \frac{P_1v_1 - P_0v_0}{1 - k}.$$

$$\text{Heat supplied} = {}_0Q_1 = 0.$$

2. Explosion (1–2).   Heat supplied at constant volume.

$$\text{Work done} = {}_1W_2 = 0.$$

$$\text{Heat supplied} = {}_1Q_2 = Wc_v(T_2 - T_1).$$

3. Expansion (2–3).   Adiabatic expansion from V_2 to V_3.

$$\text{Work done} = {}_2W_3 = \frac{P_3v_3 - P_2v_2}{1 - k}.$$

$$\text{Heat supplied} = {}_2Q_3 = 0.$$

4. Exhaust (3–0).   Considered as a cooling at constant volume.

$$\text{Work done} = {}_3W_0 = 0.$$

$$\text{Heat rejected} = c_v(T_3 - T_0).$$

For such a cycle the expression for thermal efficiency will be

$$Eff. = \frac{Q_{sup.} - Q_{rej.}}{Q_{sup.}}.$$

$$= \frac{c_v(T_2 - T_1) - c_v(T_3 - T_0)}{c_v(T_2 - T_1)}.$$

$$= 1 - \frac{T_3 - T_0}{T_2 - T_1}.$$

This can be put into the form of Eff. $= 1 - \left(\frac{1}{r}\right)^{k-1}$ * where r is the "Compression ratio," the ratio of the volume before to the volume after adiabatic compression $\frac{v_0}{v_1}$.

Attention might be called to the fact that the assumption of adiabatic action during the compression and expansion strokes is an optimum criterion. In practice the cylinder walls are cooled, but the reason for this is not thermodynamic but mechanical, i.e., the necessity of maintaining a temperature of cylinder walls sufficiently low to permit an oil film for lubrication. It is distinctly detrimental from a thermodynamic point of view.

In the discussion of the Otto cycle it was considered that the heat was withdrawn after the expansion stroke by cooling the charge at constant volume 4 to 1, Fig. (VI–28) back to the initial condition. As the engine actually operates the exhaust valves open at 4 and a free expansion to atmospheric pressure takes place with subsequent cooling at this pressure to the original temperature. However, the heat removed in either case is

$$\text{* Eff.} = 1 - \frac{T_3 - T_0}{T_2 - T_1} = 1 - \frac{T_0\left(\frac{T_3}{T_0} - 1\right)}{T_1\left(\frac{T_2}{T_1} - 1\right)},$$

but since the volume ratios are the same for both compression (0–1) and expansion (2–3), $\frac{T_3}{T_2} = \frac{T_0}{T_1}$ and thus $\frac{T_3}{T_0} = \frac{T_2}{T_1}$; therefore

$$\text{Eff.} = 1 - \frac{T_0}{T_1} = 1 - \left(\frac{v_1}{v_0}\right)^{k-1},$$

but

$$\frac{v_1}{v_0} = \frac{1}{r}$$

$$\text{Eff.} = 1 - \left(\frac{1}{r}\right)^{k-1}.$$

the same, as is shown below, and the assumption of cooling at constant volume materially simplifies the discussion.

When the exhaust valves open at 4, work is done by the outgoing charge in displacing the surrounding air, equal to

$$P_1(v_5 - v_1),$$

where v_5 is the volume, the charge would have after the sudden (irreversible) expansion to the atmospheric pressure, but before any cooling begins.[*]

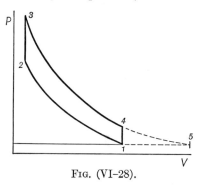

FIG. (VI–28).

The reduction in the intrinsic energy of the outgoing gases supplied the energy for doing this work and is equal to it, so

$$c_v(T_4 - T_5) = P_1(v_5 - v_1) \div J,$$

or

$$c_v(T_4 - T_5) - \frac{P_1}{J}(v_5 - v_1) = 0. \tag{1}$$

The heat withdrawn at constant pressure from 5 to 1 is

$$c_p(T_5 - T_1),$$

which may be written

$$c_v(T_5 - T_1) + \frac{P_1}{J}(v_5 - v_1) = c_p(T_5 - T_1). \tag{2}$$

Adding equations (1) and (2),

$$c_v(T_4 - T_1) = c_p(T_5 - T_1).$$

The heat rejected, therefore, when the products of combustion are cooled after release to the atmosphere is the same as if kept in the cylinder and cooled to the same temperature at constant volume.

[*] This volume would lie between the intersections with the atmospheric line of the reversible adiabatic line 3–4 extended and an isothermal line through 4.

VI–29. The Joule or Constant Pressure Cycle.—This cycle is also sometimes called the Brayton cycle. It consists of an adiabatic compression followed by a *heating* at *constant pressure* which is followed by an adiabatic expansion and this in turn by a *cooling* at *constant pressure*. The same basic assumptions are made for this cycle as were made for the preceding Otto Cycle, and in accordance with these the graphs on the *PV* and Temperature-Entropy planes are as shown in Fig. (VI–29). Zero to 1 is again adiabatic compression, 1 to 2, a burning of the charge at such a rate that the pressure remains constant, 2 to 3 represents an adiabatic expansion, and 3 to zero, a cooling of the charge at constant pressure. The expression for its thermal efficiency is as follows:

$$Eff. = \frac{Q_{Sup.} - Q_{Rej.}}{Q_{Sup.}}$$

$$= \frac{c_p(T_2 - T_1) - c_p(T_3 - T_0)}{c_p(T_2 - T_1)}$$

$$= 1 - \frac{(T_3 - T_0)}{(T_2 - T_1)}$$

and this can also be put into the form $Eff. = 1 - \left(\frac{1}{r}\right)^{k-1}$* where as before

r represents the compression ratio $\left(\frac{v_0}{v_1}\right)$ or the volume before to the volume after *adiabatic* compression.

As carried out in the actual engine the piston draws in a charge, compresses it adiabatically and combustion begins at the end of the compression stroke. The burning is so controlled, however, that the pressure remains constant and the addition of heat is thus at constant pressure. The power stroke is completed by an adiabatic expansion 2–3 and heat is withdrawn

$$* Eff. = 1 - \frac{T_3 - T_0}{T_2 - T_1} = 1 - \frac{T_0\left(\frac{T_3}{T_0} - 1\right)}{T_1\left(\frac{T_2}{T_1} - 1\right)}$$

Since the pressure range for both compression (0–1) and expansion (2–3) is identical,

$$\frac{T_2}{T_3} = \frac{T_1}{T_0} \quad \text{and} \quad \frac{T_2}{T_1} = \frac{T_3}{T_0},$$

therefore,

$$Eff. = 1 - \frac{T_0}{T_1} = 1 - \left(\frac{v_1}{v_0}\right)^{k-1}$$

but

$$\frac{v_1}{v_0} = \frac{1}{r}$$

therefore

$$Eff. = 1 - \left(\frac{1}{r}\right)^{k-1}$$

at constant pressure from 3 to 0.   As described, the engine would have to be one with unequal strokes, the suction and compression strokes of length from 0 to 1, and the power and exhaust strokes of greater length, from

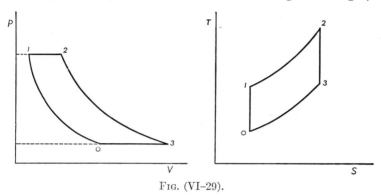

Fɪɢ. (VI-29).

0 to 3. Actually, the suction and compression are carried out in a separate cylinder of smaller volume than the working cylinder.   Fig. (VI-30) shows in diagrammatic form how this is accomplished.

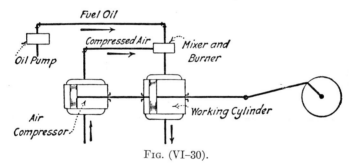

Fɪɢ. (VI-30).

The heat supplied and the work done can be figured from point to point around the cycle as follows:

1. Compression stroke (0-1).   Adiabatic compression from V_0 to V_1.

$$\text{Work done} = {}_0W_1 = \frac{P_1v_1 - P_0v_0}{1 - k}.$$

Heat supplied $= {}_0Q_1 = 0$.

2. Explosion (1-2).   Heat supplied by the combustion at constant pressure.

$$\text{Work done} = {}_1W_2 = P_2(v_2 - v_1).$$

Heat supplied $= {}_1Q_2 = c_p(T_2 - T_1)$.

3. Expansion (2–3). Adiabatic expansion from v_2 to v_3.

$$\text{Work done} = {}_2W_3 = \frac{P_3v_3 - P_2v_2}{1 - k}.$$

$$\text{Heat supplied} = {}_2Q_3 = 0.$$

4. Exhaust (3–0). Heat transferred at constant pressure.

$$\text{Work done} = {}_3W_0 = P_0(v_0 - v_3).$$

$$\text{Heat supplied} = {}_3Q_0 = c_p(T_0 - T_3).$$

It should be noted that this last will be a negative quantity, thus representing Heat *rejected*.

VI–30. The Carnot or Constant Temperature Cycle.—The third of the symmetrical cycles is the Carnot or constant Temperature cycle. This has already been discussed but it may be well to re-present it here

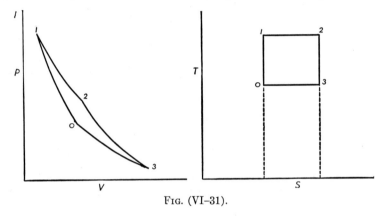

FIG. (VI–31).

for the sake of completeness. In this cycle the heat is added and rejected at constant temperature. The charge is compressed adiabatically, 0–1 (Fig. VI–31), after which heat is added at such a rate that the expansion, 1–2, takes place isothermally. The heat supply is then cut off and the expansion is completed adiabatically, 2–3, after which compression occurs with the heat withdrawn as fast as generated, isothermal compression, 3–0.

The cycle is a two stroke one though each stroke is a compound one, consisting of two processes, the expansion and the compression strokes each being composed of an isothermal followed by an adiabatic process. The cycle thus consists of alternate isothermal and adiabatic expansions and compressions. It has no supply or exhaust strokes, as the quantity of working fluid in the cylinder remains unchanged throughout the cycle.

1. Second portion of compression stroke (0–1). Adiabatic compression from $v_0 - v_1$.

$$\text{Work done} = {}_0W_1 = \frac{P_1v_1 - P_0v_0}{1 - k}.$$

$$\text{Heat supplied} = {}_0Q_1 = 0.$$

2. First portion of expansion stroke (1–2). Heat supplied at constant temperature by source, isothermal expansion v_1 to v_2.

$$\text{Work done} = {}_1W_2 = P_1v_1 \log_e \frac{v_2}{v_1}.$$

$$\text{Heat supplied} = {}_1Q_2 = \frac{P_1v_1}{J} \log_e \frac{v_2}{v_1}.$$

or, *from T–S Diagram,*

$${}_1Q_2 = T_1(S_2 - S_1).$$

3. Second portion of expansion stroke (2–3). Adiabatic expansion from $v_2 - v_3$.

$$\text{Work done} = {}_2W_3 = \frac{P_3v_3 - P_2v_2}{1 - k}.$$

$$\text{Heat supplied} = {}_2Q_3 = 0.$$

4. First portion of compression stroke (3–0). Heat rejected at constant temperature to refrigerator, isothermal compression, v_3 to v_0.

$$\text{Work done} = {}_3W_0 = P_3v_3 \log_e \frac{v_0}{v_3}.$$

$$\text{Heat supplied} = \frac{P_3v_3}{J} \log_e \frac{v_0}{v_3}.$$

or, from *T–S Diagram,*

$${}_3Q_0 = -\, T_3(S_3 - S_0).$$

$$Eff. = \frac{Q_{\text{Sup.}} - Q_{\text{Rej.}}}{Q_{\text{Sup.}}} = \frac{T_1(S_2 - S_1) - T_3(S_3 - S_0)}{T_1(S_2 - S_1)},$$

but,

$$S_2 - S_1 = S_3 - S_0,$$

therefore,

$$Eff. = \frac{T_1 - T_3}{T_1} = 1 - \frac{T_3}{T_1},$$

also since,

$$\frac{T_3}{T_1} = \frac{T_0}{T_1} = \left(\frac{v_1}{v_0}\right)^{k-1} = \left(\frac{1}{r}\right)^{k-1},$$

this may be written,

$$Eff. = 1 - \left(\frac{1}{r}\right)^{k-1}.$$

This cycle is sometimes considered as more of a purely theoretical or less practical cycle than the Otto or Joule, but there is no reason for such a distinction. All are theoretical or ideal cycles differing only on the manner heat is supplied to and rejected from the working fluid and it is possible to build engines which in their actual operation approximate closely to the processes of any of these cycles. It is quite feasible to build an engine which will operate in a cycle similar to the Carnot cycle, but it would be excessively bulky and heavy if a gas were the working medium, as the diagram on the PV plane is attenuated and has a small area indicating a small amount of work obtainable per pound of working fluid. Stated differently, the engine would be efficient but feeble.

It is interesting to note that the expression for efficiency of the Carnot cycle is identical with those derived for the Otto and Joule cycles when expressed in terms of compression ratio (r), provided the definition of compression ratio previously given be adhered to, i.e., the ratio of the volume before to the volume after the **adiabatic** compression ($v_0 \div v_1$).

VI–31. Non-Symmetrical Cycles.—Of the non-symmetrical cycles the outstanding one is that proposed by Rudolf Diesel and called by his name. It comprises the major part of the internal combusion engines that do not operate on the Otto cycle and is of the greatest practical importance. Its present form is not that originally proposed by Diesel, who had the idea of simulating the Carnot cycle, but found the maximum temperatures excessive. It consists (Fig. VI–32) of an adiabatic compression, 1–2, followed by the injection of fuel so adjusted as to burn at constant pressure as the piston moves out, thus supplying heat at constant pressure, 2–3. The rest of the outward stroke consists of the adiabatic expansion, 3–4, after which exhaust occurs, or cooling at constant volume, to the original condition, 4–1.

The expressions for work and efficiency are as follows: The cycle may be completed in two or four strokes and in practice there are about equal numbers of the two- and four-cycle types in successful operation.

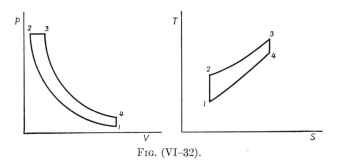

FIG. (VI–32).

1. Compression stroke (1–2).   Adiabatic Compression from v_1 to v_2.

$$\text{Work done} = {}_1W_2 = \frac{P_2v_2 - P_1v_1}{1 - k}.$$

$$\text{Heat supplied} = {}_1Q_2 = 0.$$

2. Combustion (2–3).   Heat supplied by the combustion at constant pressure.

$$\text{Work done} = {}_2W_3 = P_2(v_3 - v_2).$$

$$\text{Heat supplied} = {}_2Q_3 = c_p(T_3 - T_2).$$

3. Expansion (3–4).   Adiabatic expansion from v_3 to v_4.

$$\text{Work done} = {}_3W_4 = \frac{P_4v_4 - P_3v_3}{1 - k}.$$

$$\text{Heat supplied} = {}_3Q_4 = 0.$$

4. Exhaust (4–1).   Considered as a cooling at constant volume.

$$\text{Work done} = {}_4W_1 = 0.$$

$$\text{Heat rejected} = {}_4Q_1 = c_v(T_4 - T_1).$$

The expression for efficiency,

$$Eff. = \frac{Q_{sup.} - Q_{rej.}}{Q_{sup.}},$$

becomes,

$$Eff. = \frac{c_p(T_3 - T_2) - c_v(T_4 - T_1)}{c_p(T_3 - T_2)}$$

$$= 1 - \frac{1}{k}\left(\frac{T_4 - T_1}{T_3 - T_2}\right).$$

VI–32. The Air Standard. The preceding discussion of the various cycles for internal combustion engines has tacitly assumed that the working medium was a perfect gas (with constant specific heats) and that all so-intended events were instantaneous. The variation of the specific heat and the chemical changes occurring during combustion cause an appreciable divergence of the ideal cycle, using the actual gases from that of the ideal cycle using a perfect gas. Since, however, air preponderates in the mixture before combustion, and nitrogen, carbon-monoxide, and oxygen after, it is possible that the assumption of air for the working medium throughout, and that it behaved as a perfect gas might give a convenient and not too erroneous criterion of performance.

With this in mind and endeavoring to avoid the enormous complexity of considering the characteristics of the actual mixture throughout the cycle, a committee appointed by the British Institution of Civil Engineers devised and recommended for adoption in 1905 the so-called *air standard* as a measure of the ideal efficiency of Internal combustion engines.[*]

Thus the *air standard* is *the cycle of an ideal internal combustion engine, using air as the motive fluid.* It assumes:

1. The working fluid is air, throughout the cycle.
2. Air is a perfect gas.
3. Air has constant specific heats.
4. Constant weight of working fluid throughout the cycle.
5. No unintended heat transference.
6. Instantaneous and complete combustion.

None of these assumptions are true, that of the constancy of specific heats being particularly in error, and the air standard efficiency is always higher than the cycle efficiency computed from the true properties of the actual mixture existing in the cylinder. Its simplicity and convenience, however, have definitely fixed it in common practice.

[*] Min. Proc. Inst. Civil Engrs., Vols. 162, 163 (1905–6).

In Fig. (VI–33) is shown a comparison of the air standard efficiencies with the cycle efficiencies using the true properties of the mixture (Goodenough & Baker standard for complete combustion, but no excess air)*, from which it is apparent that comparisons of actual performances with

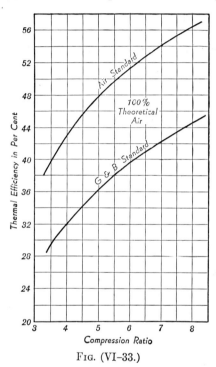

Fɪɢ. (VI–33.)

the air standard will show a greater margin for improvement than actually exists.

Example 1.—A gasoline engine working on the Otto cycle (assume air standard) has a compression ratio of 5.   A charge, composed of vaporized gasoline and air, with a heating value of 1200 B.t.u. per pound, is drawn in in a quantity such that the cylinder contains, at the end of the suction stroke, one pound of gas.   The pressure and temperature at the end of the suction stroke are 14 lbs. abs. and 80° F. respectively.

Find: (a) Pressure, Volume, and Temperature for each point; (b) For each operation of the cycle, the heat supplied or rejected, and the work done on or by the gas; (c) The net work of the cycle; (d) The thermal efficiency.

* Taken from Bul. 160 Eng. Expt. Sta. Univ. Ill., "A Thermodynamic Analysis of Internal Combustion Engine Cycles."   Goodenough and Baker.

Solution.—(Refer to Fig. (VI–28) showing Otto cycle.)

$$\text{Cylinder volume-}V_1 = V_4 = \frac{WRT_1}{P_1} = \frac{1\,(53.35)\,(540)}{14\,(144)} = 14.29 \text{ cu. ft.}$$

$$V_2 = V_3 = \frac{14.29}{5} = 2.86 \text{ cu. ft.}$$

$$\text{Vol. drawn in} = V_1 - V_2 = 14.29 - 2.86 = 11.43 \text{ cu. ft.}$$

$$\text{Wt. of charge} = \frac{14\,(144)\,(11.43)}{53.35\,(540)} = 0.8 \text{ lb.}$$

(a) Point 1: $p_1 = 14$ lbs. abs., $V_1 = 14.29$ cu. ft., $T_1 = 540°$ F. abs.

Point 2: $p_2 = p_1 \left(\dfrac{V_1}{V_2}\right)^k = 14\,(5)^{1.4} = 133.3$ lbs. abs.,

$$V_2 = 2.86 \text{ cu. ft., } T_2 = T_1 \left(\frac{V_1}{V_2}\right)^{k-1} = 540\,(5)^{.4} = 1028° \text{ F. abs.}$$

Point 3: $V_3 = 2.86$ cu. ft.

$$0.8\,(1200) = 960 \text{ B.t.u.} = {}_2Q_3 = Wc_v(T_3 - T_2)$$

$$T_3 = \frac{{}_2Q_3}{Wc_v} + T_2 = \frac{960}{.171} + 1028 = 6644° \text{ F. abs.}$$

$$p_3 = p_2 \left(\frac{T_3}{T_2}\right) = 133.3 \left(\frac{6644}{1028}\right) = 862 \text{ lbs. abs.}$$

Point 4: $V_4 = 14.29$ cu. ft.,

$$p_4 = p_3 \left(\frac{V_3}{V_4}\right)^k = 862 \left(\frac{1}{5}\right)^{1.4} = 90.6 \text{ lbs. abs.}$$

$$T_4 = T_3 \left(\frac{V_3}{V_4}\right)^{k-1} = 6640 \left(\frac{1}{5}\right)^{.4} = 3490° \text{ F. abs.}$$

(b) Compression, 1–2: ${}_1Q_2 = 0$;

$$_1W_2 = \frac{P_1V_1 - P_2V_2}{k-1} = \frac{144\,[14\,(14.29) - 133.3\,(2.86)]}{.4}$$

$$= \frac{144\,(200 - 381)}{.4} = -\,65,200 \text{ ft.-lbs.}$$

Combustion, 2–3: ${}_2Q_3 = 960$ B.t.u.; ${}_2W_3 = 0$.

Expansion, 3-4: $_3Q_4 = 0$;

$$_3W_4 = \frac{P_3V_3 - P_4V_4}{k - 1} = \frac{144 \, [862 \, (2.86) - 90.6 \, (14.29)]}{.4}$$

$$= \frac{144 \, (2464 - 1296)}{.4} = 421,000 \text{ ft.-lbs.}$$

Heat Rejection, 4-1:

$$_4Q_1 = Wc_v(T_1 - T_4) = .171 \, (540 - 3490) = -504 \text{ B.t.u.} \quad _4W_1 = 0.$$

(c) Net Work of Cycle:

$$W_{\text{Cycle}} = 421,000 - 65,200 = 355,800 \text{ ft.-lbs.}$$

or

$$W_{\text{Cycle}} = (Q_{\text{sup.}} - Q_{\text{rej.}}) \, J = (960 - 504) \, 778.6 = 456 \, (778.6) = 355,300 \text{ ft.-lbs.}$$

(d) Eff. $= \dfrac{\text{Net work}}{\text{Heat supp.}} = \dfrac{355,800}{778.6 \, (960)} = .476$

or

Eff. $= \dfrac{Q_{\text{sup.}} - Q_{\text{rej.}}}{Q_{\text{sup.}}} = \dfrac{960 - 504}{960} = .475$

or

Eff. $= 1 - \dfrac{1}{(r)^{k-1}} = 1 - \left(\dfrac{1}{5}\right)^{.4} = .475.$

Example 2.—A Diesel engine, with 7 per cent clearance, draws in, on the suction stroke, a quantity of air such that, at the end of the suction stroke, the cylinder contains one pound of gas at 14 lbs. abs., and 80° F. The fuel, with heating value of 19,000 B.t.u. per lb., is injected in the proportion of 1 lb. of fuel to 20 lbs. air induced.

Assume air standard cycle, and find: (a) Pressure, Volume, and Temperature for each point on diagram; (b) The heat supplied or rejected, and the work done on or by the gas during each process of the cycle; (c) The net work of the cycle; (d) The thermal efficiency.

Solution.—(Refer to Fig. VI-32 showing Diesel cycle.)

Cylinder volume $= V_1 = V_4 = \dfrac{WRT_1}{P_1} = \dfrac{1 \, (53.35) \, (540)}{14 \, (144)} = 14.29 \text{ cu. ft.}$

Compression ratio $= \dfrac{1.07}{.07} = 15.3$

$$V_2 = \frac{14.29}{15.3} = .934 \text{ cu. ft.}$$

Vol. air drawn in $= V_1 - V_2 = 14.29 - .934 = 13.356 \text{ cu. ft.}$

Wt. of fresh air $= \dfrac{13.356}{14.29} = 0.935 \text{ lb.}$

Wt. fuel consumed $= \dfrac{.935}{20} = 0.04675$ lb.

(a) Point 1: p_1 $= 14$ lbs. abs. $V_1 = 14.29$ cu. ft.; $T_1 = 540°$ F. abs.

Point 2: V_2 $= 0.934$ cu. ft.

$$p_2 = p_1 \left(\frac{V_1}{V_2}\right)^k = 14 \, (15.3)^{1.4} = 14 \, (45.4) = 636 \text{ lbs. abs.}$$

$$T_2 = T_1 \left(\frac{V_1}{V_2}\right)^{k-1} = 540 \, (15.3)^{.4} = 1604° \text{ F. abs.}$$

Point 3: $p_3 = 636$ lbs. abs.

$_2Q_3 = .04675 \, (19,000) = 888$ B.t.u.

$$T_3 = \frac{_2Q_3}{Wc_p} + T_2 = \frac{888}{.24} + 1604 = 5304° \text{ F. abs.}$$

$$V_3 = V_2 \left(\frac{T_3}{T_2}\right) = .934 \left(\frac{5304}{1604}\right) = 3.09 \text{ cu. ft.}$$

Point 4: $V_4 = 14.29$ cu. ft.

$$p_4 = p_3 \left(\frac{V_3}{V_4}\right)^k = 636 \left(\frac{3.09}{14.29}\right)^{1.4} = 636 \left(\frac{1}{4.63}\right)^{1.4} = 74.4 \text{ lbs. abs.}$$

$$T_4 = T_3 \left(\frac{V_3}{V_4}\right)^{k-1} = 5304 \left(\frac{1}{4.63}\right)^{.4} = 2873° \text{ F. abs.}$$

(b) Compression, 1–2: $Q_2 = 0$;

$$_1W_2 = \frac{144 \, [14 \, (14.29) - 636 \, (.934)]}{.4} = \frac{144 \, (200 - 594)}{.4}$$

$$= - \, 142,000 \text{ ft.-lbs.}$$

Combustion, 2–3: $_2Q_1 = 888$ B.t.u.;

$_2W_3 = P_{2=3} \, (V_3 - V_2) = 636 \, (144) \, (3.09 - .934)$

$= 636 \, (144) \, (2.156) = 197,500$ ft.-lbs.

Expansion, 3–4: $_3Q_4 = 0$;

$$_3W_4 = \frac{144 \, [636 \, (3.09) - 74.4 \, (14.29)]}{.4} = \frac{144 \, (1965 - 1063)}{.4}$$

$$= 325,000 \text{ ft.-lbs.}$$

Heat rejection, 4–1: $_4W_1 = 0$;

$_4Q_1 = Wc_v(T_1 - T_4) = .171 \, (540 - 2873) = .171 \, (-2333) = - \, 399$ B.t.u.

(c) Net Work $= {}_1W_2 + {}_2W_3 + {}_3W_4$

$$= - 142{,}000 + 197{,}500 + 325{,}000 = 380{,}500 \text{ ft.-lbs.}$$

or

$$W = (Q_{\text{sup.}} - Q_{\text{rej.}})\, J = (888 - 399)\, 778.6 = 489\, (778.6)$$

$$= 380{,}500 \text{ ft.-lbs.}$$

(d) Eff. $= \dfrac{\text{Net work}}{\text{Heat supplied}} = \dfrac{380{,}500}{778.6\,(888)} = 0.55$

or

Eff. $= \dfrac{Q_s - Q_r}{Q_s} = \dfrac{888 - 399}{888} = \dfrac{489}{888} = 0.55$

or

Eff. $= 1 - \dfrac{(T_4 - T_1)}{k(T_3 - T_2)} = 1 - \dfrac{(2873 - 540)}{1.4\,(5304 - 1604)} = 1 - \dfrac{2333}{1.4\,(3700)}$

$$= 1 - 0.45 = 0.55.$$

The divergence from the air standard can be represented with reasonable accuracy, as a direct function of the heating value per cubic foot of charge.

$$\textit{Eff. (Air Standard)} - \textit{Eff. (Actual Mixture)} = 0.14H$$

Where H is the lower heating value per cubic foot at standard conditions of the charge.

This divergence is so great that it has led to considerable criticism of the air standard as being a poor criterion by which to judge the performance of actual engines. For example in a series of tests carried out by Ricardo * in which *exceptional care was taken to obtain the highest thermal efficiency*, the values of the actual thermal efficiency for an engine with a compression ratio of $5 \div 1$ were about 31 per cent. The air standard for this compression ratio is 47.5 per cent. The actual engine thus had a coefficient of performance of $31 \div 47.5$ or about 65 per cent, leaving an apparent margin for improvement of 35 per cent, whereas if the true limiting efficiency (Goodenough and Baker, see p. 195) be used as the criterion the ideal efficiency is 36 per cent, giving a coefficient of performance of $31 \div 36$ or 86 per cent of the possible and leaving an actual margin for improvement of but 14 per cent.

At the present time, however, the computations for the ideal efficiency taking cognizance of the actual mixture properties is long and arduous and comparisons with it are made but occasionally. The simplicity of the

* Empire Motor Fuels Committee Report, p. 151.

air standard more than offsets its inaccuracy and it is widely used as the standard for comparison and design.

VI–33. The Effect of Clearance on Efficiency (Air Standard).—Varying the clearance affects the compression ratio directly in the relation

$$\text{Clearance} = \left(\frac{1}{r-1}\right) 100,$$

where r is the compression ratio just discussed and the clearance is expressed as a percentage of the piston displacement.

Variations in the compression ratio affect the efficiency as already shown, in the following relation

$$\text{Eff. (Air Standard)} = 1 - \frac{1}{(r)^{k-1}}$$

The relationship between these three quantities is clearly shown in the following tabulation.

TABLE VI

RELATIONSHIP BETWEEN CLEARANCE, COMPRESSION RATIO AND EFFICIENCY (A.S.)

Compression Ratio (r)	Clearance, in Per Cent, Piston Displacement	Efficiency,* Air Standard	Compression Ratio (r)	Clearance, in Per Cent, Piston Displacement	Efficiency,* Air Standard
2	100	0.242	7	16.7	0.541
3	50	.356	8	14.2	.565
4	33	.426	10	11.1	.602
5	25	.475	15	7.1	.661
6	20	.511	20	5.3	.698

* Using $k = 1.4$.

A plot of these data is given in Fig. (VI–34). It is worth noting that the gain in efficiency is very large for increases in compression ratio when the compression ratio is small and grows continuously less as the compression ratio becomes greater. The usual compression ratio for (Otto Cycle) gasoline engines now lies between 5.5 and 6.0 unless an anti-knock mixture

---

The expression Eff. $= 1 - \left(\frac{1}{r}\right)^{0.3}$ is sometimes used to compute the efficiency of the ideal cycle with variable specific heats. Here 0.3 is considered to be the average value of $(k-1)$. The efficiency is however also affected by the richness of the mixture, an element not taken cognizance of by the expression and for lean or rich mixtures it is unreliable.

is used.   Engines using gas fuels low in hydrogen frequently use compression ratios as high as 7.0.   Compression ratios higher than 7.0 give but slightly higher efficiencies and the decrease in mechanical efficiency due to the increased massiveness of the moving parts reduces it still more.

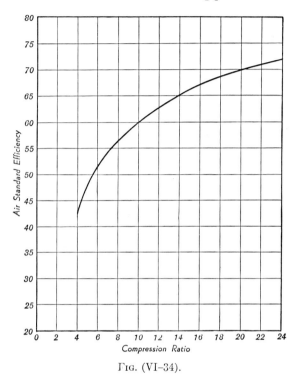

Fig. (VI–34).

For the Otto cycle the curve of brake thermal efficiency reaches a maximum at a compression ratio of about 11.*

VI–34.   The Effect of Variation of the Specific Heats.—If the temperature at the end of the constant volume explosion of the ordinary internal combustion engine be computed from the expression equating the temperature rise to the heat of combustion divided by the specific heat ($t_2 - t_1 =$ cal. val. $\div c_v$) it is much higher than that actually observed. This divergence is attributed to the increase in the specific heat of the mixture as the temperature rises thus requiring more heat to raise the mixture one degree at the high temperatures than at the low.

* See "The Internal Combustion Engine," by Ricardo, Vol. I, page 136.

Compliance with the laws of Boyle and Charles (i.e., in conformity with $Pv = RT$) carries with it the implied fact that the specific heats are independent of the pressure, but gives no information as to the effect of temperature. For example, the intrinsic energy of such a gas is given by the expression $u_2 - u_1 = c_v(T_2 - T_1)$, thus c_v is independent of pressure and since $c_p - c_v = R/J$ it follows that c_p must also be independent of the pressure.

Such is not the case for temperature variations and the assumption that the "Perfect Gas" has constancy of specific heats is an assumption additional to and independent of those properties fixed by Boyle's and Charles' laws. Moreover, while departure from these laws is but slight for most of the gases and conditions met with in engineering work, thus permitting the relationship $Pv = RT$ to be used, the divergence of the specific heats from constancy for the temperatures ordinarily met with in internal combustion engines is considerable and must be reckoned with.*

The expression for specific heat usually is of the form

$$c = a + bT + cT^2$$

and much experimental work has been done in determining the constants for the various gases. As a result of a careful study of all the best work to date the following have been recommended by the Engineering Experiment Station of the University of Illinois.† The original data of the various investigators have been correlated and combined, resultant curves determined and the units changed to bring them all into English units and Fahrenheit temperatures. Furthermore, they have been arranged to give the molal specific heats, that is the specific heat for one mol of the gas thus permitting the consolidation of the diatomic gases into one expression. The molal specific heat is the ordinary or unit weight specific heat multiplied by the molecular weight so when the given expressions are divided by the molecular weight of the gas under discussion the result is the specific heat for a unit weight (one pound).

Example 1.—Determine the instantaneous specific heats, c_p and c_v, for (a) Air (Apparent $m = 29$); (b) Carbon dioxide; (c) Methane; all for a temperature of 2040° F.

* The monatomics, such as argon, helium, mercury, have very little change at higher temperatures, the diatomics considerable and the polyatomics, H_2O, SO_2, etc., more.

† An Investigation of the Maximum Temperatures and Pressures Attainable in the Combustion of Gaseous Fuels, by G. A. Goodenough and G. T. Felbeck. Bulletin No. 139.

TABLE VII

Specific Heat Equations

mc_p = Instantaneous Molal Specific Heat at Constant Pressure
mc_v = Instantaneous Molal Specific Heat at Constant Volume
T = degree F. (abs.) $mc_p = mc_t + 1.985$

No.	Gas	Specific Heat Equation
1	CO, O$_2$, N$_2$	$mc_p = 6.93 + 0.1200 \cdot 10^{-6}T^2$ $mc_v = 4.945 + 0.1200 \cdot 10^{-6}T^2$
2	H$_2$	$mc_p = 6.00 + 0.6667 \cdot 10^{-3}T$ $mc_v = 4.015 + 0.6667 \cdot 10^{-3}T$
3	CO$_2$ ($T < 2900$)	$mc_p = 7.15 + 3.90 \cdot 10^{-3}T - 0.60 \cdot 10^{-6}T^2$ $mc_v = 5.165 + 3.90 \cdot 10^{-3}T - 0.60 \cdot 10^{-6}T^2$
4	CO$_2$ ($T > 2900$)	$mc_p = 12.196 + 0.42 \cdot 10^{-3}T$ $mc_v = 10.211 + 0.42 \cdot 10^{-3}T$
5	CO$_2$ (Entire Range)	$mc_p = 6.4587 + 5.0668 \cdot 10^{-3}T - 1.2480 \cdot 10^{-6}T^2 + 0.1086 \cdot 10^{-9}T^3$ $mc_v = 4.5637 + 5.0668 \cdot 10^{-3}T - 1.2480 \cdot 10^{-6}T^2 + 0.1086 \cdot 10^{-9}T^3$
6	H$_2$O	$mc_p = 8.33 - 0.276 \cdot 10^{-3}T + 0.423 \cdot 10^{-6}T^2$ $mv_v = 6.345 - 0.276 \cdot 10^{-3}T + 0.423 \cdot 10^{-6}T^2$
7	CH$_4$	$mc_p = 3.459 + 10.56 \cdot 10^{-3}T$ $mc_v = 1.474 + 10.56 \cdot 10^{-3}T$
8	C$_2$H$_2$	$mc_p = 6.19 + 8.10 \cdot 10^{-3}T$ $mc_v = 4.205 + 8.10 \cdot 10^{-3}T$
9	C$_2$H$_4$	$mc_p = 6.67 + 6.80 \cdot 10^{-3}T$ $mc_v = 4.685 + 6.80 \cdot 10^{-3}T$
10	C$_2$H$_6$	$mc_p = 7.10 + 8.60 \cdot 10^{-3}T$ $mc_v = 5.115 + 8.60 \cdot 10^{-3}T$
11	C$_6$H$_6$	$mc_p = 4.00 + 31.80 \cdot 10^{-3}T$ $mc_v = 2.015 + 31.80 \cdot 10^{-3}T$
12	C$_8$H$_{18}$ (Gasoline)	$mc_p = 38.327 + 38.00 \cdot 10^{-3}T$ $mc_v = 36.342 + 38.00 \cdot 10^{-3}T$
13	C$_{12}$H$_{26}$ (Kerosene)	$mc_p = 57.154 + 56.67 \cdot 10^{-3}T$ $mc_v = 55.169 + 56.67 \cdot 10^{-3}T$
14	Amorphous Carbon	$mc = +4.533 \cdot 10^{-3}T - 0.9092 \cdot 10^{-6}T^2$

Solution.—

(a) For Air:

$$mc_p = 6.93 + 0.12 \ (10)^{-6} \ T^2 = 6.93 + \frac{.12 \ (2500)^2}{1,000,000} = 6.93 + .75$$

$$= 7.68 \text{ B.t.u. per mol. per deg. F.}$$

$$mc_v = 7.68 - 1.985 = 5.695 \text{ B.t.u. per mol. per deg. F.}$$

$$c_p = \frac{7.68}{29} = 0.265 \text{ B.t.u. per lb. per deg. F.}$$

$$c_v = \frac{5.695}{29} = 0.1963 \text{ B.t.u. per lb. per deg. F.}$$

(b) For CO_2:

$$mc_p = 7.15 + 3.9 \ (10)^{-3} \ T - 0.6 \ (10)^{-6} \ T^2$$

$$c_v = \frac{11.16}{44} = 0.23 \text{ B.t.u. per lb. per deg. F.}$$

(c) For Methane:

$$mc_p = 3.459 + 10.56 \ (10)^{-3} \ T = 3.459 +$$

$$c_v = \frac{27.866}{16} = 1.74 \text{ B.t.u. per lb. per deg. F.}$$

Example 2.—Twelve pounds of air at 40° F. are heated without change in pressure to a temperature of 2040° F.

Considering the variation in specific heats, find the heat necessary to produce this temperature rise.

Solution.—$_1Q_2 = mc_p(T_2 - T_1)$.

In this case, it is the *mean* c_p, between 500° and 2500° that is required.

$$mc_p \text{ (mean)} = A + \frac{B}{2} \ (T_2 + T_1) + \frac{C}{3} \ (T_2{}^2 + T_2T_1 + T_1{}^2)$$

$$A = 6.93, \quad B = 0, \quad C = .12 \ (10)^{-6}.$$

$$mc_p \text{ (mean)} = 6.93 + \frac{.12 \ [(2500)^2 + 2500 \ (500) + (500)^2]}{3 \ (1,000,000)}$$

$$= 6.93 + \frac{930,000}{3,000,000} = 6.93 + .31 = 7.24 \text{ B.t.u. per mol' per °F.}$$

$$c_p = \frac{7.24}{29} = 0.25 \text{ B.t.u. per lb. per °F.}$$

$$_1Q_2 = 12 \ (.25) \ (2500 - 500) = 6000 \text{ B.t.u.}$$

Example 3.—For the conditions of the preceding example, find the change in (a) Intrinsic energy; (b) Heat content; per pound of air during the heating.

Solution.—

a) $\int_1^2 du = u_2 - u_1 = \int_1^2 c_v dT$

$mu_1 = 500 [4.945 + .04 (10)^{-6} T^2] = 500 (4.955) = 2477.5$ B.t.u. per mol.

$u_1 = \dfrac{2477.5}{29} = 85.4$ B.t.u. per lb.

$mu_2 = 2500 [4.945 + .04 (10)^{-6} (6,250,000)]$

$\qquad = 2500 [4.945 + .04 (6.25)] = 12,980$ B.t.u. per mol.

$u_2 = \dfrac{12,980}{29} = 447.5$ B.t.u. per lb.

$u_2 - u_1 = 447.5 - 85.4 = 362.1$ B.t.u. per lb.

or

mc_p (mean) [from previous example] $= 7.24$

c_v (mean) $= \dfrac{7.24 - 1.985}{29} = .181$ B.t.u. per lb. per deg.

$u_2 - u_1 = \int_1^2 c_v dT = .181 (2500 - 500) = 362$ B.t.u. per lb.

(b) Heat added at constant pressure is equivalent to the change in heat content during the process.

From previous example, $h_2 - h_1 = \dfrac{6000}{12} = 500$ B.t.u. per lb.

or, from previous example,

$h_2 - h_1 = \int_1^2 c_p dT = .25 (2500 - 500) = 500$ B.t.u. per lb.

or

$mh_1 = T[6.93 + .04 (10)^{-6} (500)^2 = 500 \left[6.93 + \dfrac{.04 (250,000)}{1,000,000} \right]$

$\qquad = 500 (6.94) = 3470$ B.t.u. per mol.

$h_1 = \dfrac{3470}{29} = 119.6$ B.t.u. per lb.

$mh_2 = 2500 \left[6.93 + \dfrac{.04 (6,250,000)}{1,000,000} \right] = 2500 (7.18)$

$\qquad = 17,950$ B.t.u. per mol.

$h_2 = \dfrac{17,950}{29} = 619$ B.t.u. per lb.

$h_2 - h_1 = 619 - 119.6 = 499.4$ B.t.u. per lb.

VI–35. Determination of Thermal Properties Allowing for Variable Specific Heat.—Since the heat supplied and the work done both on and by the gas can be determined with reasonable accuracy for the operating cycle of any actual engine (the first from the calorific value of the fuel and the second from the indicator diagram) it is possible to carry out a step-by-step analysis of the cycle and determine the transfers of heat between the working fluid and the cylinder during all the working events, provided there is available accurate data giving the intrinsic energy and the heat content of the working fluid at the various temperatures.

For example, beginning at 0, Fig. (VI–31), since no combustion has occurred

$$U_1 = U_0 + {}_0W_1/J.$$

${}_1W_2$ can be determined from the indicator diagram, and if U_1 is known then the total intrinsic energy is known at point 1, but for the temperature of 1, figured from the perfect gas relationship $PV^k = \text{Const.}$, the intrinsic energy *actually* present is less by the amount of the loss to the cylinder walls.   The intrinsic energy at 1 can be taken from a curve of U on temperature and curves of this sort for the gases commonly met with are now available from the same source as that previously mentioned for specific heats.

The specific heats listed above are the *Instantaneous* specific heats or the specific heats **at** the given temperature.   If the **mean** specific heat is desired it is

$$Mc \text{ (mean)} = \frac{Q}{T_2 - T_1} = \int_{T_1}^{T_2} Mcdt \div (T_2 - T_1),$$

if Mc has the form

$$c = a + bT + cT^2,$$

then,

$$Mc \text{ (mean)} = \frac{a(T_2 - T_1) + \dfrac{b}{2}(T_2{}^2 - T_1{}^2) + \dfrac{c}{3}(T_2{}^3 - T_1{}^3)}{T_2 - T_1},$$

$$Mc \text{ (mean)} = a + \frac{b}{2}(T_2 + T_1) + \frac{c}{3}(T_2{}^2 + T_2T_1 + T_1{}^2).$$

For 1 mol of the diatomic gases at constant volume

$$a = 4.945$$
$$b = 0$$
$$c = 0.1200 \times 10^{-6}.$$

If, then, the mean specific heat be desired for the range of temperatures of from 200° F. to 2000° F.,

$$Mc_v \text{ (mean)} = 4.945 + 0 + 0.040 \times 10^{-6}[(2460)^2 + 2460 \times 660 + (660)^2]$$

$$= 4.945 + 0 + 0.04 \times 8.111$$

$$= 5.269$$

Say $= 5.27$.

Then the specific heats of a unit weight (c_v) will be

$$O_2 = 5.27 \div 32 = 0.165 = c_v \text{ (mean)}$$

$$N_2 = 5.27 \div 28 = 0.188 = c_v \text{ (mean)}$$

$$CO = 5.27 \div 28 = 0.188 = c_v \text{ (mean)}$$

$$\text{Air} = 5.27 \div 29 = 0.182 = c_v \text{ (mean)}.$$

The equations for intrinsic energy and enthalpy follow from those of the specific heat by the following transformation, and are tabulated below:

$$du = c_v dT.$$

If

$$c_v = a + bT + cT^2,$$

then

$$du = adT + bTdT + cT^2 dT,$$

and

$$u_2 - u_1 = a(T_2 - T_1) + \frac{b}{2}(T_2{}^2 - T_1{}^2) + \frac{c}{3}(T_2{}^3 - T_1{}^3).$$

Similarly, for Heat Content we have,

$$dh = c_p dt,$$

or expressed for a mol,

$$Mdh = Mc_p dt$$

and

$$Mc_p = Mc_v + 1.985,$$

hence

$$Mc_p = a' + bT + cT^2$$

TABLE VIII

MOLAL INTRINSIC ENERGY EQUATIONS

B.t.u. required to Raise Temperature of 1 mol of Gas at constant volume from 0 deg. F. (abs.) to T deg. F. (abs.)

No.	Gas	Intrinsic Energy
1	CO, O_2 and N_2	$= T(4.945 + 0.0400 \cdot 10^{-6}T^2)$
2	H_2	$= T(4.015 + \frac{1}{3} \cdot 10^{-3}T)$
3	CO_2, $T < 2900$	$= T(5.165 + 1.95 \cdot 10^{-3}T - 0.2 \cdot 10^{-6}T^2)$
4	CO_2, $T > 2900$	$= T(10.211 + 0.21 \cdot 10^{-3}T) - 4878$
5	H_2O	$= T(6.345 - 0.138 \cdot 10^{-3}T + 0.141 \cdot 10^{-6}T^2)$
6	CH_4	$= T(1.474 + 5.28 \cdot 10^{-3}T)$
7	C_2H_2	$= T(4.205 + 4.05 \cdot 10^{-3}T)$
8	C_2H_4	$= T(4.685 + 3.40 \cdot 10^{-3}T)$
9	C_2H_6	$= T(5.115 + 4.30 \cdot 10^{-3}T)$
10	C_6H_6	$= T(2.015 + 15.90 \cdot 10^{-3}T)$
11	C_8H_{18} (Gasoline Vapor)	$= T(36.342 + 19.0 \cdot 10^{-3}T)$
12	$C_{12}H_{26}$ (Kerosene Vapor)	$= T(55.169 + 28.333 \cdot 10^{-3}T)$
13	H (Atomic Hydrogen)	$= 2.978T$

where $a' = a + 1.985$ from the preceding table.
Thus,

$$M(h_2 - h_1) = a'(T_2 - T_1) + \frac{b}{2}(T_2^2 - T_1^2) + \frac{c}{3}(T_2^3 - T_1^3).$$

Figure (VI–35) shows curves of intrinsic energy and heat content for the diatomic gases O_2, N_2 and CO derived in this manner and plotted on temperature.

Recently spectroscopic methods for determining the specific heats of gases have been developed which appear to give data at high temperatures more reliable than those obtained by direct measurement. Sweigert and Beardsley have collected these data for the gases most commonly dealt with in combustion problems and developed empirical equations which represent them closely.* An accuracy within $\frac{1}{2}$ of 1 per cent is claimed for the diatomic gases O_2, H_2, N_2, and CO, and from 1 to 2 per cent for the others except for methane, CH_4, where the accuracy is set at 3 per cent.

The general effect of using these newer values of specific heat is to lower appreciably the maximum temperatures computed for combustion. In general the new values are higher for temperatures up to 3000° R. and lower for temperatures above 4000° R. (except for CO_2), a fact which explains the apparent anomaly that while individual values of specific heat may differ as much as 10 per cent from the Goodenough & Felbeck values, intrinsic energy and enthalpy differ by a much smaller percentage. For example, the new specific heat for nitrogen at 2500° R. is over 10 per cent greater than the G. & F. value, yet the temperature for equal enthalpies is but 250° less at 4000° R.

Working with these same spectroscopic data R. C. H. Heck has prepared a tabulation of the values of instantaneous specific heat, enthalpy and intrinsic energy over a temperature range from 600° R. to 5500° R.† An abstract of this tabulation follows: The temperatures are in degrees Rankine and the enthalpy and intrinsic energy are measured from a datum of 540° R.   The specific heats are for one mol. of gas.

VI–36. Temperature After Adiabatic Compression When Specific Heats Vary.—The temperature change which accompanies an adiabatic expansion or compression of a gas is readily figured for the perfect gas by

---

* "Empirical Specific Heat Equations Based upon Spectroscopic Data," by R. L. Sweigert and N. W. Beardsley, Bulletin No. 2 of the State Engineering Experiment Station, The Georgia School of Technology.

† "The New Specific Heats," R. C. H. Heck, Spring Meeting A.S.M.E., Worcester, Mass., May 1940.

	Nitrogen $N_2(M = 28.016)$				Oxygen $O_2(M = 32.00)$		
T	C_p	H	U	T	C_p	H	U
600	6.968	418	299	600	7.075	423	304
1000	7.140	3,231	2,318	1000	7.570	3,345	2,432
1500	7.571	6,905	5,000	1500	8.119	7,279	5,373
2000	7.971	10,795	7,897	2000	8.452	11,431	8,533
2500	8.247	14,853	10,962	2500	8.669	15,712	11,822
3000	8.444	19,028	14,144	3000	8.840	20,091	15,208
3500	8.581	23,287	17,411	3500	8.998	24,552	18,677
4000	8.684	27,605	20,736	4000	9.148	29,092	22,224
4500	8.761	31,967	24,106	4500	9.290	33,701	25,841
5000	8.820	36,364	27,510	5000	9.423	38,382	29,529
5500	8.869	40,783	30,937	5500	9.546	43,118	33,272

	Carbon Monoxide $CO(M = 28.00)$				Hydrogen $H_2(M = 2.016)$		
T	C_p	H	U	T	C_p	H	U
600	6.971	419	300	600	6.933	416	297
1000	7.207	3,243	2,330	1000	7.001	3,205	2,292
1500	7.684	6,966	5,061	1500	7.096	6,727	4,822
2000	8.076	10,910	8,012	2000	7.323	10,329	7,430
2500	8.343	15,020	11,129	2500	7.600	14,056	10,165
3000	8.519	19,239	14,356	3000	7.887	17,931	13,048
3500	8.645	23,533	17,657	3500	8.139	21,937	16,062
4000	8.739	27,880	21,012	4000	8.349	26,062	19,195
4500	8.808	32,267	24,406	4500	8.530	30,283	22,423
5000	8.862	36,686	27,833	5000	8.686	34,589	25,736
5500	8.908	41,023	31,379	5500	8.822	38,961	29,116

	Carbon Dioxide $CO_2(M = 44.00)$				Water $H_2O(M = 18.016)$		
T	C_p	H	U	T	C_p	H	U
600	9.283	547	428	600	8.044	481	362
1000	11.049	4,637	3,724	1000	8.523	3,784	2,871
1500	12.445	10,538	8,633	1500	9.299	8,236	6,331
2000	13.298	16,994	14,096	2000	10.127	13,092	10,194
2500	13.839	23,785	19,895	2500	10.883	18,353	14,463
3000	14.205	30,803	25,920	3000	11.505	23,951	19,068
3500	14.460	37,975	32,100	3500	12.000	29,833	23,958
4000	14.644	45,253	38,385	4000	12.388	35,940	29,072
4500	14.797	52,614	44,754	4500	12.695	42,210	34,349
5000	14.922	60,045	51,192	5000	12.935	48,623	39,770
5500	15.021	67,528	65,683	5500	13.124	55,134	45,289

computing the terminal temperature from the p and T, or v and T relations, derived in Chapter IV. These relations hold, however, only for the *perfect* gas with its constancy of specific heats. Variation in the specific heat of a gas will materially affect its temperature after such changes and there are many instances in which it is important to make predictions as to final qualities of gases which conform in general to the equation $Pv = RT$, but

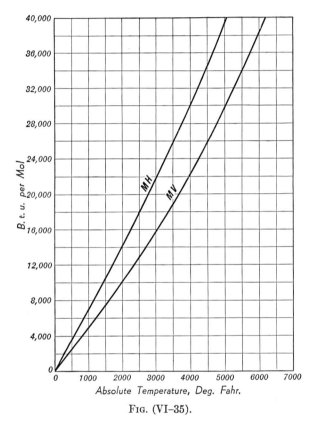

Fig. (VI–35).

for which the specific heats are known to vary appreciably. Thus it is important to be able to compute the final temperature after such change taking cognizance of this variation in the specific heats.

Reverting to the fundamental energy equation,

$$dQ = dU + \frac{dW}{J}$$

for adiabatic action

$$dQ = 0,$$

$$0 = dU + \frac{dW}{J} = Wc_v dt + \frac{PdV}{J},$$

substituting for P and dividing by T,

$$0 = Wc_v \frac{dt}{T} + \frac{R}{J}\frac{dV}{V},$$

substituting molecular weight M for W, to obtain molal values,

$$0 = Mc_v \frac{dt}{T} + \frac{MR}{J}\frac{dv}{v}.$$

Substituting for MR/J the universal gas value, 1.985,

$$0 = Mc_v \frac{dt}{T} + 1.985\frac{dv}{v}. \tag{1}$$

The expression for the molal specific heat is of the form

$$Mc = A + BT + CT^2,$$

substituting in equation (1),

$$0 = (A + BT + CT^2)\frac{dT}{T} + 1.985\frac{dv}{v},$$

simplifying and integrating between limits,

$$0 = A\,\log_e \frac{T_2}{T_1} + B(T_2 - T_1) + \frac{C}{2}(T_2{}^2 - T_1{}^2) + 1.985\log_e \frac{V_2}{V_1}. \tag{2}$$

In this equation T_1, V_1, and V_2 are usually known, thus leaving T_2 as the only unknown.

Similarly, in terms of T and P,

$$0 = A\,\log_e \frac{T_2}{T_1} + B(T_2 - T_1) + \frac{C}{2}(T_2{}^2 - T_1{}^2) + 1.985\log_e \frac{P_1 T_2}{P_2 T_1}$$

$$0 = (A + 1.985)\log_e \frac{T_2}{T_1} + B(T_2 - T_1)$$

$$+ \frac{C}{2}(T_2{}^2 - T_1{}^2) + 1.985\log_e \frac{P_1}{P_2}. \tag{3}$$

In this the known quantities are usually, T_1, P_1, and P_2.

The use of these equations is perhaps best illustrated by an example. Let it be required to find the temperature of air having an initial temperature of 40° F., after an adiabatic compression from 15 lbs. abs. to 1500 lbs. abs.

Using equation (3), with the constants A, B, and C, taken from the equation for the specific heat at constant volume for air, as given on page 210, there remains only the single unknown T_2. The equations for the Specific Heats of air repeated for convenience are:

$$Mc_p = 6.93 + 0.1200 \times 10^{-6}T^2$$

$$Mc_v = 4.945 + 0.1200 \times 10^{-6}T^2.$$

Thus: $A = 4.945$; $B = 0$; $c = 0.1200 \times 10^{-6}$.

Substituting in (3),

$$0 = (4.945 + 1.985) \log_e \frac{T_2}{500} + 0$$

$$+ 0.1200 \times 10^{-6}(T_2{}^2 - 250,000) + 1.985 \log_e \frac{1}{100}$$

$$0 = 6.93 \log_e \frac{T_2}{500} + 0.1200 \times 10^{-6}(T_2{}^2 - 250,000) - 1.985 \log_e 100.$$

This is most readily solved by graphical methods. If successive values be assumed for T_2 and substituted into the equation, a graph can be plotted, using the error as ordinates on the assumed temperatures as abscissae. Where the curve connecting these points crosses the axis will give the correct temperature. To obtain an approximate value of T_2 for the first trial we may take a value near that given for the perfect gas expansion, $p\,T = $ const. This gives 1865° F. abs. For the first trial value use 1850°.

Substituting this in equation (3),

$$0 = 6.93 \log_e \frac{1850}{500} + 0.1200 \times 10^{-6}(3,422,000 - 250,000) - 1.985 \log_e 100$$

$$0 = 9.07 + .3808 - 9.141$$

$$0 = .310.$$

$$\text{Error} = + .310.$$

Assuming $T_2 = 1800°$,

$$0 = 6.93 \log_e \frac{1800}{500} + 0.1200 \times 10^{-6}(3,240,000 - 250,000) - 1.985 \log_e 100$$

$$0 = 8.875 + .358 - 9.141$$

$$0 = 0.092.$$

$$\text{Error} = + .092$$

Assuming $T_2 = 1750°$,

$$0 = 6.93 \log_e \frac{1750}{500} + .1200 \times 10^{-6}(3,062,000 - 250,000) - 1,985 \log_e 100$$

$$0 = 8.680 + .3375 - 9.141$$

$$0 = -0.123.$$

$$\text{Error} = -0.123.$$

Plotting these errors as ordinates on the assumed temperatures as abscissae, the correct value for T_2 is found as $1779°$ F. abs.

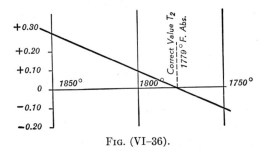

FIG. (VI–36).

With the final temperature and pressure known, the final volume may be determined from the common characteristic equation $Pv = RT$, or for greater accuracy from some one of the more correct characteristic equations, such as Keyes (page 110).

VI–37. **The Divergence of the Actual from the Ideal Cycle.**—The series of processes which constitute the working cycle of any actual engine differs materially from the idealized cycles which have been taken as representative of their performance. The divergence is due to two different effects, *mechanical* and *cyclical*, i.e., when the underlying assumptions concerning the mechanical characteristics and operation are violated and when the assumptions as to processes and characteristics of the working fluid are departed from.

Mechanical imperfections cause leakage of gas by the piston, non-instantaneous events, and frictional losses. The first causes the expansion and compression lines to depart from that of the tight piston assumed, the second causes a rounding of all corners, and the third, including both fluid and mechanical friction, is responsible for pumping losses and a generally reduced output.

Obviously, the more correct the assumptions as to thermodynamic action the less the divergence between actual and theoretical cycles, but, as already pointed out, it is sometimes preferable to sacrifice accuracy for convenience, and thus we find two major standards, the Air Standard and the Goodenough and Baker * or Variable Specific Heat Standard, and between these limits a host of secondary ideal cycles that are occasionally used for standards. Mechanical imperfections have practically the same effect regardless of the standard selected, but the thermodynamic assumptions made for the various standards will have a very great effect on the nearness of the approach of the ideal cycle to that of the actual engine.

Chief among the thermodynamic effects causing departure from ideal action may be mentioned, mixing with clearance gases, non-adiabatic action, variation in the chemical composition and mass of the working fluid, and the complex nature of the combustion phenomena.

In the air standard none of these is taken into consideration, as adiabatic action and constancy of properties of the working fluid are specifically assumed and the combustion is considered as simply the complete liberation of the full calorific value of the fuel, all going to raise the temperature of the air at constant specific heats.

In the Goodenough and Baker standard, assumptions are made for the effect of mixing with the clearance gases, for the variation in the chemical composition of the working fluid throughout the cycle and for the complex nature of the combustion process. This includes consideration of thermal equilibrium and variable specific heats. The cycle, moreover, is not a closed one, as, in conformity with actual operation, it assumes a throttling into the atmosphere of the burned gases at the end of the expansion stroke, instead of the cooling of a constant mass at constant volume as is done by the air standard.

In order to permit lubrication the cylinders of any actual engine are cooled by circulating air or liquid around them, with the result that neither

* A Thermodynamic Analysis of Internal-Combustion Engine Cycles. Goodenough and Baker. Bul. No. 160, Eng. Expt. Sta., Univ. of Illinois.

expansion nor compression are adiabatic, and, further, heat is also transferred throughout the suction and exhaust strokes. All this, however, is thermodynamically undesirable and the proper criterion for any standard is the *optimum* one of *adiabatic action*.

The summation of all these divergences gives the total amount of the difference between the performance of an actual engine and the performance which might be expected of an ideal engine, and thus, with a correct standard, should represent the margin available for improvement. The ratio of the indicated power to the ideal, usually called the diagram factor, ranges from 0.50 to 0.60 when the air standard is used for comparison, and from about 0.70 to 0.80 if the Goodenough and Baker standard be used. Thus, as already mentioned, the air standard, because of the crudeness of its assumptions, over-indicates the possibility of improvement, though its use in many cases is warranted by its simplicity. In using the Goodenough and Baker standard with its more accurate thermodynamic assumptions, the chief divergence is due to the non-adiabatic action of the actual engine, and this cooling of the cylinders and other heat transfers accounts for practically all of the divergence.

VI–38. Detonation.—From the foregoing the desirability of high-compression ratios for internal combustion engines is obvious, the principal deterrent to their adoption lies in a chemical phenomenon known as detonation which occurs when certain explosive mixtures are highly compressed as in the cylinder of the internal combustion engine. It consists apparently of an automatic ignition followed by a very rapid combustion of a portion of the fuel which sends a high-pressure wave down through the charge so violently that its impact against the piston gives the familiar knock met with in gasoline engines. It occurs only in certain classes of fuels, being worst in the petroleum derivatives (including kerosene and gasoline) and practically absent in the coal-tar derivatives (including benzol) and in alcohol. There are many reagents which tend to suppress detonation, bromine compounds, iodine compounds and lead compounds. Of these tetra-ethyl lead is the one of greatest commercial importance as the suppression of detonation is accomplished by the addition of but a very small quantity (about 1 to 12,000 by volume) and it can be produced commercially at reasonable price. By its use it has been possible to raise the compression ratio of an automobile engine from 4.0 to 7.0. With a corresponding gain in the air standard thermal efficiency of from 42.6 per cent to 54.1 per cent, or a **27** per cent $\left(\dfrac{54.1 - 42.6}{42.6} = 27.0 \text{ per cent} \right)$ improvement in the ideal thermal efficiency. As the actual thermal efficiency is about the same fraction of the ideal thermal efficiency over a wide range of compression ratios we should expect a similar reduction in actual fuel consumption and experiments bear this out.

VI–39.—Air Refrigeration Machines.—Any refrigerating machine is essentially a heat engine reversed, or a heat pump.   In the case of the heat

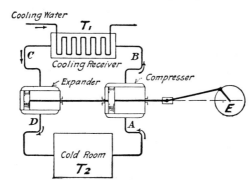

FIG. (VI–37).

engine, the heat Q_1 is supplied, the work W is done, and the heat Q_2 is rejected, the law of the conservation of energy requiring that $W = Q_1 - Q_2$ or $W + Q_2 = Q_1$.   Similarly, in the case of refrigerating machines, the heat Q_2 is taken into the working fluid, work W done upon it and a quantity of heat Q_1, larger by the amount of work energy added to it, is delivered to

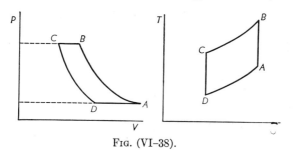

FIG. (VI–38).

the receiving agent, usually the circulating water.   One of the best illustrations of this is the refrigerating machine using air for its working fluid, such as the Allen Dense Air Ice Machine shown diagrammatically in the accompanying sketch.   Air at temperature T_2 is taken into the compressor cylinder A, compressed and delivered at B, hotter by virtue of the work done upon it.   From B it passes through the cooling receiver where it is cooled to the temperature of the cooling water T_1. From here, at T_1 it goes to the expander cylinder D, where it pushes the piston out, doing work and thus cooling itself to $< T_2$. Then the cold air passes to the cold room where it takes on heat, Q_2, at T_2 to maintain the desired temperature in the cold room.

Example.—An air-refrigerating machine, working on the reversed Joule cycle, operates between pressure limits of 14 lbs. abs. and 150 lbs. abs. The temperatures of the air leaving the cooling receiver and the cold room are 60° F. and 0° F. respectively. Ten pounds of air are circulated per minute. Assume the ideal cycle as in Fig. VI–38.

Find: (a) Pressure, temperature and volume of the air at each point; (b) Work done in compressor cylinder, and Hp.; (c) Work done in expander cylinder, and Hp.; (d) Net work and Hp.; (e) Heat taken on by air in cold room —B.t.u. per minute; (f) Heat rejected by air in air cooler—B.t.u. per minute.

Solution: (a) Point C: $p_C = 150$ lbs. abs.; $T_C = 60 + 460 = 520°$ F. abs.;

$$V_C = \frac{10\,(53.35)\,(520)}{150\,(144)} = 12.83 \text{ cu. ft. per min.}$$

Point D: $p_D = 14$ lbs. abs.; $V_D = \sqrt[1.4]{\dfrac{p_C V_C^{1.4}}{p_D}} = \sqrt[1.4]{\dfrac{150\,(12.83)^{1.4}}{14}}$

$$= \sqrt[1.4]{381.3} = 70 \text{ cu. ft. per min.}$$

$$T_D = \frac{14\,(144)\,(70)}{10\,(53.35)} = 265° \text{ F. abs.} = -195° \text{ F.}$$

Point A: $p_A = 14$ lbs. abs.; $T_A = 460°$ F. abs.;

$$V_A = 70 \left(\frac{460}{265}\right) = 121.5 \text{ cu. ft. per min.}$$

Point B: $p_B = 150$ lbs. abs.; $V_B = \sqrt[1.4]{\dfrac{14\,(121.5)^{1.4}}{150}}$

$$= \sqrt[1.4]{77} = 22.2 \text{ cu. ft. per min.}$$

$$T_B = \frac{150\,(144)\,(22.2)}{10\,(53.35)} = 900° \text{ F. abs.}$$

(b) Work of Compression $= \dfrac{1.4}{1.4 - 1}\,(144)\,[14\,(121.5) - 150\,(22.2)]$

$$= 504\,(1630) = 822,000 \text{ ft.-lbs. per min.}$$

$$\text{Hp.} = \frac{822,000}{33,000} = 24.9$$

(c) Work of Expansion $= \dfrac{1.4}{1.4 - 1}$ (144) [150 (12.83) $-$ 14 (70)] $=$ 504 (945)

$$= 476,000 \text{ ft.-lbs. per min.}$$

$$\text{Hp.} = \frac{476,000}{33,000} = 14.4.$$

(d) Net work $=$ 822,000 $-$ 476,000 $=$ 346,000 ft.-lbs. per min.

Net Hp. $=$ 24.9 $-$ 14.4 $=$ 10.5 Hp.

(e) Heat supplied to air in cold room $= Wc_p(T_A - T_D) =$ 10 (.24) (460 $-$ 265)

$$= 468 \text{ B.t.u. per min.}$$

(f) Heat rejected by air in air cooler $= Wc_p(T_C - T_B) =$ 2.4 (520 $-$ 900)

$$= 912 \text{ B.t.u. per min.}$$

CHAPTER VII

GASEOUS MIXTURES

The solution of problems dealing with gaseous mixtures rests mainly on two common fundamental natural laws; namely, Avogadro's Law and Dalton's Law, the former relating to molecular size and the latter to the independence of action of two or more groups of molecules which are intermingled.

VII–1. Avogadro's Law.—Avogadro's Law states that equal volumes of perfect gases under the same conditions of temperature and pressure contain the same number of molecules. This same conclusion follows directly from the kinetic theory of heat which considers pressure as the result of the molecular impacts against the restraining walls and temperature a function of the kinetic energy of the moving molecules, both expressed by the relation,

$$P = \tfrac{1}{3}n \, m \, vel^2.$$

For two gases at the same temperature the average kinetic energy of a molecule in each is the same, $m \, vel^2$ is therefore constant and if the pressure is the same, n must be the same for both gases.

The number of molecules in one mol of any gas is called Avogadro's number; for the pound-mol it is 2.75×10^{26} and for the metric gram-mol it is 6.062×10^{23}.

VII–2. Dalton's Law.—Sometimes called the Law of Partial Pressures, as originally enunciated by Dalton stated that the pressure exerted on the walls of a vessel containing a mixture of two or more gases is equal to the sum of the pressures which each gas would exert if it occupied the vessel separately (i.e., with none of the others present). $P_{mix.} = P_a + P_b$ where P_a and P_b are the pressures the ingredient gases of the mixture would exert if each occupied the space separately and at the same temperature. For the ideal gas, this is correct, for the perfect gas it is a very close approximation, diverging only by the influence of the volumes of the molecules themselves, and for actual gases and vapors the closeness of its approximation is of the same order as the closeness that these gases conform to the perfect gas laws. In general, we are justified in using it in engineering work when the ingredients of the mixture are customarily dealt with by the perfect gas characteristic equation, $PV = WRT$.

VII–3. **Molecular Mechanics of Mixtures.**—Dalton's Law is essentially a statement of the effect on one property, pressure, of the mixing together of equal volumes of different gases. When two gases mix what apparently takes place is that the molecules of one slip into the intermolecular spaces of the other and each gas behaves as if it occupied the vessel separately. The number of molecular collisions is of course increased, but such affect direction of travel only and are without effect on energy. For example, imagine two phantom cubes each containing a perfect gas. Assume the molecular arrangement at some instant to be as

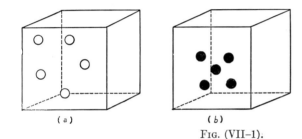
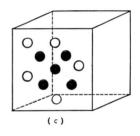

(a)   (b)   (c)

FIG. (VII–1).

shown in Fig. (VII–1). If cube (a) be slipped into coincidence with cube (b) the two gases would then occupy one cube as in (c) and obviously there would be more molecules and the pressure (the result of the molecular impacts) would be increased.* Dalton's Law specified that prior to the mixing, the temperature, i.e., the average molecular kinetic energy, of the two gases should be the same, thus, after mixing, this property remains the same and the resulting pressure is the sum of the partial pressures exerted by each acting as if it were alone in the cube. Had the temperatures prior to mixing been different the collisions between the molecules of the different gases would have resulted in a redistribution of the kinetic energy with consequent equalizing of temperature throughout the mixture.

Passing to the consideration of other properties such as Intrinsic Energy, Specific Heat, Heat Content, Temperature, Specific Volume and Entropy we find in general that where the property is a *specific* one,

* The assumption of the molecules of one gas clearing those of the other gas is quite legitimate as the result would be the same if two were shown as occupying the same spot. Such a representation would indicate a collision from which both molecules immediately rebound and continue on their respective ways.

i.e., evaluated for a unit weight of the gas, the result of any mixing is for the mixture to have the *sum* of the properties brought in by the ingredient gases, when ingredient gases are reversibly miscible.

VII–4. Properties of a Mixture. *Intrinsic Energy.*—From the foregoing it is obvious that the intrinsic energy of a mixture will be the sum of the individual intrinsic energies brought in by the component gases at the time of mixing, thus,

$$U_{\text{mix.}} = U_1 + U_2 + U_3 + \text{etc.}$$

If the *specific* intrinsic energy, i.e., the intrinsic energy *per pound* (u) be desired it can be obtained by dividing the total intrinsic energy by the total weight of the mixture.

$U = Wu$, where W denotes the weight under consideration and, u, the specific intrinsic energy.

$$u_{\text{mix.}} = \frac{W_1 u_1 + W_2 u_2 + W_3 u_3 + \text{etc.}}{W_1 + W_2 + W_3 + \text{etc.}} = \frac{\Sigma W u}{\Sigma W}.$$

Specific Heat.—Specific Heat is a Thermal Capacity of a unit weight and is defined as the heat supplied divided by the change in temperature, $\left(\dfrac{dq}{dt}\right)$. Since each gas in a mixture behaves as if it were alone, the thermal capacity $\left(\dfrac{dQ}{dt}\right)$ of the mixture is equal to the sum of the individual thermal capacities of the component gases, thus,

$$\frac{dQ}{dt} = \left(\frac{dQ}{dt}\right)_1 + \left(\frac{dQ}{dt}\right)_2 + \left(\frac{dQ}{dt}\right)_3 + \text{etc.}$$

The heat supplied, Q, is equal to that supplied per unit of weight, q, multiplied by the weight, W.

$$Q = Wq,$$

therefore,

$$c_{\text{mix.}} = \left(\frac{dq}{dt}\right)_{\text{mix.}} = \frac{W_1\left(\dfrac{dq}{dt}\right)_1 + W_2\left(\dfrac{dq}{dt}\right)_2 + W_3\left(\dfrac{dq}{dt}\right)_3 + \text{etc.}}{W_1 + W_2 + W_3 + \text{etc.}}$$

or

$$c_{\text{mix.}} = \frac{W_1 c_1 + W_2 c_2 + W_3 c_3 + \text{etc.}}{W_1 + W_2 + W_3} = \frac{\Sigma W c}{\Sigma W}.$$

Heat Content.—Heat Content, defined as $U + APV$, may also be evaluated as,

$$H = \int (dQ)_p = W \int c_p dt.$$

It is essentially an energy quantity thus, for a gaseous mixture,

$$H_{\text{mix.}} = H_1 + H_2 + H_3 + H_4 + \text{etc.}$$

For *specific* consideration, i.e., for one pound, this becomes,

$$h_{\text{mix.}} = \frac{W_1 h_1 + W_2 h_2 + W_3 h_3 + \text{etc.}}{W_1 + W_2 + W_3 + \text{etc.}} = \frac{\Sigma W h}{\Sigma W}.$$

Temperature.—Temperature is not a *specific* property, it is a measure of the *average* molecular kinetic energy possessed by a gas and thus indirectly a measure of the average (square root mean square) velocity of the molecules. It is the intensity factor of the sensible heat of the gas and therefore not a complete or true energy quantity and therefore not additive when considering a mixture. Two gases at the same temperature when mixed still retain their original temperatures. The temperature of a mixture must then be arrived at by summing the intrinsic energies and finding the temperature corresponding to this sum. For perfect gases,

$$U_{\text{mix.}} = W_{\text{mix.}} \, c_{v_{\text{mix.}}} \, T_{\text{mix.}}$$

thus,

$$T_{\text{mix.}} = U_{\text{mix.}} \div W_{\text{mix.}} \, c_{v_{\text{mix.}}} \quad \text{or} \quad u_{\text{mix.}} \div c_{v_{\text{mix.}}}.$$

For actual gases where the specific heat may not be constant,

$$U_{\text{mix.}} = W_{\text{mix.}} \, T_{\text{mix.}} \, [c_v]_{\text{mean val. for mixture}}$$

Entropy.—The entropy of a mixture will be the sum of the entropies of the component gases *provided* the mixing has occurred *reversibly.* If several gases, all at the same temperature, are quietly mixed the resulting entropy of the mixture will be the sum of the individual entropies but if the mixing involves any *irreversible* processes such as conduction, impact, etc., the entropy of the mixture will be greater than the sum of the individual entropies because of the degradation of energy accompanying the irreversible action. Thus we may write, for a **reversible** mixing,

$$S_{\text{mix.}} = S_1 + S_2 + S_3 + \text{etc.}$$

$$s = \frac{W_1 s_1 + W_2 s_2 + W_3 s_3 + \text{etc.}}{W_1 + W_2 + W_3 + \text{etc.}} = \frac{\Sigma W s}{\Sigma W},$$

and for an *irreversible* mixing,

$$S_{mix.} > S_1 + S_2 + S_3 + \text{etc.}$$

and

$$s > \frac{\Sigma Ws}{\Sigma W}.$$

Volume.—In any mixture of gases that is in a state of equilibrium the temperature is the same throughout the mixture and the temperature of each ingredient gas is identical with that of the mixture. We may therefore consider the mixture as having been arrived at by either of two routes, one, by putting them consecutively into a vessel of fixed volume in which case the temperature and volume remain the same for each gas and the resulting mixture, while the pressure builds up successively as each gas is added, or by starting with them all at the same pressure and temperature and putting them successively into an elastic vessel which is capable of expanding as necessary to accommodate them.

For the first case (identical temperatures and volumes) the resulting pressure is the sum of the partial pressures exerted by each of the component gases. For the second (identical temperatures and pressures) the resulting volume is the sum of the volumes of the component gases as added. $V_1 + V_2 + V_3 + \text{etc.} = V_{mix.}$, and each gas has filled the entire space of the resultant volume, i.e., each gas has expanded at constant temperature until it has filled the increased space and its pressure has accordingly dropped. From this, $P_{mix.}V_1 = P_1V_{mix.}$ also $P_{mix.}V_2 = P_2V_{mix.}$ and $P_{mix.}V_3 = P_3V_{mix.}$

By division $V_1/V_2 = P_1/P_2$ and $V_2/V_3 = P_2/P_3$, etc.

hence

$$V_1 : V_2 : V_3 : \text{etc.} = P_1 : P_2 : P_3 : \text{etc.}$$

Thus the volumes of the ingredient gases, as expressed by a volumetric analysis, are proportional to the partial pressures.*

VII–5. Apparent Molecular Weight of Mixture.—The specific volume of a mixture of gases is usually determined by assuming the mixture a single gas having properties equivalent to the average of those of its constituent gases. This is done by determining a pseudo-molecular weight for the mixture which can be used for M in the general characteristic equation,

$$Pv = \frac{1545}{M} T.$$

---

* Where the gases depart radically from perfect gas behavior these relations do not hold exactly.

When the percentage composition by volume is known it is equivalent to knowing the number of molecules of each gas present in 100 molecules of the mixture. If the percentage by volume of each constituent gas be multiplied by its molecular weight, summed, and the sum divided by 100 there will result a figure which represents the average molecular weight of the mixture. If the component gases follow the perfect gas characteristic equation there is little error in assuming the mixture a simple gas having this for its molecular weight. If, however, the mixture contains either vapors or gases in states close to the critical state the error may be large and the above method should not be used. Such cases will be reserved for later discussion, Chapter XII.

VII–6. Molal Properties.—When the unit of quantity be taken as the *mol*, the various properties are referred to as **molal** properties. For gaseous mixtures the molal property refers to an amount of the mixture represented by M pounds where M is the apparent molecular weight above-mentioned. Thus the *molal intrinsic energy* would be the intrinsic energy of one mol of the gas or mixture under consideration. For a mixture it would, obviously, be the sum of the molal intrinsic energies of its ingredient gases, each multiplied by the fraction of a mol (n) which represented that gas.

Molal intrinsic energy $= Mu = n_1(m_1u_1) + n_2(m_2u_2) + n_3(m_3u_3) +$ etc.

Molal heat content $\quad = Mh = n_1(m_1h_1) + n_2(m_2h_2) + n_3(m_3h_3) +$ etc.

Molal specific heat $\quad\; = Mc = n_1(m_1c_1) + n_2(m_2c_2) + n_3(m_3c_3) +$ etc.

While commonly spoken of as a unit of weight, the mol is essentially a unit of number like the dozen, yet it is used to indicate quantities on both a weight and a volume basis and care is sometimes necessary to avoid confusion. Since there are always 2.75×10^{26} molecules in one mol, it may be helpful to think of equations using molal values as referring to molecular statistics. The statement of the composition of a mol of a gaseous mixture in terms of mols of the component gases is a statement of its volumetric composition.

VII–7. Conversion of Analyses by Weight and Volume.—Analyses of mixtures of gases may be given by quoting the ingredients in percentages by weight or percentages by volume. Each system possesses advantages for certain types of problems and the translation of analyses from one system to the other is a problem of everyday occurrence. Consider the following analysis of a mixture of gases in which the ingredients are given in percentages by volume:

$CO_2 = 12$ per cent; $N_2 = 73$ per cent; $CO = 7$ per cent; $O_2 = 8$ per cent.

According to Avogadro's Law equal numbers of molecules of all these ingredient gases occupy identical spaces, so that if a sample of a hundred molecule size were taken, it would contain 12 molecules of CO_2, 73 molecules of N_2, 7 molecules of CO, and 5 molecules of O_2. Since the relative weight of each of these molecules is known, the product of the percentage by volume and the molecular weight gives the weight of the individual gas contained in 100 molecules.

Gas	Per Cent by Volume		Molec- ular Weight		Weight of 100 Molecules or Function of Weight				Per Cent by Weight
CO_2	12	×	44	=	528	528 ÷ 3024	=		17.4
N_2	73	×	28	=	2044	2044 ÷ 3024	=		67.6
CO	7	×	28	=	196	196 ÷ 3024	=		6.5
O_2	8	×	32	=	256	256 ÷ 3024	=		8.5
Total for 100 molecules					3024				100.0

Conversely, when the analysis is given in percentage by weight, if the sample be considered as of one hundred unit weights in size, dividing the weight of each ingredient by its individual molecular weight will give the number of molecules (and, therefore, a function of the volume occupied).

For example, in a mol of the above gas, there would be .12 mol of CO_2, .73 mol of N_2, .07 mol of CO, and .08 mol of O_2 for each of the gases, just as if we had a measure filled with balls, all of the same size but of various densities, such as Aluminum, Silver and Lead, and the total weight of each group were known; then dividing the weight of Aluminum by the weight of one Aluminum ball would give the number of Aluminum balls, and since all of the balls are of the same size this number would be proportional to the volume occupied by the Aluminum.

To illustrate, the following analysis by weight is converted to one by volume.

Gas	Per Cent by Weight		Molec- ular Weight		Number of Mols, or Function of Volume				Per Cent by Volume
H_2	5	÷	2	=	2.5	2.5 ÷ 6.75	=		37.1
N_2	28	÷	28	=	1.0	1.0 ÷ 6.75	=		14.8
CO	35	÷	28	=	1.25	1.25 ÷ 6.75	=		18.5
CH_4	32	÷	16	=	2.0	2.0 ÷ 6.75	=		29.6
Total mols in 100 units of weight					6.75				100.0

If one mol be taken as the size of the sample and the composition of a mixture of gases be given in terms of the fraction of a mol present of each of the component gases, it is equivalent to quoting the composition on a percentage by volume basis, since a mol contains the same number of molecules for all gases.* As the total mols in 100 units of weight of the mixture is 6.75, the molecular weight of the mixture is 100 ÷ 6.75 = 14.80.

VII–8. **Determination of the Specific Heat of a Mixture** (Constant Specific Heats).—The specific heat, using the pound as the unit of weight, is denoted by c, and when the mol is taken as the unit of weight, it is Mc. If the analysis be on a weight basis, the specific heat, c, of the mixture is the sum of the products of the specific heat of each gas by its fraction by weight.

For example, taking the analysis by weight of page 224:

Gas	Per Cent by Weight		Specific Heat at Const. Pressure, c_p		Function of Specific Heat
H₂............	5	×	3.42	=	17.10
N₂............	28	×	0.24	=	6.72
CO............	35	×	0.24	=	8.40
CH₄............	32	×	0.59	=	18.88

$$51.10 \div 100 = .511 = c_p \text{ (mixture)}$$

If the analysis be on a mol basis the sum of the products of each gaseous fraction by its molal specific heat will give the molal specific heat of the mixture. For example:

Gas	Number of Mols		Specific Heat per Mol, Mc_p		Function of Mc_p
H₂.........	0.371	×	6.84	=	2.537
N₂.........	0.148	×	6.72	=	0.994
CO.........	0.185	×	6.72	=	1.243
CH₄.........	0.296	×	9.44	=	2.790

$$7.564 \quad \text{Specific heat per mol } (Mc_p)$$

Dividing this molal specific heat (Mc_p) by the apparent molecular weight of the mixture will give the specific heat per lb. (c_p). The apparent molecular weight of the mixture is 14.80.

$$7.564 \div 14.80 = .511 = c_p \text{ (mixture)}.$$

VII–9. **Combustion.**—Combustion is commonly defined as the rapid oxidation of a substance accompanied by the evolution of considerable heat, a definition which is not very satisfying because of the vagueness of the qualifying adjectives. Oxidation is a chemical phenomenon of rea-

---

* The volume of one mol of any perfect gas at 32° F. and atmospheric pressure is 358.7 cu. ft. See Art. IV–4.

sonably definite character, but what shall constitute a *rapid* oxidation depends upon the standard by which the event is measured. Unfortunately, oxidation has been rechristened with a series of semi-technical or popular terms which are mainly indicative of the rapidity with which the oxidation process is consummated. Thus a very slow oxidation is called *corrosion* or rusting, a more rapid one, *combustion*, a still more rapid oxidation constitutes an *explosion* and where the process is completed in a still more minute time interval, we have to deal with the phenomenon of *detonation*. The same amount of heat energy is brought into existence when a unit weight is oxidized by any of these processes, but where, as in the case of corrosion, the dissipation of the heat energy goes on at a pace almost equal to its generation, the effect on our senses is negligible.

VII–10. Molecular Mechanics of Combustion.—Combustion is essentially a transformation of chemical energy into heat energy, from the viewpoint of molecular mechanics it is the transformation of molecular energy of the potential form into that of the kinetic form. Molecular structures retained in certain aggregations against intermolecular attractions (including chemical affinity) are toppled over when the temperature and thus the translatory velocity of the molecules becomes sufficiently high. They then fall into other combinations, new molecules, which move off with greatly increased translatory velocities and corresponding kinetic energies, thus the substance acquires sensible heat as a consequence of the chemical reaction.

Consider the combustion of carbon monoxide in oxygen, a mixing of the two gases at ordinary atmospheric temperature results in the simple mechanical mingling of the two sets of molecules, each going serenely on its way unaffected by the other. If now some hot point be introduced, such as a glowing platinum wire or the arc across a spark plug, the molecules immediately adjacent to that are speeded up and soon achieve a velocity sufficient to upset the dynamic equilibrium of the separate CO and O_2 molecules to such an extent that the O_2 combines with the CO to form the new molecule, CO_2. . . . This union results in an even higher velocity of the newly formed CO_2 molecule which proceeds on its way and in turn brings about similar changes by imparting kinetic energy to the molecules immediately adjacent to it.

Thus the combustion proceeds until all unions have been completed and the whole mass of the products has acquired the sensible heat producible by the union

Even though the entire process occur in an immeasurably small interval of time, it is not instantaneous in the strict sense of the word as it is necessarily a progressive action. Moreover, in any combustion there is a continuous dissemination of heat to outside surroundings and while the reaction begins at the ignition temperature and proceeds with progressively increasing temperatures as the successive amounts of fuel are burned, the dissipation of heat also progressively increases and the maximum temperature will be reached when evolution and dissipation are equal. Moreover, when the temperature reaches a certain intensity, the reaction halts and the mixture attains a state of equilibrium even though all the fuel has not been combined. This is due to dissociation.

As the combustion proceeds, the products molecules (in this case CO_2) move about with ever-increasing velocities as more and more energy is received, finally a point is reached where they are moving so rapidly that their own motion disrupts the atomic grouping of the molecule and it is dissociated into its component groups. This requires energy to accomplish and the effect is the same as that of cooling or heat dissipation. Later a reassociation may occur with a re-evolution of heat as at first but a time interval has intervened during which the regular loss to outside has been going on so that when reassociation occurs it is in a group with a lowered total sensible heat, and the combustion proceeds at this temperature of equilibrium between the dissipation and evolution of heat, or as Clerk* states, " at the highest temperature produced by combustion the product cannot exist in a state of complete combination. It will be mixed, to a certain extent, with the free constituents which cannot combine further until the temperature falls, as the temperature falls combustion will continue till all the free gases are combined."

VII-11. General Combustion Equations.—Combustion is essentially an atomic and molecular rearrangement and the solution of problems involving the weight and volume of the participating gases, both before and after combination, is most simply handled by considering molecular weights and volumes.

Consider the equation for the combustion of CO:

$$2CO + O_2 \rightarrow 2CO_2.$$

This states that one molecule of oxygen combines with two molecules of carbon monoxide forming as a result, two molecules of carbon dioxide. Remembering that, according to Avogadro's Law, the space occupied by a molecule is the same for any gas regardless of its structure this combustion has resulted in two molecules merging into one with the consequence that the products of combustion will occupy but two-thirds of the space occupied

* Dugald Clerk in "The Gas, Petrol and Oil Engine," p. 123.

by the ingredients before combustion, or a chemical contraction of $33\frac{1}{3}$ per cent. This, of course, is measured when the products have been brought to the same temperature and pressure as the mixture before ignition.

The molecular weights of the gases forming the mixture were as follows: $CO = 28$, $O_2 = 32$, thus $2 \times 28 = 56$ parts by weight of CO combined with 32 parts by weight of O_2, resulting (since the weight of a molecule of CO_2 is 44) in 88 parts by weight of CO_2. Or 56 lbs. of CO will combine with 32 lbs. of O_2 and give 88 lbs. of CO_2.

The equation, therefore, may be written as follows:

$$2CO + O_2 \rightarrow 2CO_2.$$

By weight, $56 + 32$ $=$ $88.$
By volume, $2 + 1$ become $2.$

For the three simple gases fundamental in combustion problems, the atomic and molecular weights are:

	Atomic Weight		Molecular Weight	
	Approximate	Exact	Approximate	Exact
Hydrogen (H_2).................	1	1.008	2	2.015
Oxygen (O_2)....................	16	16.00	32	32.00
Nitrogen (N_2).................	14	14.01	28	28.02

The round number values are usually used. Carbon has an atomic weight of 12 and the molecular weight of any compound molecule, such as methane (CH_4) is the sum of the weights of the atoms composing it, $12 + 4 = 16$; or, for alcohol (C_2H_6O), $24 + 6 + 16 = 46$. The composition of air is approximately $0.232 O_2$ and $0.768 N_2$ by weight; or $0.21 O_2$ and $0.79 N_2$ by volume.

Assuming that the water vapor in the products of combustion is at a temperature and pressure to warrant its being considered perfectly gaseous, the following reaction equations describe the combustion of some of the common fuels.

Methane CH_4

$$CH_4 + 2O_2 \rightarrow CO_2 + 2H_2O$$

By weight, $16 + 64$ $=$ $44 + 36.$
By volume, $1 + 2$ become $1 + 2.$

Acetylene C_2H_2

$$H_2 + 5O_2 \rightarrow 4CO_2 + 2H_2O$$

By weight, $52 + 160$ $=$ $176 + 36.$
By volume, $2 + 5$ become $4 + 2.$

Benzol (Benzene) C_6H_6

$$2C_6H_6 + 15O_2 \rightarrow 12CO_2 + 6H_2O$$

By weight, $156 + 480 = 528 + 108.$
By volume, $2 + 15$ become $12 + 6.$

Gasoline Vapor C_8H_{18}

$$2C_8H_{18} + 25O_2 \rightarrow 16CO_2 + 18H_2O$$

By weight, $228 + 800 = 704 + 324.$
By volume, $2 + 25$ become $16 + 18.$

Alcohol (ethyl) C_2H_6O

$$C_2H_6O + 3O_2 \rightarrow 2CO_2 + 3H_2O$$

By weight, $46 + 96 = 88 + 54.$
By volume, $1 + 3$ become $2 + 3.$

It is interesting to note that when certain fuels as hydrogen and carbon monoxide burn, the specific volume of the products of combustion, when returned to the original temperature and pressure, becomes smaller, i.e., there is a chemical contraction. This change of specific volume may be of any sort, depending upon the composition of the fuel, from a contraction for the fuels just mentioned, through zero change for the combustion of methane (CH_4), to the chemical expansion resulting from the combustion of the richer hydrocarbons, such as gasoline.

If the volumetric composition be known, the change of specific volume which a mixed gaseous fuel undergoes during combustion can be determined by calculating the change each ingredient passes through and summing these effects. For example, the following holds true for producer gas of the following composition, burned in Oxygen:

| | Composition by Volume | Volume of O_2 Needed | Volume of Products | | |
			H_2O	CO_2	N_2
Carbon dioxide, CO_2.......	5.6	....	....	5.6	....
Carbon monoxide, CO.....	22.9	11.5	....	22.9	....
Hydrogen, H_2............	15.3	7.6	15.3	....	....
Methane, CH_4............	1.0	2.0	2.0	1.0	....
Nitrogen, N_2.............	55.2	....	....	....	55.2
	100.0	21.1	17.3	29.5	55.2

121.1 becomes ⟶ 102.0

or a chemical contraction of 19.1 volumes

Considering this gas to be exploded with the least air that could be used, i.e., the richest mixture, 21.1 volumes of oxygen would be required, or

21.1 ÷ 0.209 = 101 volumes of air, since the oxygen component of dry air is 20.9 per cent of its volume. The chemical contraction of the fuel and its oxygen was 19.1 mols, and this contraction took place in 100 volumes of fuel plus 101 volumes of air so that contraction of the charge was 19.1 in 201 or 9.5 per cent. In actual practice an excess of air is used and the charge is further diluted products of the previous combustion entrapped in the clearance space so that this figure would be materially reduced.

VII–12. Heat of Combustion or Heating Value.—As a result of the chemical oxidation process that we call combustion, the products of combustion are at a much higher temperature than the original substances. The amount of heat which it is necessary to *withdraw from the products of combustion to return them to the original temperature* is variously called, *heat of combustion, heating value,* or *calorific value,* of the fuel.* It is intended to represent the heat liberated by any given combustion, in reality it is an experimental determination of the heat which must be withdrawn from the *products* to reestablish the initial temperature prior to combustion, and the value will differ according to whether the cooling (and burning) has taken place at constant pressure or at constant volume. Thus, for a combustion occurring at constant volume the heating value of the fuel would be the difference in the intrinsic energy of the products of combustion between the maximum and original temperatures, assuming

adiabatic combustion, $(\text{Htg. Val.})_v = U_2 - U_1 = W \int_1^2 c_v dt$. Similarly, for a combustion occurring at constant pressure, the heating value is the difference

in enthalpy, or $(\text{Htg. Val.})_p = H_2 - H_1 = W \int_1^2 c_p dt$. The difference,

however, is slight, rarely amounting to more than one-half of one per cent, except in the case of pure carbon where it may run as high as 3 per cent.

VII–13. Higher and Lower Heating Value.—For fuels containing hydrogen there is another aspect, however, that must be considered. Such fuels have as a product of combustion, water vapor and the experimental determination of the heating value differs materially when all products remain in the gaseous state, or when the water vapor is condensed out. Thus all fuels containing hydrogen may have two heating values, a lower and a higher. *Lower heating value* may be defined as the heat which must be removed from the products of combustion to return them to their

---

* To be strictly accurate the cooling of the products back to the original temperature should be accomplished by a process or processes the reverse of those occurring during the combustion, i.e., constant volume, constant pressure, or polytropic cooling.

original temperature, *assuming all products to remain in the gaseous phase.*
Higher heating value may be defined as the heat which must be removed
from the products of combustion to return them to their original temperature, including the heat of vaporization of all the water vapor of combustion. For accurate work the temperature at which the heating value was
determined should be specified. In Fig. (VII–2) ABC represents the cooling at constant volume of the products of combustion from T_A (which is
assumed to be the temperature after an adiabatic combustion as in a non-
conducting bomb) to T_c, the original temperature, with the further assumption that the products all remain in the gaseous phase. Actually, the

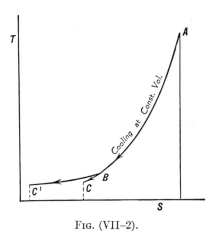

FIG. (VII–2).

cooling will result in the state point moving along the curve AC until it
reaches T_B, the dewpoint, a temperature such that the water vapor begins
to condense. After this, more and more water vapor condenses out, but
not all of it, and the state point moves along BC'. The area under the
curve ABC represents the *lower* heating value while that under ABC' is
equivalent to the *higher* heating value. The difference is, of course, equal
to the heat of vaporization of as much moisture as has been condensed
out of the mixture up to the final temperature T_c. Had the combustion
and subsequent cooling occurred at constant pressure, the only difference
in the figure would have been that the curves ABC and C' would have
been less steep.

From an extensive survey, Goodenough and Felbeck have compiled
a table giving the lower heats of combustion of the common fuels, selecting
the best experimental work available on each fuel and by weighted averages

determining mean values which represent probably the best information yet published.

TABLE IX

HEATS OF COMBUSTION (IN MEAN B.T.U.) OF THE COMMON FUELS *

(Lower Heating Value)

Fuel	Symbol	At Constant Pressure and 62° F.			At Constant Volume and 62° F.		
		Per Mol	Per Lb.	Per Cu. Ft.	Per Mol	Per Lb.	Per Cu. Ft.
Hydrogen.........	H_2	103,530	51,354	272	103,010	51,096	271
Carbon monoxide...	CO	122,130	4,362	321	121,610	4,343	320
Carbon (amorphous) to CO_2..........	C	174,250	14,521	....	174,250	14,521	....
Methane..........	CH_4	345,920	21,577	909	345,920	21,577	909
Acetylene.........	C_2H_2	542,170	20,840	1425	541,650	20,820	1423
Ethylene..........	C_2H_4	575,370	20,525	1512	575,370	20,525	1512
Ethane...........	C_2H_6	610,340	20,312	1604	610,850	20,329	1605
Benzene..........	C_6H_6	1,359,400	17,418	3572	1,359,920	17,424	3573
Gasoline vapor.....	C_8H_{18}	2,143,200	18,800	5631	2,146,840	18,830	5641
Kerosene vapor....	$C_{12}H_{26}$	3,456,100	20,330	9081	3,461,800	20,360	9096

* Abstract from Bulletin 139, Engineering Experiment Station, University of Illinois.

Referring again to the fundamental energy equation,

$$-\Delta U = -\Delta Q + \frac{\Delta W}{J}$$

when either of the terms of the right-hand member is made zero, the entire energy of the reaction goes to the other; for example, if no external work is done, as in a combustion at constant volume, the energy of the reaction is equal to the heat of combustion, as determined by cooling the products at constant volume.

$$-\Delta U = -\Delta Q = (Ht. \text{ of } C)_v.$$

When the combustion is adiabatic, i.e., thermally isolated, $\Delta Q = 0$, and all the energy of the reaction may go into the doing of external work plus the heating of the products of combustion. If the combustion occur at constant pressure,

$$-\Delta U = -\Delta Q + \frac{\Delta W}{J} = -\Delta Q + \frac{P\Delta V}{J}$$

or,

$$-\Delta U - \frac{P\Delta V}{J} = (Ht. \text{ of } C)_p = -\Delta H.$$

Thus the heat of combustion at constant pressure includes within it the heat equivalent of the work done in changing the volume of the products from the final to the original volume existing before combustion.

For adiabatic combustions, therefore, we say that when the burning occurs at *constant volume* the heat of combustion is equal to the increase in the **intrinsic energy** of the products, and when the burning occurs at *constant pressure* the heat of combustion is equal to the increase in the **heat content** of the products, or

At constant volume, $_1Q_2 = (Ht \text{ of } C)_v = U_2 - U_1$

At constant pressure, $_1Q_2 = (Ht \text{ of } C)_p = H_2 - H_1$.

For a mol of fuel burned these may be written,

At constant volume, $_1Q_2 = Mu_2 - Mu_1$

At constant pressure, $_1Q_2 = Mh_2 - Mh_1$.

VII–14. Temperature-Entropy Diagrams.—For a perfect gas the characteristic equation and the equations for the property relations for all of the processes commonly are so simple that arithmetical solution of the problems is the easiest and simplest. When, however, actual gases are dealt with, for which the perfect gas assumptions no longer hold, the solution of problems involving the common changes are much more complex. For example, for the adiabatic compression of a perfect gas, we have the relation

$$P_1V_1^k = P_2V_2^k = \text{Const.}$$

If, however, the gas has a specific heat which varies with temperature, the relation is as follows:

$$\left(a + \frac{R}{J}\right)\log_e \frac{T_2}{T_1} + b\,(T_2 - T_1) + \tfrac{1}{2}c\,(T_2{}^2 - T_1{}^2) = \frac{R}{J}\left(\log_e \frac{P_2}{P_1}\right)$$

where a, b, and c are the constants in the equation for specific heat.

However, it is possible to construct for actual gases temperature-entropy charts by means of which the solution of problems of the above nature can be obtained graphically and with great simplicity.

Ordinary air is considered as sufficiently close to the perfect gas laws to permit customary perfect gas relations to be used. However, when the internal-combustion engine is dealt with, the temperature of the working mixture becomes so high that failure to recognize the variation in specific heats leads to absurd results. Accordingly, there have been constructed a number of temperature-entropy diagrams for actual gases which find considerable use.

The item of major importance dealing with actual gases as distinguished from the perfect gas is undoubtedly the variation of specific heat with temperature. However, temperature-entropy charts allowing for this can be readily constructed. There follows a brief discussion of the salient features in the construction of such a diagram.

Entropy changes corresponding to heating (or cooling) at constant pressure or at constant volume can be simply determined; for example, treating air as a perfect gas with constant specific heat a series of entropy changes for a series of isothermal compressions can be readily figured. With these data, and using temperature and entropy for axes, a series of points can be plotted as shown in Fig. (VII–3). Curves drawn through

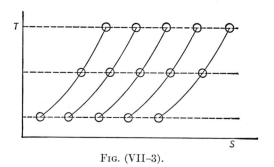

Fig. (VII–3).

the points representing the same volume would give curves of constant volume on the temperature-entropy coördinates, as shown in Fig. (VII–3).

These constant volume curves would be in the nature of contour curves on T–S axes, and by a similar process there could be developed a family of constant pressure lines. It would be necessary to assume some initial condition as the datum from which the entropy changes were measured. A completed diagram would have something the appearance of Fig. (VII–4). Such a diagram would have the convenient features that adiabatic and isothermal changes would be represented by vertical and horizontal lines respectively, and for various compressions and expansions one could spot the initial state, draw a line representing the change and then read values of pressure, temperature and volume for the final state directly.

However, when dealing with perfect gases, the algebraic computation for these changes are themselves so simple that there is no gain in a graphical solution, and such a figure is never used. When dealing with actual gases at high temperatures, as in combustion problems, the assumption of constant specific heat is too grossly in error to permit its retention, even though the expressions for the true or varying specific heat are somewhat involved. Then the algebraic computation for adiabatic or other changes becomes complex and cumbersome, and a temperature-entropy diagram, similar to that outlined above but constructed taking cognizance of the variation in specific heat, permits ready graphical solution of problems.

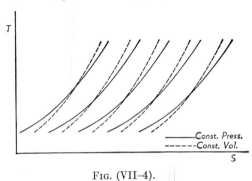

FIG. (VII–4).

VII–15. Temperature-Entropy Diagram for the Diatomic Gases. (Variable Specific Heats).

—In air compressors, internal-combustion engines, and many combustion problems the range of temperature is sufficient to make it entirely improper to retain our early assumption of a constant specific heat. Provided there is a good representative equation for the specific heat and temperature relation, a temperature-entropy diagram such as mentioned in the preceding paragraph can be readily constructed, and its use is helpful in the solution of problems. The commonest gases encountered in problems of the type above-mentioned are oxygen, nitrogen, carbon monoxide, air, carbon dioxide, and water vapor. Goodenough* has given one equation which is applicable to all of the first four gases, provided that we deal with them on a mol basis. Using this, a temperature-entropy diagram for these diatomic gases has been constructed and is reproduced as Fig. (VII–5).

Details of the computations necessary for its layout have already been discussed and are covered in the original paper.† Problems involving adiabatic or isothermal changes of these diatomic gases, with the specific heat variation taken account of can be readily solved graphically. For

* Bul. 139, University of Illinois Engineering Experiment Station.
† "A Temperature Entropy Diagram for Air and the Diatomic Gases," *Mechanical Engineering*, Nov., 1926, Vol. 48, No. 11a.

example, it may be interesting to note the solution of a problem analytically and compare it with the graphical solution.

USE OF THE DIAGRAM FOR THE SOLUTION OF PROBLEMS

I.—Let it be required to find the final pressure resulting from the adiabatic compression of nitrogen from an initial pressure of 8 lbs. per sq. in. and a temperature of 500° F. abs. to a final temperature of 2500° F. abs.

The solution by direct computation is as follows: *

$$a \log_e \frac{2500}{500} + b\,(2500 - 500) + \frac{c}{2}\,(2500^2 - 500^2) = \frac{R}{J} \log_e \frac{P_2}{P_1}$$

where a, b, and c are the constants in the equation for the specific heat at constant pressure and are 6.93, 0, and 0.1200×10^{-6}, respectively. Substituting,

$$6.930 \log_e 5 + 0 + \frac{0.1200}{2}\,(2500^2 - 500^2) \times 10^{-6} = 1.985 \log_e \frac{P_2}{P_1}$$

or

$$11.51314 = 1.985 \log_e \frac{P_2}{P_1}$$

whence

$$P_2 = 2642 \text{ lbs. per sq. in.}$$

From the chart, Fig. (VII–2), entering at 8 lbs. per sq. in. and 500°, go vertically upward to the 2500° line, where the final pressure is read by interpolation as 2640 lbs. per sq. in.

II.—Similarly, for a mol of oxygen compressed adiabatically from $P_1 = 4$ lbs. per sq. in. and $T_1 = 1500°$ F. abs., to $T_2 = 5000°$, the final pressure will be

$$6.93 \log_e \frac{5000}{1000} + 0 + \frac{0.12 \times 10^{-6}}{2}\,(5000^2 - 1500^2) = 1.985 \log_e \frac{P_2}{P_1}$$

whence

$$\log \frac{P_2}{P_1} = 4.880$$

and

$$P_2 = 4 \times 131.7 = 527.$$

* Principles of Thermodynamics, by Goodenough.

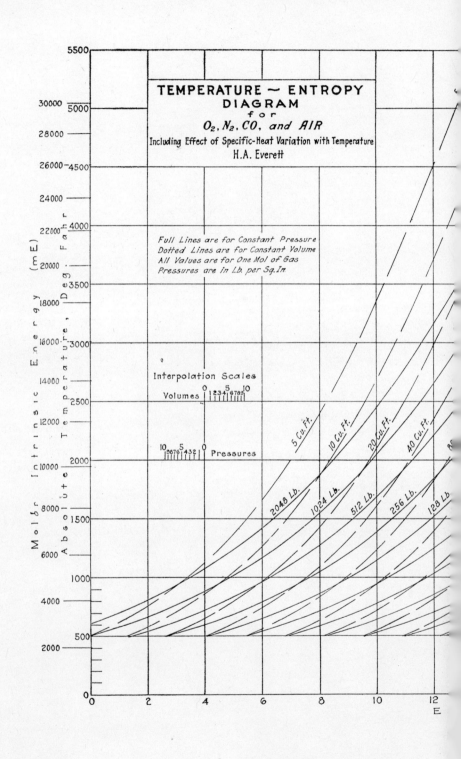

TEMPERATURE ~ ENTROPY
DIAGRAM
for
O_2, N_2, CO, and AIR
Including Effect of Specific-Heat Variation with Temperature
H.A. Everett

Full Lines are for Constant Pressure
Dotted Lines are for Constant Volume
All Values are for One Mol of Gas
Pressures are in Lb. per Sq.In.

Interpolation Scales

Volumes | 0 1 2 3 4 5 6 7 8 9 10

10 9 8 7 6 5 4 3 2 1 0 Pressures

Molar Intrinsic Energy (mE)

Absolute Temperature, Deg. Fahr.

5 Cu. Ft.

10 Cu. Ft.

20 Cu. Ft.

40 Cu. Ft.

2048 Lb.

1024 Lb.

512 Lb.

256 Lb.

128 Lb.

E

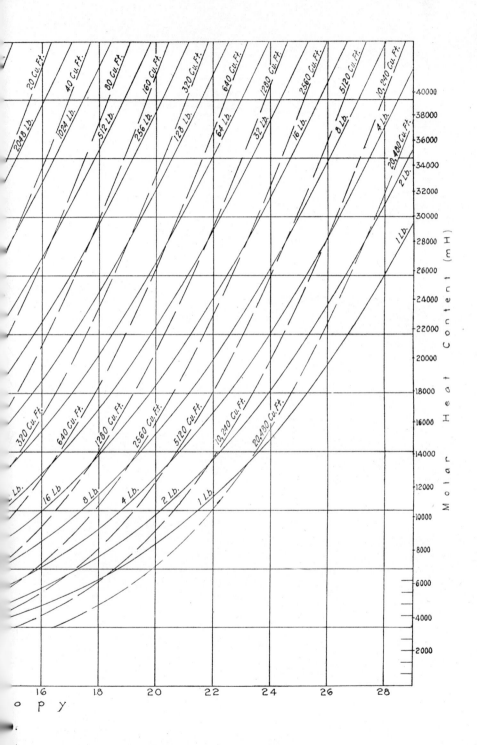

From the diagram, entering at $P_1 = 4$ lbs. and $T_1 = 1500°$ a vertical line to $5000°$ temperature gives the pressure of 530 lbs. per sq. in.

The curves have been placed horizontally on equal increments of entropy which gives the corresponding pressure and volume scales a logarithmic character, thus the use of the interpolation scales for intermediate pressures and volumes is essential. The values of the successive pressure and volume curves are in a ratio of 2 to 1, and the interpolation for intermediate values is not proportional to the space, but, as just mentioned, logarithmic and the small scales at the left of the diagram have been provided to facilitate interpolation.

For example, if we wish to locate the curve for 90 lbs. on the diagram, this lies between the 64-lb. curve and the 128-lb. curve, the interval between being 64 lbs. Since 90 lbs. is 26 lbs. in excess of 64 lbs., the 90-lb. curve will cross the lines of constant temperature $\frac{26}{64}$ or 0.41 of the interval to the *left* of the 64-lb. curve. Using the pressure interpolation scale, measure 0.41 and lay off this distance *along the lines of constant temperature* for a series of points on the 90-lb. curve.

Conversely, to find the value of any point lying between two curves, measure the distance to the next smaller curve, read this interval as a decimal from the proper interpolation scale, and multiply the value of the small curve by one plus the interpolated decimal. For example, a point lying between the volume curves of 80 and 160 cu. ft., scales from the volume-interpolation-curve scales 0.35 (measured from 80 toward 160 cu. ft.). Multiplying 80 by 1.35 gives 108 cu. ft., which is the interpolated volume.

If one is willing to assume that the working substance in internal-combustion engines, may with sufficient accuracy be considered as these diatomic gases, it is easy to plot cycles representative of any assumed action. It will be remembered from the earlier discussion of the Air Standard as adopted for internal combustion engine cycles that the assumption as to constancy of specific heats and the assumption that the chemical characteristics remain unchanged throughout were both widely divergent from actual conditions, however, the most grossly inaccurate assumption is that of constant specific heats, and that is rendered unnecessary by using this temperature-entropy diagram. For example, let it be required to

III.—Plot and find the thermal efficiency of an ideal Otto-cycle engine with compression ratio of 5, when the heat liberated per mol of charge is 23,450 B.t.u. If the charge be considered to behave as air (or O_2, N_2, or CO) and initial conditions be assumed, the various events of the cycle can be plotted on the temperature-entropy diagram and the ratio of the net to the gross areas is equal to the thermal efficiency.

The following have been taken for initial conditions: $P_1 = 8.46$ lbs. per sq. in., $T_1 = 779°$ F. abs., $V_1 = 990$ cu. ft. (per mol). The condition at the end of the compression stroke will be (adiabatic compression from 990 cu. ft. to 990/5 cu. ft.) $P_2 = 77.6$ lbs. and $T_2 = 1440°$. From point 2 the liberation of 23,450 B.t.u. at constant volume will give $T_3 = 5100°$

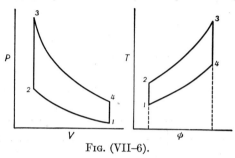

FIG. (VII–6).

and $P_3 = 276$ lb. From point 3 adiabatic expansion to the initial volume (990 cu. ft.) gives the point 4 with $P_4 = 33.6$ lbs. and $T_4 = 3200°$. The efficiency of this cycle is found by taking the ratio of the area enclosed by the figure 1, 2, 3, 4 to the area of the figure lying between the curve 2, 3 and the base line. This works out to be 42.6 per cent.

VII–16. Approximate Determination of Maximum Temperature of Combustion.—Integration of the curve, Fig. (VII–7), along the tempera-

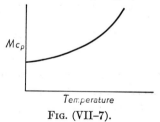

FIG. (VII–7).

ture axis will give the heat corresponding to any temperature rise, since

$$_1Q_2 = W \int_{T_2}^{T_1} c \, dT$$

and if the integral curve be constructed,* each ordinate of the integral

* The integral curve of any given curve may be constructed by determining the area between the base and the curve up to successive terminal ordinates and plotting these areas on the successive terminal ordinates.

curve will represent $\int McdT$ from the origin to the temperature under consideration and therefore the heat necessary to raise one mol of the mixture (or any one) of these gases through that temperature range. If the process of heating take place at constant volume the integral curve will be obtained by integrating the curve of Mc_v and its ordinates will represent the intrinsic energy change of the gases $\left(M \int c_v dT\right)$; if at constant pressure the ordinates will represent the change in heat content,

$$\left(M \int c_p dT\right).$$

For a known quantity of heat supplied the ordinate of the integral curve equal in value to this heat that has been supplied will be located at the temperature corresponding to the final temperature provided the origin of the integral curve coincides with the original temperature of the gases.

Curves similar to those just described have been constructed for the diatomic gases and are given in Fig. (VII–8). This figure is constructed from the Goodenough equation for the diatomic gases of

$$mc_p = 6.93 + 0.1200 \times 10^{-6}\ T^2$$

$$mc_v = mc_p - 1.985$$

where c_p = instantaneous specific heat at constant pressure;
c_v = instantaneous specific heat at constant volume;
T = absolute temperature expressed in degrees fahrenheit;
m = molecular weight of the gas. Therefore mc is the specific heat of one mol.

By *instantaneous* specific heat is meant the specific heat *at* any given temperature. If *mean* specific heat is desired for a range of temperatures from T_1 to T_2, it is given by the following relation:

$$c_{mean} = \frac{Q}{T_2 - T_1} = \frac{Wcdt}{T_2 - T_1}.$$

VII–17. **Exothermic and Endothermic Reactions.**—The heat of combustion is, of course, but a specialized form of the more general term *Heat of Reaction* used for all chemical reactions and it may be well to call attention to the fact that all chemical reactions do not *evolve* heat in the sense just used. Similar to the combustion phenomena just discussed are many of the common reactions such as the dissolving of zinc in dilute sulfuric acid with the appearance of zinc sulfate and water as the products. For such the temperature of the products has risen above the original temperature and heat must be *withdrawn from them* to recover the original tem-

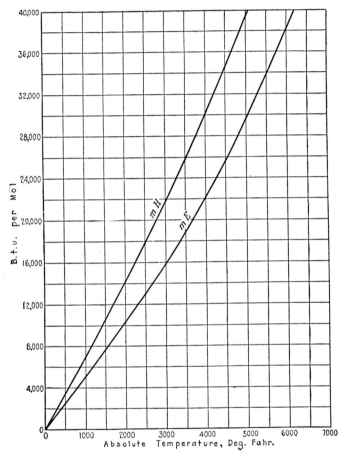

Fig. (VII–8). Curves of mH and mE for 1 Mol of O_2, N_2, Co, and Air.

perature. Such reactions are said to be **exothermic** because they produce or develop heat. On the other hand, there are some reactions which operate conversely and heat has to be *supplied to* the products to return them to the original temperature and to these is given the name **endothermic.** An example of this sort is the combination of oxygen with nitrogen in the electric furnace. Most of the reactions occurring at low temperatures are exothermic, but at very high temperatures endothermic reactions are common, as for example, the dissociation of CO_2, etc., and exothermic ones are rare.

A chemical combination at low temperatures may evolve heat, yet at high temperatures the reaction may be reversed and the products resulting from the original association be torn apart into the elements of the initial

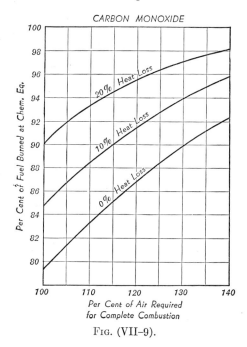

CARBON MONOXIDE

Fig. (VII-9).

mixture, such a process is called *dissociation* and it is essentially an exothermic reaction.

Dissociation phenomena, where compound products revert to their elements, require the supplying of the same amount of heat energy that the association of the elements under like conditions will give up; in other words, dissociation absorbs the same amount of heat that association (combustion) liberates. Dissociation plays an important part in combustion and most of the common combustion reactions may proceed in either direction, dependent only upon the temperature, as for example,

$$2CO + O_2 \longleftrightarrow 2CO_2 \quad \text{and} \quad 2H_2 + O_2 \longleftrightarrow 2H_2O.$$

VII–18. Chemical Equilibrium.—Any combustion is a progressive process even though the time interval is extremely small. After ignition occurs, the chemical combination results in a rising temperature of the entire mixture due to the increased energy of the products. A detailed analysis of the process considers that the combustion proceeds with an eagerness, or "driving force," progressively less as the temperature increases. It is obvious that this temperature may soon become so high that further association becomes impossible unless some heat is dissipated. If this occurs before all the original mixture has been combined, there

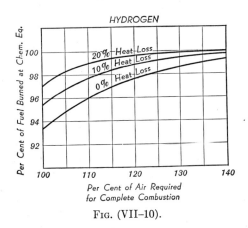

FIG. (VII–10).

results a mixture of uncombined elements (unburned fuel) and products of combustion existing in a state of chemical equilibrium and further action is halted. If heat is dissipated, further combination may occur, but the maximum temperature will oscillate an infinitesimal amount about this temperature of chemical equilibrium as the successive infinitesimal heat quantities are liberated and dissipated. A state is thus achieved which establishes a definite maximum of temperature and this usually occurs when an appreciable amount of the fuel remains unburned. Obviously, if only a portion of the fuel has been burned only that portion of the heating value has been liberated and the temperature rise is consequently less than would be obtained if combustion had proceeded to completion without interruption.

Most actual combustions reach the state of chemical equilibrium though it is quite possible with much excess air or large heat losses for the combustion to be completed without acquiring the equilibrium temperature. The magnitude of this incompleteness of combustion is rather surprising, for example, to cite the case of the combustion of CO, at constant volume and without any heat loss, the percentage burned by the time chemical equilibrium has been attained is but 49 per cent when burned in an oxygen atmosphere, and 80 per cent when burned in the correct amount of air.

The following tabulation, compiled from Bul. 139, University of Illinois Engineering Experiment Station, amplifies this information for the two major fuels (CO, and H_2) met with in common practice, as the hydrocarbon fuels are disintegrated into these prior to burning at the chemical equilibrium state.

TABLE X

GIVING THE AMOUNT OF FUEL BURNED TO ACHIEVE CHEMICAL EQUILIBRIUM FOR CONSTANT VOLUME COMBUSTION IN AIR

Initial temperature = 520° F. abs.; initial pressure = 1 atmosphere

Per Cent of Air Required for Complete Combustion	Per Cent of Fuel Burned when Chemical Equilibrium is Reached					
	CO			H_2		
	Heat Loss as Per Cent of Heat of Combustion			Heat Loss as Per Cent of Heat of Combustion		
	0	10	20	0	10	20
100	79.5	85.0	90.0	93.1	95.2	97.0
110	83.5	88.5	93.3	95.9	97.6	98.8
120	86.8	91.6	95.6	97.5	98.7	99.4
130	89.7	93.9	97.1	98.4	99.2	99.7
140	92.2	95.8	98.2	99.0	99.5	99.9

VII–19. **Maximum Temperature of Combustion.**—Any combustion at first proceeds with rising temperature and is headed toward chemical equilibrium. Whether it reaches it or not is largely a matter of the relative rates of evolution and dissipation of the heat energy. If the combustion be adiabatic, i.e., without any heat dissipation, the temperature quickly rises to the maximum imposed by chemical equilibrium when, if still adiabatic, further combustion ceases. If heat is carried away, but less rapidly than evolved, the temperature may still rise to that of chemical equilibrium but less rapidly. If, however, heat is carried away more rapidly than it is being evolved, as in the later stages of many combustions, the temperature may cease to rise and even decrease.

The temperature corresponding to the chemical equilibrium state furnishes a maximum which cannot be exceeded. Values for several of the common fuels, as computed by Goodenough and Felbeck, are tabulated below and probably represent the best data for this limiting temperature

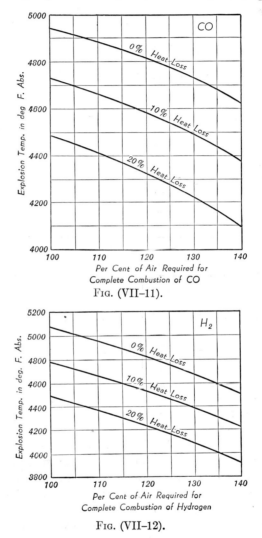

Fig. (VII–11).

Fig. (VII–12).

now available. In addition to these, the curves shown in Figs. (VII–11) and (VII–12) indicate the maximum temperature attainable for the primary fuels for various air-fuel ratios and heat dissipations.

TABLE XI

MAXIMUM TEMPERATURES ATTAINABLE IN COMBUSTION

No Excess Air

(From Bull. 139, by Goodenough and Felbeck, University of Illinois Engineering Experiment Station)

For Gas-Air Mixtures (constant volume combustion)

Gas B.t.u. per Cu. Ft. of Mixture	Maximum Temperature, Deg. F. Abs. Adiabatic Combustion	10% Heat Loss
Hydrogen (79.9).............	5070°	4800°
Carbon monoxide (94.4).....	4950	4730
Natural gas (86.0)..........	....	4520
Producer gas (61.6).........	....	3860
Blast furnace gas (56.1).....	....	3600

For Liquid Fuels (constant volume combustion)

Gasoline..	5140°
Kerosene.......................................	5350
Benzol...	5340

Welding Flames (constant pressure combustion)

	Without Dissociation of H_2O into Atoms	With Dissociation of H_2O into Atoms
Oxyhydrogen.........	6170°	5730°
Oxyacetylene.........	7750	6460

The temperature reached in any actual burning is dependent upon the following factors:

1. The chemical energy of the mixture,
2. The initial temperature of the mixture,
3. The heat losses,
4. The external work done by the gases,
5. The specific heat of the mixture,
6. Chemical equilibrium.

Of these, the first, the heating value of the fuel, is capable of accurate experimental determination and is usually well known. The initial temperature of the mixture before combustion begins is also usually well known, and thus the original intrinsic energy at start; to this then is added the energy liberated by the combustion process.

The next four items, however, are not so easily dealt with. The heat losses are rarely known with any degree of certainty. The work done by the gases can, in the case of the internal-combustion engine, be estimated from the indicator diagram but in many cases is not readily obtainable. The specific heat varies with the temperature and the composition of the mixture as combustion proceeds, and the chemical equilibrium state is difficult to predict with any certainty, as it involves assumptions with reference to practically all of the other items.

All of these last four tend to reduce the maximum temperature attained in actual combustions far below that of an ideal complete combustion.

A method for the complete calculation taking cognizance of all of the above-mentioned factors has been outlined by Goodenough and Felbeck in the Bulletin 139 already referred to. This should be followed when an exact estimate is desired as it is the only logical method, but the calculations are involved and tedious and are incapable of summarization for presentation here. However, certain simplifying assumptions may be made which will permit obtaining approximate values with a minimum of effort.

The two influences of major importance are variation of specific heats and chemical equilibrium. If reasonable approximations to the effect produced by each of these can be made the result is a reasonable estimate of the maximum temperature. Complete specific heat data are available and a specific heat equation for any products mixture can be set up with excellent accuracy. It is possible to make a reasonable estimate of the percentages of CO and H_2 which have been burned at the equilibrium state for any given combustion. See Table X. Multiplying the heating value of the fuel by this percentage will give the heat liberated.

To illustrate, let it be required to estimate the maximum temperature that will be reached by the adiabatic combustion in air of carbon monoxide when burned at constant volume, with no excess air and an initial temperature of 500° F. abs.

The heating value of one mol of CO is 121,610 B.t.u.

$$T - T_1 = \text{Htg. Val.} \div (\text{Sp. Ht.} \times \text{mols of products}).$$

In the combustion of CO in air there are 2.89 mols of products per mol of CO burned.

Consider first the result obtained if all minimizing factors be neglected, then the specific heat would be that of air at normal conditions ($mc = 29 \times 0.17 = 4.95$), and the heating value 121,610.

$$T - 500° = 121,610 \div (4.95 \times 2.89) = 8500°$$

$$T = 9000° \text{ F. abs.}$$

This is a result grossly larger than the correct one of 4950° F. abs. as reported in Table XI. Even if a value of the mean specific heat were used, the result would still be greatly in error. The products are composed of 1.89 mols of nitrogen and 1.00 mol of carbon dioxide. Using the mean specific heats given in the table below, the mean specific heat of the mixture between 500° F. abs. to 5000° F. abs. is

$$\frac{1.89 \times 10.69 + 1 \times 6.055}{2.89} = 7.65.$$

The maximum temperature is, then

$$\frac{121,610}{2.89 \times 7.65} + 500 = 6000° \text{ F. abs.}$$

VALUES OF THE MEAN SPECIFIC HEAT OF AIR (B.T.U. PER LB. OR MOL) FROM 500° F. ABS. TO VARIOUS TEMPERATURES

Upper Temperature, Deg. F. Abs.	Mc_v	Mc_p	c_v	c_p
3000	5.015	7.000	0.173	0.242
2000	5.155	7.140	.178	.246
3000	5.375	7.360	.185	.254
4000	5.675	7.660	.196	.264
5000	6.055	8.040	.209	.277
6000	6.515	8.500	.225	.293

NOTE: The values of Mc_v and Mc_p, the molal specific heats of air are the same for the diatomics, nitrogen, oxygen and carbon monoxide.

VALUES OF THE MEAN SPECIFIC HEAT OF CARBON DIOXIDE AND WATER VAPOR (B.T.U. PER MOL) FROM 500° F. ABS. TO VARIOUS TEMPERATURES

Upper Temperature, Deg. F. Abs.	Carbon Dioxide		Water Vapor	
	Mc_v	Mc_p	Mc_v	Mc_p
1000	7.60	9.59	6.39	8.38
2000	9.00	10.99	6.74	8.73
3000	9.84	11.83	7.34	9.33
4000	10.34	12.33	8.28	10.27
5000	10.69	12.68	9.50	11.49
6000	11.09	13.08	10.98	12.97

However, if a factor to allow for the incomplete combustion that exists at chemical equilibrium be selected from Table X, and applied to the heating value, this latter computation becomes:

$$T_{max.} = \frac{121{,}610 \times .795}{2.89 \times 7.65} + 500 = 4870° \text{ F. abs.}$$

This temperature, calculated by these greatly simplifying assumptions, is only 1.6 per cent lower than the true temperature as calculated by the more laborious process, as outlined by Goodenough and Felbeck. Of course, if the combustion is at constant pressure, the molal specific heats at constant pressure are to be used.

VII–20. Chemical Contraction.—By chemical contraction is meant the shrinkage met with when the products of combustion are volumetrically less than the ingredients before combustion when reduced to the precombustion temperature and press. It is really the change in specific volume of the charge before and after combustion. The products of the combustion of some fuels have a smaller specific volume, some others have the same, and still others have a larger specific volume. For example, when hydrogen burns to water two molecules of hydrogen unite with one of oxygen to form two molecules of water with a corresponding chemical contraction of from three to two.

$$2H_2 + O_2 = 2H_2O$$

by Vol. 2 + 1 give 2.

When methane burns to CO_2 and H_2O there is no chemical contraction,

$$CH_4 + 2O_2 = CO_2 + 2H_2O$$

by Vol. 1 + 2   give 1 + 2

3   give 3,

and when some of the heavier hydrocarbons, such as gasoline, burn there is an increase of specific volume

$$2C_8H_{18} + 25O_2 = 16CO_2 + 18H_2O$$

by Vol.   2   + 25 give 16   + 18

27 give 34.

With the fuel mixtures ordinarily met with there is usually some chemical contraction but it is small, rarely exceeding 2 per cent and usually no consideration is taken of it.

CHAPTER VIII

FLOW OF FLUIDS (Gases)

VIII-1. General Equation for Flow.—By fluid is meant any substance that will flow; the speed of the flow does not enter into the definition, hence, strictly speaking, a comprehensive discussion of the phenomena of flow should apply to the entire gamut of non-crystalline substances from the very slowest flowing, the pseudo-solids like pitch, tar, etc., through the more rapidly moving, the liquids, to and including the fastest flowing substances, the gases. For all cases the two basic assumptions are (1) that the total energy in the approaching column is equal to the energy of the leaving column plus any energy abstractions (or minus any energy additions) which have occurred between the points under consideration, and (2) that the total mass approaching is equal to the total mass leaving, plus any abstractions en route. These will be recognized as the physical laws (1) of the Conservation of Energy and (2) of the Conservation of Mass.

Where the velocities may range from a few inches per year to thousands of feet per second it is apparent that factors having an important influence in one case may be negligible in another; for example, it is important to allow for the velocity of approach when considering rapidly moving liquids and gases, but for the very low moving plastics it may be neglected; similarly the effect of compression or expansion must be taken into account when dealing with gases yet may be omitted when dealing with the practically incompressible liquids and solids. Hence it has become customary to isolate the flow discussions and narrow the treatment to the particular state of matter, solid, liquid, or gaseous, under consideration. Such treatment has the merit of utility but the student should not forget that the broad fundamentals above mentioned apply to all problems of flow.

In gases the change of volume with pressure is marked and the work of expansion or compression is an important factor in the energy balance. Consider the flow of a gas, a compressible fluid, from region 1 to region 2 of any enclosed duct or pipe line, Fig. (VIII–1). Assuming no leakage, interest narrows to a consideration of the energy equation. The total energy supplied by the stream across Section 1 must equal the energy carried away by the stream across Section 2 plus (or minus) any energy deductions (or additions) enroute from 1 to 2, and this is independent of the relative sizes of the sections at 1 and 2 and the character of the change from 1 to 2; i.e., whether gradual or abrupt, smooth or rough, straight or curved, etc.

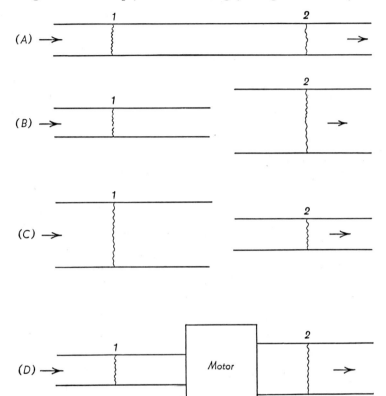

Fig. (VIII–1).

For the simple case the total energy brought in through section 1 will be the sum of the internal energy (U_1) the kinetic energy of the flowing stream and the work done against P_1 to force the fluid by section 1.

Considering a unit weight passing section 1,

$$(\text{Total Energy})_1 = u_1 + \frac{\text{Vel.}_1{}^2}{2gJ} + \frac{P_1 v_1}{J}$$

$$= h_1 + \frac{\text{Vel.}_1{}^2}{2gJ}$$

and similarly for section 2, $(\text{Total Energy})_2 = h_2 + \dfrac{\text{Vel.}_2{}^2}{2gJ}$,

$$h_1 + \frac{\text{Vel.}_1{}^2}{2gJ} = h_2 + \frac{\text{Vel.}_2{}^2}{2gJ} \qquad \text{(VIII–1)}$$

or

$$\frac{1}{2gJ}\,(\text{Vel.}_2{}^2 - \text{Vel.}_1{}^2) = h_1 - h_2 \qquad \text{(VIII–2)}$$

This is a basic equation for simple adiabatic flow of compressible fluids; it states that, *the change in the kinetic energy of any adiabatically flowing stream is equal to the difference in enthalpies* (heat contents) *at the points under discussion.*

If the flow between Sections 1 and 2 is not adiabatic and there is a leakage of heat as such, out of $(-_1Q_2)$ or into $(+_1Q_2)$ the flowing stream the expressions become,

$$h_1 + \frac{\text{Vel.}_1{}^2}{2gJ} = h_2 \pm {}_1Q_2 + \frac{\text{Vel.}_2{}^2}{2gJ} \qquad \text{(VIII–3)}$$

If in addition there is any energy transmitting device between 1 and 2, such as a compressed air engine, which transforms some of the energy into useful work and delivers it outside the flowing stream, as case D in Fig. (VIII–1), that amount of energy will have to be accounted for. Then equations (VIII–1) and (VIII–2) become:

$$h_1 + \frac{\text{Vel.}_1{}^2}{2gJ} = h_2 \pm {}_1Q_2 + \frac{{}_1W_2}{J} + \frac{\text{Vel.}_2{}^2}{2gJ}. \qquad \text{(VIII–4)}$$

when $_1W_2$ is the gross work delivered from the flowing stream between sections 1 and 2. For an engine this would be the net work delivered externally plus all engine friction and heat losses.

An important field in engineering is that dealing with formation of high velocity jets of gases and vapors the kinetic energy of which is then transformed into useful work by turbines or similar mechanical devices. For such equations (VIII–1) and (VIII–2) are directly applicable and nozzles are designed or performance predicted by their aid.

In many practical cases the fluid is originally at rest, as in a tank, in which case, $\text{Vel.}_1 = 0$, and (VIII–2) becomes, for the velocity of efflux,

$$\text{Vel.} = 223.8\ \sqrt{h_1 - h_2}. \qquad \text{(VIII–5)}$$

The velocity is in feet per second and if the expansion can be considered adiabatic and frictionless, h_1 and h_2 are at the same entropy. Equation (VIII–5) is in the form most commonly used for calculating the velocity acquired by *any expanding fluid initially at rest* when passing as a jet through nozzles or other directive passageways.

Restricting its application to perfect gases, for which $h = C_p T$, there results:

$$\text{Vel.} = 223.8 \sqrt{c_p(T_1 - T_2)} \qquad \text{(VIII-6)}$$

or

$$\text{Vel.} = 223.8 \sqrt{\frac{c_p}{R}(P_1 v_1 - P_2 v_2)}.$$

and if its application be further restricted to adiabatic and frictionless action, $(P_1 v_1{}^k = P_2 v_2{}^k)$ it can be transformed into a form involving only initial pressure and volume and secondary pressure (P_2), as follows:

$$\text{Vel.} = \sqrt{\frac{2gk}{k-1}\left[1 - \left(\frac{P_2}{P_1}\right)^{\frac{k-1}{k}}\right]P_1 v_1}. \qquad \text{(VIII-7)}$$

This special case of equation (VIII-6), holds only when the expansion is isentropic and the expression PV^k = const., truly represents the expansion.

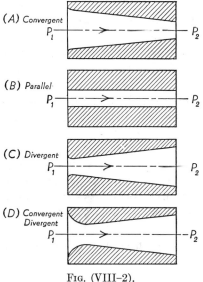

(A) Convergent
P_1 — P_2

(B) Parallel
P_1 — P_2

(C) Divergent
P_1 — P_2

(D) Convergent Divergent
P_1 — P_2

Fig. (VIII-2).

VIII-2. Nozzle Characteristics.— A nozzle is a directive channel whose prime function is the conversion of pressure or thermal energy of a fluid into kinetic energy of the issuing stream. Whenever the purpose is the generation of velocity as distinguished from simple transference, the passageway serves as a nozzle. Nozzles are preferably circular in cross-section, since then the perimeter and therefore the frictional resistance for a given sectional area is a minimum, but for mechanical reasons they are frequently made rectangular.

Since the same weight of fluid passes every section in a unit of time, the quantity flowing, cubic feet per second (V), will be for any section

$$V = A \times \text{Vel.},$$

where A = the area of the cross-section in square feet.

Vel. = the velocity of the flowing stream in feet per second, but this quantity flowing (V) is equal to the weight flowing per second, in pounds, multiplied by the specific volume (v), so that the area per pound of flowing fluid (A) is,

$$\text{area} = \frac{v}{\text{Vel.}}. \qquad\qquad \text{(VIII-8)}$$

For liquids, since the specific volume remains nearly constant, the area of cross-section of the nozzle is a function of but one variable, decreasing in direct proportion to the increasing velocity. For elastic fluids, however, the sectional area of the passage at any point is a function of two variables, the velocity of the stream at that point and the specific volume of the flowing fluid at that point. Both of these quantities are readily determined for the ideal case of frictionless, isentropic flow.

To illustrate this point, the nozzle for a liquid passing from P_1 to a lower pressure P_2 should have a continually decreasing sectional area corresponding to the increasing velocity (the specific volume remaining constant), as shown in A of Fig. (VIII-2). If, however, the nozzle were for an hypothetical fluid whose specific volume increased at the same rate as the velocity increased, then v/Vel. would remain constant and the sectional area would be the same throughout as in B. If the specific volume were to increase at a faster rate than the velocity, then the nozzle contour would be like that of C. Actually, in most gases and vapors, the rates of velocity and specific volume increase are independent of each other, the velocity at first increasing more rapidly than the specific volume and for further expansion less rapidly, thus giving the longitudinal section of the nozzle a convergent-divergent form, as in D.

This is best illustrated by a concrete example, for instance, let us find the sectional areas for a nozzle expanding air from an initial pressure of 200 lbs. per sq. in. abs. to 20 lbs. abs. without heat losses or frictional resistance, i.e., isentropically, the initial temperature to be 180° F. and 75 lbs. of air to be delivered per minute.

By the time the pressure has fallen to 160 pounds, the temperature will have dropped to

$$\left(\frac{P_{200\,\text{lbs.}}}{P_{160\,\text{lbs.}}}\right)^{\frac{k-1}{k}} = \frac{T_{200\,\text{lbs.}}}{T_{160\,\text{lbs.}}}$$

$$\left(\frac{200}{160}\right)^{.286} = \frac{640}{T_{160\,\text{lbs.}}}$$

$$T_{160\,\text{lbs.}} = 601°.$$

The enthalpy (measured from absolute zero) then will be

$$h = c_p T = .24 \times 601 = 144.2 \text{ B.t.u.}$$

and the difference between this and the original enthalpy of 153.6 is

$$153.6 - 144.2 = 9.4 \text{ B.t.u.}$$

which has gone into producing velocity of flow in the jet. The velocity corresponding is

$$\text{Vel.} = 223.8 \sqrt{h_1 - h_2}$$

$$= 223.8 \sqrt{9.4} = 686 \text{ ft. per second.}$$

The specific volume at this point will be

$$v = \frac{RT}{P} = \frac{53.35 \times 601}{160 \times 144} = 1.39 \text{ cu. ft.}$$

and the area necessary to pass one pound per second will be

$$a = \frac{v}{\text{Vel.}} = \frac{1.39}{686} = 0.00203 \text{ sq. ft.}$$

$$= .2923 \text{ sq. in.}$$

and the area (A) to pass the desired quantity of 75 lbs. per minute will be

$$A = \frac{75}{60} \times .2923 = 0.365 \text{ sq. in.}$$

Similarly, the areas corresponding to other drops in pressure are tabulated below:

Pressure, Lbs. Abs. p	Temperature, Deg. F. Abs. T	Enthalpy,* B.t.u. H	Adiabatic Heat Drop, B.t.u. $H_1 - H_2$	Velocity, Ft. per Sec.	Specific Volume, Cu.Ft. v	$\dfrac{v}{\text{Vel.}}$	Area, Sq.In. A
200	640	153.6	0	0	.....	......	.....
180	621	149.0	4.6	480	1.277	0.00266	0.479
160	601	144.2	9.4	686	1.391	.00203	365
140	578	138.7	14.9	864	1.528	.00177	.318
120	552	132.5	21.1	1027	1.704	.00166	.299
100	524	125.8	27.8	1180	1.942	.00164	.296
80	492	118.1	35.5	1332	2.279	.00171	.307
60	453	108.7	44.9	1498	2.797	.00187	.336
40	402	96.4	57.2	1692	3.725	.00219	.395
20	329	78.9	74.7	1933	6.09	.00315	.568

* Using specific heat (c_p) for air $= 0.240$. The mean specific heat for this range of temperatures by the method of Chap. VI is 0.2401.

In the above example it will be noted that the ratio of volume/velocity at first decreases till it reaches a minimum and then increases and, therefore, the proper form to give a nozzle which has a large pressure drop, and consequent heat drop, to be converted into kinetic energy of the stream, should be one in which the area of cross-section first decreases to a minimum (called the throat), and then gradually increases till the exit or *mouth* is reached, where the pressure has dropped to that of the back pressure.

This fact was first used commercially by DeLaval when he incorporated this feature into the nozzles of his steam turbine. A nozzle of this type is shown in Fig. (VIII–3), but here instead of arranging the areas equidistant along the central axis, which would have ensured an equal drop in pressure per unit length of nozzle travelled, the distance to the throat is made much less than from throat to exit. This is done to shorten the length of the nozzle and thus reduce frictional resistance. It can be done from entrance to throat because the velocities of the flowing stream are low and rather abrupt contraction can be tolerated. From throat to exit is also made as short as possible, but must have an angle of divergence no greater than the steam will follow, usually a taper of about one in ten on diameters.

VIII–3. Acoustic Velocity.—In any fluid medium if there be a disturbance in one portion of it, consequent disturbances travel throughout the mass with the same velocity that sound waves are transmitted through

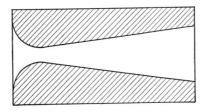

FIG. (VIII–3).

the medium, the acoustic velocity. For example, an increment of pressure, such as an explosion, is propagated throughout the gas with a definite velocity equal to the acoustic velocity.

The equation is usually expressed in the following form:

$$\text{Ac. Vel.} = \sqrt{Pvgk}, \qquad\qquad \text{(VIII–9)}$$

where, Ac. Vel. = Acoustic Velocity in ft. per second,

      P = Pressure in fluid expressed in lbs. per sq. ft.

      v = Specific Volume of fluid at P in cu. ft.

      g = Acceleration due to gravity (32.17 ft. sec.^{2})

      k = adiabatic index $\left(\dfrac{c_p}{c_v}\right)$.

Considering a flowing stream, it is obvious then that any impulse given to the fluid at the downstream end will be transmitted back through the fluid with the acoustic velocity, but if a stationary point adjacent to the stream be chosen for receiving the signal, the time required for its transmission will be lengthened because its velocity of travel with reference to this point has been decreased by the amount of the stream velocity. Simimilarly, if the stream were flowing with a velocity equal to or faster than its acoustic velocity, the adjacent point upstream would never receive notice or be affected by disturbances originating lower down. Knowledge of this is essential for understanding the action of nozzles and jets.

VIII–4. Throat Pressure and Limitation of Discharge.—For elastic fluids undergoing large ratios of expansion the proper nozzle is always of the convergent-divergent type. In such the section of smallest area is called the throat. It is an interesting and important fact that, for any given gas, the pressure at the throat (p_t) is always directly proportional to the initial pressure (p_1) or, p_t = const. $\times$ p_1.

If there occurs a change of pressure in a flowing stream this increment or decrement of pressure is propagated as a wave throughout the medium and the flow of the entire stream, above the point where the change occurred, will be altered into conformity with the new condition. Information of the change in the downstream conditions is transmitted upstream with a rapidity equal to the acoustic velocity and, so long as the stream itself is flowing with velocity below the acoustic, upstream conditions are altered into conformity. If, however, the stream be flowing at a velocity equal to the acoustic, nothing that occurs on the downstream side of the imaginary section will affect the character of flow through the section.

The equation for acoustic velocity of the preceding paragraph may be written, Ac. Vel. = $\sqrt{R\,T\,g\,k}$, and for fluids in which k remains constant (perfect gases) the acoustic velocity is directly proportional to the square root of the absolute temperature.

For air, the equation becomes,

$$\text{Ac. Vel.} = 49.0\sqrt{T}.$$

Combining this with the general expression for the velocity obtainable by adiabatic expansion permits the determination of the temperature at which the acoustic velocity will have been reached when any perfect gas expands adiabatically. Considering air as the fluid, the general equation is,

$$\text{Vel.} = 223.8\sqrt{h_1 - h_2}$$
$$= 223.8\sqrt{c_p T_1 - c_p T_2}$$
$$= 109.6\sqrt{T_1 - T_2}.$$

Where T_2 now represents the temperature at which the acoustic velocity has been achieved (T), or $T_2 = T$.

Equating these two,

$$49.0\sqrt{T} = 109.6\sqrt{T_1 - T}$$
$$T = 5(T_1 - T)$$
$$T = 5/6\,T_1 = 0.833\,T_1.$$

This may also be expressed as a pressure relation. See Art. (IV–36).

$$P = .527P_1.$$

For any nozzle discharging an elastic fluid the acoustic velocity occurs at the smallest section and the *maximum* quantity (lbs.) which can be delivered by it is equal to the product of the acoustic velocity and the area, divided by the specific volume, *all determined for this point.*

This can be illustrated most simply by an experiment of the following nature:

Consider two adjacent chambers A and B with the air pressure always maintained at 100 pounds abs. in A. There is a connecting nozzle between, and the pressure in chamber B can be regulated at will. Chamber B connects to a metering device so that air from A can be measured after passing through B. Consider now a series of runs made with varying

pressure in B, but always the same pressure (100 lbs.) in A.   With 90 lbs.
there will be a certain quantity delivered; if the pressure in B be reduced,
to say 80 lbs., there will be an increased quantity delivered, and if another
run is made with a back pressure of 70 lbs., a still greater quantity will flow
through.   This is to be expected, for, obviously, the greater the difference
between the pressures in A and B the harder is B pulling the stream and,
therefore, the faster it should flow.   But this does not continue indefinitely,
for when the pressure in B has been lowered to about 53 lbs. the stream
has come up to the acoustic velocity, and after that no matter what
change in the character of the stream is made by lowering the pressure in
B, information of this change never reaches A, and, therefore, adjustment to
conform to it is impossible, consequently no greater quantity is delivered.

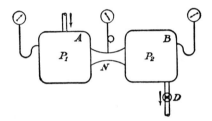

FIG. (VIII–4).

Thus lowering the pressure in B to 40, 20, 10 or 5 lbs. will send not a whit
more fluid through.   What really occurs is, that when the first reduction of
the pressure in B takes place, the character of the stream issuing into B
changes and the medium all around is affected as the surface of a quiet
pool is affected by a stone dropped in it.   This change is transmitted by
wave action and, going up stream faster than the stream is flowing down,
changes the character of the stream approaching the outlet to B, with the
result that more fluid passes out.   When the pressure has dropped to 53
lbs., however, the stream is flowing with a velocity equal to the acoustic
velocity, and, therefore, a further reduction of the pressure in B can
have no influence on the stream coming to it since its wave propagated
signals can not ascend the downflowing stream.

The relation between the throat pressure and the initial pressure for
any elastic fluid obeying the laws of perfect gases can be derived as follows:
The velocity resulting from any pressure drop expressed in terms of
heat contents is, by (equation VIII–5), $\sqrt{2g(h_1 - h_2)J}$, and the velocity at

the throat will be equal to the acoustic velocity (equation VIII–9), so that we may write

$$\sqrt{2g(h_1 - h_t)J} = \sqrt{P_t v_t gk},$$

where h_1 and h_t are the heat contents of the initial and throat conditions respectively.

Removing the radicals and cancelling

$$2J(h_1 - h_t) = RT_t k$$

but

$$R/J = c_p - c_v \quad \text{and} \quad k = \frac{c_p}{c_v},$$

so

$$2(h_1 - h_t) = k(c_p - c_v)T_t$$

and

$$T_t = \frac{2(h_1 - h_t)}{\dfrac{c_p}{c_v}(c_p - c_v)} = \frac{2(h_1 - h_t)}{c_p(k - 1)}.$$

For a perfect gas $h = c_p T$, therefore,

$$T_t = \frac{2(T_1 - T_t)}{k - 1}$$

$$\frac{T_t}{T_1} = \left(\frac{2}{k + 1}\right). \tag{VIII–10}$$

Moreover, since $PV^k = C$, from which

$$\frac{T_t}{T_1} = \left(\frac{P_t}{P_1}\right)^{\frac{k-1}{k}},$$

the relation of throat pressure to initial pressure is

$$\frac{P_t}{P_1} = \left(\frac{2}{k + 1}\right)^{\frac{k}{k-1}}$$

or

$$P_t = \left(\frac{2}{k + 1}\right)^{\frac{k}{k-1}} P_1. \tag{VIII–11}$$

Below are tabulated values of the Ratio $\dfrac{P_t}{P_1}$ for varying values of the adiabatic ratio k.

TABLE XII

k	P_t/P_1	k	P_t/P_1
1.1	0.587	1.5	0.512
1.2	.564	1.6	.497
1.3	.545	1.7	.483
1.4	.528		

Callendar * states that superheated steam expanding through a nozzle behaves much like a perfect gas with $k = 1.3$ and experiments of late have confirmed this. This gives the throat pressure for such steam nozzles as 55 per cent of the initial pressure. For air $k = 1.4$ and the throat pressure is 53 per cent of the initial pressure.

The amount of fluid passing a given section in a unit of time is equal to the product of the sectional area by the velocity or $wt \times v = A \times \text{Vel.}$, where wt is the quantity in pounds per second, v is the specific volume, A is the area of the cross-section in square feet and Vel. is the velocity by the given section expressed in feet per second.

The fundamental expression for the velocity resulting from any expansion (equation (VIII–5)) is for any fluid.

$$\text{Vel.} = \sqrt{2gJ(h_1 - h_2)},$$

where h_1 and h represent the enthalpy of the fluid at entrance and at the section under discussion respectively.

For a perfect gas, $h = c_p T$; $Pv = RT$; and for adiabatic expansion $Pv^k = \text{const.}$; or $Tv^{k-1} = \text{const.}$

The weight discharged per unit of sectional area at any section along the nozzle is,

$$\frac{\text{Weight}}{\text{Area}} = \frac{\text{Velocity}}{v} = 223.8 \sqrt{\frac{c_p(T_1 - T)}{v^2}} \qquad \text{(VIII–12)}$$

In the preceding article attention was directed to the limit on the quantity discharged placed by the acoustic velocity. It was also shown that

* *Proc.*, Inst. Mech. Eng., Feb., 1915.

the pressure allowing sufficient drop to produce this acoustic velocity could be expressed as a fraction of the initial pressure and, similarly, the specific volume and temperature as fractions of corresponding initial properties. If this were a correct explanation the same values for these throat properties should result from determining the algebraic maximum of equation (VIII–12).

Substituting for T its value from $\dfrac{T_1}{T} = \left(\dfrac{v}{v_1}\right)^{k-1}$ and reducing, equation (VIII–12) becomes,

$$\frac{T_1 - T}{v^2} = T_1 \left(\frac{1}{v^2} - v_1^{k-1} v^{k-1}\right).$$

Differentiating and placing the first differential equal to zero

$$T_1 \left[-\frac{2}{v^3} + \frac{(k+1)v_1^{k-1}}{v^{k+2}} \right] = 0,$$

from which

$$\left(\frac{v_1}{v}\right)^{k-1} = \frac{2}{k+1} \quad \text{or} \quad \frac{v_1}{v} = \left(\frac{2}{k+1}\right)^{\frac{1}{k-1}}$$

and

$$\frac{v}{v_1} = \left(\frac{k+1}{2}\right)^{\frac{1}{k-1}} \tag{VIII–13}$$

This may also be stated as

$$\frac{p}{p_1} = \left(\frac{2}{k+1}\right)^{\frac{k}{k-1}} \quad \text{or} \quad \frac{T}{T_1} = \frac{2}{k+1},$$

all of which are identical with those derived assuming the acoustic velocity was the limiting criterion.

Utilization of these so-called "critical" ratios offers an easy method of computing discharges as follows, (1) determine the characteristic properties (P, v, or T) at the section where the acoustic velocity occurs (throat) and hence the enthalpy at that point; (2) the enthalpy drop then substituted into equation (VIII–5) determines the acoustic or throat velocity. Knowing the throat velocity and the specific volume the discharge per unit of area of throat section follows directly and this is the maximum that the nozzle can deliver.

This does not mean that *velocities* in excess of the acoustic velocity may not be generated, since the velocity of the flowing stream continues to increase after passing the throat, but the quantity delivered remains unchanged regardless of the pressure drop from the throat to the exit.

Perhaps this may be made clearer if we consider the graphs (for a perfect gas) of the quantity discharged and the velocity for a large range of pressure drops.

Considering it solely from a mathematical point of view, the expression for the quantity delivered (equation VIII–12) becomes zero for two values

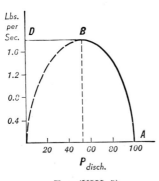

Fig. (VIII–5).

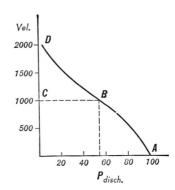

Fig. (VIII–6).

of T, i.e., T_1 and zero. These correspond to delivery into a chamber having the same pressure as the initial pressure and into one in which exists a perfect vacuum, respectively. The first is reasonable but the second is obviously untrue since experimental evidence shows that the delivery remains constant from the point B on, as is shown by the line BD Fig. (VIII–5). The explanation of this apparent discrepancy lies in the fact that the pressure at the section where the acoustic velocity has been attained remains constant regardless of decrease of pressures beyond that point, and, therefore, so far as delivery is concerned, there is no further change in the pressure ratio p/p_1.

The graph of the velocity for various pressure drops continues to rise with increasing pressure drops, but once a throat condition is reached the velocity *at that section* does not change, though beyond that point the pressure may be less and the velocity correspondingly greater, provided the expansion is directed or controlled, i.e., without turbulence. The velocity throughout such a nozzle will be that corresponding to the various ordinates of the curve ABD, while the velocity at the throat will be that indicated by the line *BC*, Fig. (VIII–6), regardless of what the pressures below it may be.

From the foregoing a convenient summary to carry in mind is that, two distinct conditions arise affecting the flow from an orifice or nozzle, one for pressure drops less than the critical ratio and the other for pressure drops greater. The pressure corresponding to this critical ratio is that where the drop has been sufficient to generate the acoustic velocity. When dealing with expansions to or greater than the critical ratio it is the throat conditions that govern the *amount delivered*, and it is the exit conditions that govern the *final velocity*.

VIII–5. The Effects of Friction.—The effects of friction on a jet flowing through a nozzle are a reduction of the velocity of the issuing

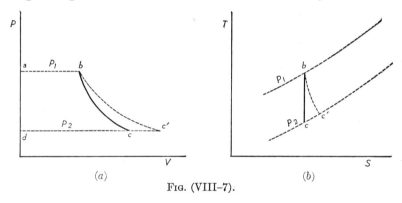

Fɪɢ. (VIII–7).

stream and an increase of its specific volume above that which it would have in an isentropic (adiabatic) expansion. The path of the state point on both the *P–V* and *T–S* planes is shown above, Fig. (VIII–7), *bc* indicating the reversible adiabatic expansion (frictionless and isentropic), and *bc′*, the action when the expansion is adiabatic (in the sense that no heat enters or leaves the medium from any external source), but taking cognizance of the friction between the fluid and the sides of the nozzle and that due to the internal turbulence of the fluid. Both result in the degradation of energy of flow, into heat, with the result that after a drop to a given pressure the fluid has a greater heat content and specific volume than when the flow is frictionless.

Considering the expansion as a whole we may imagine what is happening, to consist of two distinct actions, first, an isentropic expansion to the lower pressure with consequent acquisition of velocity and kinetic energy by the jet, and second, the reduction by friction of part of this energy and its reconversion into heat at this lower pressure. The final state of the fluid is correctly represented by c', but it has not been reached by a reversible expansion such as we have heretofore been accustomed to, and certain of the properties we have habitually associated with curves showing reversible expansions no longer hold. For example, the area under the curve bc' of Fig. (VIII–7a) does not represent the external work done or kinetic energy acquired during this expansion and the area under the curve bc' of Fig. (VIII–7b) does not represent the heat required from an external source for this change. The curves bc' in every case correctly represent the travel of the state point and the final state is correctly represented by b', but all proper ties of this curve of expansion which were derived on the assumption that the expansion was a reversible process are now void because it is an irreversible one.

If the whole expansion be broken up so that it takes place in several stages instead of all at once, we may gain a clearer conception of what goes on. In Figs. (VIII–8 and 9) the expansion has been broken up into four stages, with the two component actions shown for each stage.

The first action is a conversion of heat energy into kinetic energy of flow by the normal process of isentropic expansion from the pressure at b to the pressure at 1 as shown by the line b–1. The second action is the reconversion, at this lower pressure, of part of the kinetic energy just acquired, into heat. This step is simply a degradation of energy, an irreversible process, and one during which $\int Pdv$ does not represent useful external work because it is accomplished only at the expense of the work already done in creating kinetic energy in flowing stream. No heat is supplied from any outside source but comes from the kinetic energy of the eddies within the fluid itself. As these quiet down and lose their velocity, the kinetic energy due to their motion goes back into heat energy and the high grade energy of motion becomes low grade energy, heat. Thus a certain amount of heat has been let down from the high pressure state to the lower pressure without doing work, just as when heat travels by conduction from a high temperature to a lower temperature, a purely irreversible process.

From $1'$–2–$2'$ the same events occur, first an isentropic expansion to 2 along a path exactly similar to bc and then reheating at constant pressure to $2'$. Continuing this throughout the entire range, we get the broken line b–1–$1'$–2–$2'$–3–$3'$–4–c'. The general effect is much the same as if the fluid expanded in a cylinder pushing the piston out in a series of steps, each terminated by a bump which converted some of the available work back into heat. The substance would thus arrive at its final pressure with increased volume and heat content, but having done less effective work than if the expansion had been balanced and without impact throughout.

Thus the net result of the entire expansion, instead of producing work in excess of the adiabatic, *abcd.* is the production of an amount *less* than

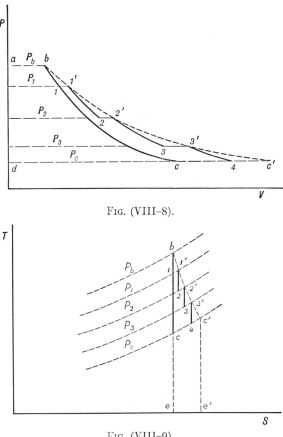

FIG. (VIII-8).

FIG. (VIII-9).

the adiabatic by that heat necessary to change the state from c to c' at constant pressure. This is equal to the difference between the heat contents at c' and c, $(h_{c'} - h_c)$. Stated differently, the net amount of work done is equivalent to *the actual drop in heat contents.*

Considering the temperature-entropy graph, bc represents the ideal adiabatic expansion which is frictionless and isentropic and bc' the path of the state-point when the expansion is retarded by friction. Here $ebc'e'$ represents the heat supplied by friction during the expansion, but since no heat has come from any external source (adiabatic expansion), it must have come from the reconversion of the kinetic energy of the jet, a process taking place continuously as the expansion progressed. Therefore the difference between the initial and terminal heat contents will be the actual amount converted into kinetic energy of the issuing jet. The heat content of the terminal state at c' is greater than that after isentropic expansion (c) by the area $ecc'e'$. The net heat really utilized then is equivalent to

$$(h_b - h_c) - (h_{c'} - h_c) = h_b - h_{c'}, \qquad \text{(VIII-14)}$$

or the actual drop in heat contents as before noted.

VIII–6. Nozzle Design.—Since the effect of friction reduces the effectiveness of the transformation of heat energy into the kinetic energy of the issuing jet, it is desirable that frictional resistances be reduced to a minimum and therefore that the surface over which the jet rubs should have the smallest area possible.

For nozzles with large pressure drops there are two cross-sections that are of interest, that at exit and that at the throat, between these the character of the channel has but little effect upon the jet provided its change of section from place to place be not so abrupt as to cause eddying or turbulence. It is customary, therefore, to compute the throat area and the exit area and to connect these by a passage increasing in area uniformly between these two and at a rate such that the angle of the cone does not exceed one that the fluid can follow, this is a connecting passage and possesses the minimum rubbing surface. For the portion from the entrance to the throat, since the velocity of flow is low, there can be a much greater angle of divergence with corresponding reduction in axial length and rubbing surface. For nozzles in which the pressure drop is small (when p_2/p_1 is less than the critical ratio), there will be but one sectional area that need be computed, namely, the throat, since for this small pressure drop the nozzle is a simple convergent one and the throat coincides with the exit.

This can be made clearer by solving an actual example, suppose a nozzle is wanted which shall deliver 75 lbs. of air per minute, working between the pressures of 200 lbs. and 20 lbs. per sq. in. absolute, the same conditions as those used for the example of page 254, but taking account of the effect of friction.

If we let y represent the fraction of the available heat energy that was not used in producing velocity because of the friction or, in other words, the percentage lost by friction, there will be left $(1 - y)$ times the available heat, as the effective head for producing velocity. Therefore, at the exit the velocity will be

$$\text{Vel.} = \sqrt{2gJ(h_1 - h_2)(1 - y)},$$

$$= 224\sqrt{74.7(1 - y)}.$$

Assuming that y has the value of 10 per cent, i.e., that 10 per cent of the available heat energy has been used up in overcoming friction, then the actual velocity to be expected at exit will be

$$\text{Vel.} = 224\sqrt{74.7 \times 0.90}$$

$$= 1836 \text{ ft. per sec.}$$

The throat or smallest section occurs at that point where the pressure has dropped to 0.528 of the initial pressure as explained in Art. (VIII–4), which will be $200 \times .528 = 105.6$ lbs. After adiabatic expansion to this pressure the heat content will be 127.8, obtained in the same manner as those tabulated in computation of Art. (VIII–2).

The available heat is then,

$$153.6 - 127.8 = 25.8 \text{ B.t.u.}$$

and the actual velocity at the throat will be

$$\text{Vel.} = 224\sqrt{25.8 \times 0.90}$$

$$= 1078 \text{ ft. per sec.}$$

The actual heat contents at exit and throat will be

$$153.6 - (74.7 \times 0.90) = 86.4 \text{ B.t.u.},$$

and

$$153.6 - (25.8 \times 0.90) = 130.4 \text{ B.t.u.},$$

respectively. These correspond to absolute temperatures at exit and throat of 360° and 543° respectively and for these temperatures and the pressures existing at these places the specific volumes are

$$\text{at exit,} \quad v = \frac{53.35 \times 360}{144 \times 20} = 6.666 \text{ cu. ft.,}$$

$$\text{at throat,} \quad v = \frac{53.35 \times 543}{144 \times 105.6} = 1.903 \text{ cu. ft.}$$

The areas at exit and throat of proper size to pass the required amount (75 lbs.) of air per minute will be

$$\text{Area exit} = \frac{75 \times 6.66}{1836 \times 60} = 0.004538 \text{ sq. ft.}$$

$$= 0.6535 \text{ sq. in.}$$

$$\text{Dia.} = 0.912 \text{ in.}$$

$$\text{Area throat} = \frac{75 \times 1.903}{1078 \times 60} = 0.00221 \text{ sq. ft.}$$

$$= .318 \text{ sq. in.}$$

$$\text{Dia.} = 0.636 \text{ in.}$$

It will be noted that these areas are appreciably different from those obtained when friction was neglected (.568 sq. in. and .297 sq. in.), more so than might at first thought have been expected, but the effect of friction has been a twofold one in that it has slowed down the velocity and also increased the specific volume. The increase of specific volume has resulted from the reheating effect due to the kinetic energy of the jet lost by friction, reappearing in the form of heat within the flowing fluid.

If now a maximum allowable taper be decided upon, the construction dimensions of the nozzle may be determined. Accepting a taper of one in ten on diameters, the length of the nozzle from throat to exit will be 2.76 ins. The length from entrance to throat is made as short as possible, usually about one-twentieth of the length from throat to exit. From these data the longitudinal section of the nozzle may be laid out as in Fig. (VIII–10).

VIII–7. Discharge Formulas.—It is a convenience to be able to determine the weight of fluid discharged from a given opening and for this purpose there have been proposed from time to time a number of expressions. Some of these are empirical and some are logical. Since the volume issuing from any opening is equal to the product of the velocity of efflux by the area of the opening, and the corresponding weight is equal to this volume divided by the specific volume of the fluid at that point

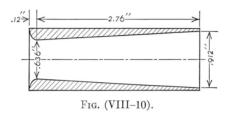

Fig. (VIII–10).

the problem becomes one of predicting the velocity and specific volume at the exit section. However, since the weight passing the exit section is the same as that passing any other section of the passage, it is perfectly allowable to select some other section for the measurement provided the velocity and specific volume can be determined more readily for that section. For the velocity the fundamental expression derived on (Art. VIII–1) Vel. $= \sqrt{2gJ(h_1 - h_2)}$, is used though its form may be modified to incorporate expressions for the heat content that apply to the particular fluid that is being used. Similarly, the specific volume may be replaced by an expression involving other properties of that fluid. For a given initial pressure, the quantity discharged will be of increasing magnitude, as the back pressure is lowered until the back pressure reaches the throat value, after which there will be no increase in the quantity discharged.

The formulae, therefore, fall into two groups, one dealing with pressure drops greater than the critical and the other with pressure drops less than the critical. For the first group, the discharge is a maximum and is independent of the back pressure. It is, therefore, only necessary to substitute the values of k and R for the gas under consideration in equation (VIII–13).

Substituting the values for air of $k = 1.40$ and $R = 53.35$, gives, when $P_b < .53P_1$,

$$wt = 0.53 \frac{Ap_1}{\sqrt{T_1}}. \qquad \text{(VIII–15)}$$

For the second group, where the pressure drop is less than the critical, i.e., when the back pressure is greater than the critical, substitution must be made directly in the general equation (VIII–12).

Substituting the values for air, this gives, when $P_b = P_2 > .53P_1$,

$$wt = 2.056 \frac{Ap_1}{\sqrt{T_1}} \left[\left(\frac{P_2}{P_1}\right)^{\frac{10}{7}} - \left(\frac{P_2}{P_1}\right)^{\frac{12}{7}} \right]^{\frac{1}{2}}. \qquad \text{(VIII–16)}$$

As a result of extensive experiments upon the flow of air, Fliegner proposed the following equations for well-rounded orifices which have been extensively used.

$$p_1 > 2p_a \qquad wt = 0.53A \frac{p_1}{\sqrt{T_1}}. \qquad \text{(VIII–17)}$$

$$p_1 < 2p_a \qquad wt = 1.06A \sqrt{\frac{p_a(p_1 - p_a)}{T_1}}. \qquad \text{(VIII–18)}$$

For the foregoing,

A = area in sq. ins.

wt = lbs. per sec.

p_1 = initial pressure in lbs. per sq. in.

p_b = back pressure in lbs. per sq. in.

p_a = pressure of atmosphere lbs. per sq. in.

T_1 = absolute initial temperature of air in degrees Fahrenheit.

It is interesting to note that equation (VIII–15) and (VIII–16) are logical and apply to air simply by restricting the general equations to that particular fluid and that equation (VIII–15) and (VIII–17) (Fliegner's) are identical, though arrived at by different methods. Fliegner's equation (VIII–18), for the pressure drop less than the critical, differs appreciably from equation (VIII–16), the logical one for the same case. A comparison of these two shows that Fliegner's equation (VIII–18) gives discharges that are less than those of equation (VIII–16) by from 1 to 3 per cent as the ratio of $\frac{p_2}{p_1}$ increases from .6 to .9.

VIII–8. Kinetic Engines.—The term Kinetic Engine is sometimes used to designate that group of heat engines in which the actual movement of the driving parts is caused by a change in the velocity of the motive fluid as a whole. In the ordinary type of heat engine, which for distinction may be called a pressure engine, the piston is moved outward by the conversion of the energy of the molecules of the working substance directly into mechanical energy of the piston, i.e., the molecular impacts push the piston along. In a kinetic engine, such as a turbine, this molecular energy or heat is first converted into kinetic energy of flow of the substance itself (which is, of course, a form of mechanical energy) and this kinetic energy of the jet is then absorbed by the moving mechanical parts (vanes), and by them transmitted as a rotative force to the driven shaft.

For example, it has been shown (Art. VI–18) that a compressed-air engine, working upon a normal cycle such as Fig. (VI–10), can transform the heat content available from adiabatic expansion into work,

$$\frac{W}{J} = c_p\,(T_1 - T_2) = h_1 - h_2.$$

Considering next an impulse turbine driven by an air jet issuing from a nozzle which has expanded it from P_1 to P_2.

The velocity at exit from the nozzle will be equal to

$$\text{Vel.} = \sqrt{2gJ(h_1 - h_2)}$$

where, as before, $h_1 - h_2$ is the adiabatic difference in heat contents. (See Art. VIII–1.)

Thus the issuing jet has a kinetic energy of

$$\frac{\text{Vel.}^2}{2g} = J(h_1 - h_2),$$

and if the vanes are suitably proportioned so as to entirely abstract the velocity of this jet, all its kinetic energy will be transformed into work, thus giving for the ideal case $_1W_2/J = h_1 - h_2$, as before.

Thus it is obvious that the amount of work theoretically obtainable for a given set of limiting conditions is identical, the only difference coming from the mechanical characteristics of the engine converting the heat energy into mechanical energy.

CHAPTER IX

VAPORS

IX-1. General Discussion of Vapor Pressure.—Matter may exist in three distinct states or phases: solid, liquid and gaseous. There is not always a line of rigid demarcation between these various phases, and it is sometimes even difficult to specify when a substance is in the solid state and when in the liquid state. A plastic material like tar, for instance, will slowly flow while apparently in a very solid state. It is customary for the chemist to accept as solids only those which are in crystalline form. Similarly, the passage from the liquid to the gaseous state is not always obvious to our senses, but in general, liquids undergo a distinct transition period— the boiling period—when passing into the gaseous phase. The definition of a vapor * is not particularly satisfactory for the simple reason that it is modified by terms *saturated* and *superheated* to cover two distinct states of a gaseous phase. The transition period from the liquid to the gaseous phase, which begins when the liquid has all boiled away, is purely an intermediate stage and partakes of certain characteristics of both phases. During the boiling-off period there is a definite tying together of the pressure-temperature relation, i.e., for any given pressure there is a definite boiling temperature and the liquid will not boil until it has reached that temperature. Moreover, throughout the boiling or vaporization period we are dealing with a mixture of the liquid and its vapor, instead of a homogeneous substance, and that makes it necessary to take into consideration the relative wetness or dryness of the mixture we are dealing with. Thus, where it was possible in the case of gases to deal with the pressure and temperature as *independent* variables, we lose this independence when dealing with fluids passing through the vaporization process or in the saturated vapor region and the equations which have been derived for perfect gases no longer hold. We have in effect the combination of P and T into one variable and the addition of another variable in the injection of quality into our consideration.

This fixing of the relationship between pressure and temperature during the vaporization period may be explained best by a reiteration of

* "An elastic fluid rendered aeriform by Heat."—Worcester.

272

the kinetic theory, see Fig. (IV-13). In the solid phase the molecules are vibrating or oscillating but with permanence of their relative positions. In the liquid phase the molecules are wandering, that is, the attracting bonds of their immediately adjacent neighbors were insufficient to restrain them in a definite position, and they are continuously flying out from the field of attraction of one group and into corresponding fields of attraction of other groups, thus rambling in a heterogeneous manner throughout the substance. In the gaseous phase the molecules are considered to have broken away from the restraint of their neighbors completely and are moving in straight lines in random directions and with random velocities. Now consider the aggregation of molecules in the solid phase receiving heat, with the resulting increase in molecular velocities and rising temperature; this action continues until the molecular velocities become sufficient to overcome the attraction of neighboring molecules which had heretofore maintained relative fixity of location for each molecule. Molecules thus breaking away commence a random wandering, drawn hither and yon by successive attractions but moving too rapidly to settle down into an oscillation about some fixed location. The velocities of individual molecules differ widely, but as the high-speed molecules pass from the activity of the solid phase to the activity of the liquid phase, the remaining molecules successively increase in speed until this critical speed is reached when they in turn follow into the liquid phase. The important fact is that during this transition period the temperature (a function of the average molecular kinetic energy) remains constant, for, as each molecule reaches the critical velocity it changes its mode of motion and until all have been so changed the heat received is used in accelerating the others to this critical velocity.

Continuing the heating process after the substance has been completely liquefied, the temperature of the mass will rise until the boiling point corresponding to that pressure were reached, and then there will be a repetition of what occurred during the transition from solid to liquid, namely, sporadic molecules will fly off from the orbital paths of the liquid phase into the rectilinear paths of the gaseous phase, and as heat is continued to be supplied more molecules will be forced into this change of path, and again we shall find that during the entire vaporization period from the liquid phase to the gaseous phase the temperature will remain constant. This process might be continued still further, the vapor on continued heating would undergo a rise in temperature until its molecular velocities become so great as to tear apart the individual molecular structures, atoms composing it would be thrown apart and we would have a molecular structure such as CO_2 dissociated into its component parts, and it is even conceivable that were the heating to still further continue, a condition might be reached in which the atomic structure might be destroyed into its subatomic components. Fig. (IV–13) illustrates such a history.

IX–2. Pressure Temperature Relation.—From the foregoing, the item of paramount importance is the fact that when one of these transitional processes (melting or vaporization) begins *there is no change in temperature* until it has been finished. In other words, when melting begins the substance remains at the melting temperature until the entire mass has changed from the solid to the liquid, when boiling begins the temperature remains constant until the entire mass has boiled away and the substance gone from the liquid to the vapor phase, etc. The temperature at which the change may occur is not independent of pressure. In other words, ice may melt at a certain temperature for one pressure and

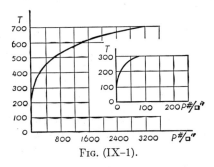

FIG. (IX–1).

at a different temperature for another pressure, and similarly water will boil at atmospheric pressure at 212° F., but if the pressure is 80 lbs. it will not boil until the temperature has reached 312° F., and at a pressure of 1.35 lbs. absolute it will boil at 112° F, see Fig. (IX–1). Thus, for every pressure there is a corresponding boiling temperature. *When a substance exists at boiling temperature for any given pressure, it is said to be saturated.* If we are dealing with a substance in any of these transitional phases (melting or vaporization), we then have the enormous asset of knowing that if we know *either* the pressure or the temperature we have also knowledge of the other, provided experimental information exists. In engineering work, the transition process from liquid to the gaseous phase, or the vaporization process, is of tremendous importance as much of our work with steam lies in this region, and this is also true of many other substances such as the various refrigerants. We have to deal with them through and on either side of the vapor phase. The question is sometimes raised as to why a special name, vapor, is given to the gaseous part of the substance during the vaporization phase, and the only reason is precedence and convenience. It has been customary to consider a fluid existing in the gaseous phase *in conjunction with its liquid* as a vapor, from the belief that it had arrived at that state by a slow process of vaporization, and it was not fully realized that gases, particularly the so-called permanent gases which the early workers had been unable to liquefy, went through exactly the same phase change if they were subjected to sufficiently low temperature and proper pressure.

IX–3. Saturated and Superheated Vapors.—As soon as the term vapor was used in the sense we have just discussed, it was recognized that we might have a substance in the actual transition period of vaporization, i.e., in that section on the temperature-entropy diagram that lies between the liquid and the dry saturation line, and that we might have the same substance lying in the region to the right of the saturation line, in which case it still ought to be a vapor but it was of distinctly different character from when it was in the process of vaporization. Thus, it was necessary to distinguish between these two states, and the words saturated and superheated were evolved to take care of this condition. The difference, in fact the one difference, between these two states is the fact that for any given pressure a saturated vapor exists at the temperature at which it was evolved, whereas a superheated vapor exists at a temperature in excess of this saturation temperature. On the *T–S* Diagram, for any state within the boundaries of the liquid and dry saturation lines, the substance is a saturated vapor and for a given pressure has an equivalent temperature. Therefore, in the light of present information, our definition of *saturated vapor* should be a vapor *which is at the boiling temperature corresponding to the pressure at which it exists.* The term saturated in thermodynamics means nothing more than this. It is quite obvious then that we may have a vapor which is very wet or one only slightly wet, or even one with no particles of liquid in it, and, therefore, dry; and, provided that they are at the boiling temperature for their pressure they are all saturated vapors. Thus, we may have dry saturated steam, wet saturated steam or even a saturated liquid, and the one outstanding feature of them all is that they exist at the boiling temperature for their pressure. Once the definition of saturated vapor is clearly in mind, the definition for superheated is obvious; namely, any vapor which exists at a temperature in excess of the boiling temperature for the given pressure.

IX–4. Quality and Moisture Content.—Since in the saturated region we may deal with a mixture of a vapor and its liquid, it is necessary to have some means of determining the relative proportions of these two. We could have a wetness factor or a dryness factor, which should indicate the percentage of moisture in the mixture or the percentage of dry saturated vapor in the mixture, and either would be satisfactory. Both are used but it is more common to use the latter. This is termed the *quality* of the mixture, and is denoted by x. x is thus the dryness factor of a mixture or vapor and its liquid. It is the percentage of dry vapor in a mixture of a vapor and liquid. If x is .95, then we have $1 - x$ or .05 as representing the fraction of the mixture that is liquid or the moisture content. This latter is often called the *Priming*.

IX–5. Energy Relations.—While the laws of perfect gases do not apply to a mixture of a vapor and its liquid and we cannot use the perfect gas characteristic equation for the solution of problems, nevertheless, the fundamental thermodynamic equations apply. For example, with the heat dQ added to a substance there will result a change in the intrinsic energy (dU) and a doing of work external to the substance $\dfrac{(dW)}{J}$, but in this case the increase of intrinsic energy has not been confined to increasing sensible heat only as was true for perfect gases. The intrinsic energy of the body has been increased but it may have been increased in two ways: (1) by a rise in temperature and therefore in sensible heat (dU_k), and (2) by an increase in the potential energy of the molecules or rather the energy which the substance possesses by virtue of the position of the molecules which has been due to change in phase from the liquid aggregation to the gaseous aggregation (dU_p). This latter, dis-aggregation or dis-gregation energy (dU_p) corresponds to the energy stored up in stretched springs. It is as if we had a group of molecules close together and later the group was expanded so that their distances apart were much greater, then the connecting bonds would be stretched and it would have required the expenditure of energy to make the change, but this energy would be stored up in the potential energy of the new molecular configuration.

In lieu of a simple characteristic equation it has been customary to determine the principal properties of vapors experimentally, or analytically from the general thermodynamic relations, and tabulate them with pressure or temperature as arguments for entering the table.

IX–6. Tables of Vapor Properties.—The properties of vapors most commonly assembled in tabular form are pressure, temperature, volume, heat content or total heat, entropy, and sometimes intrinsic energy. These properties assembled in tabular form are usually given for one pound of dry saturated vapor, i.e., specific properties. Since most of our work deals with a mixture of a liquid and a vapor, it is desirable to have besides the properties of the dry saturated vapor the same properties for a pound of the liquid and for the vaporization process; thus making it possible to get properties for any intermediate states of varying quality. The properties of heat content, entropy, and specific volume in the dry saturated state are obtained by summing the values for the liquid state, plus the change undergone during vaporization. Thus the properties of the dry saturated vapor consist of the sum of the property in the liquid phase and the increment acquired during the vaporization process. When a mixture of a liquid and its vapor exists, the determination of the properties for a known dryness fraction consists in simply adding to the property of the saturated liquid the augmentation due to as much of the vaporization process as has taken place, and thus indicated by the dryness fraction or quality. For example, for steam the entropy of one pound of the liquid at 50 lbs. pressure is .4110 and the entropy of the vaporization process (sometimes called entropy of vaporization) is 1.2474. If, therefore, we have steam with a quality of 0.9, the entropy for a pound of such a mixture will be equal to $0.4110 + 0.9 \times 1.2474 = 1.5337$. Similarly, the heat content of a pound of moist steam of 0.9 quality will be equal to the heat content of the liquid plus 0.9 of the heat content of vaporization process, or at 50 lbs., $250.1 + 0.9 \times 924.0 = 1081.7$ B.t.u. If the intrinsic energy were desired, it could be obtained most readily from the heat content. By definition heat content is $H = U + APV$ or U is equal to $H - APV$. Thus, if we know the heat content of the liquid, it will simply be necessary to subtract the APV product from it to obtain the intrinsic energy of the liquid, and similarly, if we desire the intrinsic energy for a wet mixture or a dry saturated vapor, it is readily obtained by subtracting from the heat content the APV product. Specific volume is usually treated in a slightly different manner, although it can be handled in exactly the same way as heat content and entropy, namely, if to the specific volume of the water under the conditions specified, we add the increase in specific volume, due to the vaporization process, we shall have the resultant specific volume for a mixture of any quality. In other words, if v_{fg} represents the increase in volume due to vaporization process, and v_g represents the specific volume of dry saturated vapor and v_f represents the volume of a pound of water, then, the specific volume of a wet mixture will then be v_x is equal to $v_f + xv_{fg}$. Usually the tables list specific volume of water, the increase of specific volume during vaporization, and the specific volume of dry saturated vapor. The above equation may be rewritten as $v_x = xv_g + (1 - x)v_f$. Because the volume of water is usually small compared with the volume of steam except at very high pressures and the dryness fraction is usually high, the second term $(1 - x)v_f$ is small and frequently negligible. When this is neglecced the volume of wet steam becomes $v_x = xv_g$, approximately. For work not requiring great accuracy and where the specific volume of the resultant mixture equals 2.0 cu. ft. or greater, the approximate equation suffices.

IX–7. **Steam Tables.**—Since our commonest motive fluid is steam much interest is centered on the establishing of tables giving the properties of water and steam. In each of the major countries, there have been one or two sets of such compilations which have been accepted as standard. In this country the latest table is that compiled by Keenan and Keyes,* abstracts from which are given in Appendix I. In Great Britain tables by Callender have been preferred, while in Germany the tables by Knoblauch are widely used. The various sets differ inappreciably below 400 lbs. pressure, but at the higher pressures show considerable divergence. A recent International conference held in London in 1929 to minimize these discrepancies effected an agreement upon a series of values scattered throughout the ranges covered by all the tables and an international acceptance of a tolerance for the values at these points. Thus, any set of tables, which at these points has values that come within these tolerances, will be acceptable as an international table. Moreover, as fast as additional information comes out it is proposed at future conferences to reduce the limits of these tolerances and thus gradually work toward a very precise and universally accepted tabulation of properties.

Unfortunately, there has been no unity in the past in either the nomenclature or the symbols adopted for the various properties and what should be a simple problem for the student has frequently been made difficult by this divergence in nomenclature and symbols. For example, the increment of heat content during the vaporization process, since this process always occurs at constant pressure, is equal to the heat supplied to produce the change and the heat so supplied is a quantity capable of direct experimental determination. To this was given the name of heat of vaporization by some writers, by others latent heat, etc. Also, in this country it was variously given the symbol r and L, and they meant exactly the same thing, namely, the change in heat content or enthalpy that takes place during the vaporization process.

Recently there has been promulgated, largely through the efforts of

---

* Thermodynamic Properties of Steam, by J. H. Keenan and F. G. Keyes. Published by John Wiley & Sons, Inc. The pioneer tabulation in this country was by C. H. Peabody and this served as the standard for many years. Later Marks and Davis and G. A. Goodenough brought out Tables which were also accepted. Revisions incorporating current data have been made by the first mentioned.

the ASME, a simplified system of nomenclature which has some rationality and bids fair to become widely used. In this the property of the liquid carrier carries the subscript f and of the dry saturated state the subscript g while the change of the property for the vaporization process has the subscript fg.

Thus h_f denotes the heat content of saturated liquid, h_g the heat content of dry saturated vapor and h_{fg} the increment in heat content for the vaporization process.

IX–8. **Temperature-Entropy Diagram.**—With the tabulation of the properties as data, graphs may be constructed which are helpful in visualizing changes and in solving numerical problems. Using temperature and entropy as coördinate axes, a graph may be drawn of the temperature-entropy relation for saturated water (liquid line) by simply plotting against the successive temperatures the various entropies listed in the table. Similarly, a line may be drawn representing the entropy of dry saturated steam (saturation line) for a series of successive temperatures. These two curves are essentially boundary curves and liquid exists to the left and dry vapor to the right and if the state point is in the region lying between them, the substance is a wet saturated vapor. If continued to sufficiently high temperatures, these two boundary lines, the liquid and the dry saturated line, merge into one at a point called the critical point where the physical distinction between the liquid and vapor phase vanishes, of which more will be said later. Using these boundary curves, there can be constructed intermediate curves of constant quality. For example, since for vaporization at constant pressure (also constant temperature), the increase in entropy is directly proportional to the heat supplied, the quality will be proportional to the distance traveled along a horizontal line, i.e., when we have vaporized, one-half of the liquid we shall have supplied one-half of the entropy of vaporization. Any horizontal line drawn between the liquid and the dry saturated lines shows by its magnitude the increase of entropy due to the vaporization process. If this, then, is divided into a series of equal divisions, they will represent equal increments of quality and we can, therefore, by dividing a few of these horizontal lines into equal parts spot in contour curves of constant quality.

In a somewhat similar manner, we may establish contour curves for constant heat content lines as follows:

$$\text{Heat content, } h_x = h_f + x h_{fg}.$$

For a given temperature everything in this equation except x is fixed. Thus, assuming a series of values for h_x at one temperature, it is possible to solve for concordant values of the quality x, and if this be repeated for a series of temperatures, there will be obtained a series of quality points of equal heat content. A curve passing through these values of x will then be a line of constant heat content. For example, to construct the 1000 B.t.u. heat content curve if we start at a temperature of 400° F.

$$h_f = 374.97 \qquad h_{fg} = 826.0.$$

Our equation is then,

$$1000 = 374.97 + x826.0$$

$$x = 0.757.$$

This is one point on the curve. Another point at 300° F. by the same process is

$$h_f = 269.6 \qquad h_{fg} = 910.1.$$

$$1000 = 269.6 + x910.1$$

$$x = 0.803.$$

Lines of constant volume may be established in a similar manner. Thus for the saturated region there can be shown curves giving values of quality, volume, heat content and entropy and on the temperature coördinate axis there can be superposed the saturation pressures equivalent to the successive temperatures. In a similar manner, curves may be plotted for the superheated region, using the data of the superheated steam tables. Here, however, quality is replaced by degree of superheat, and curves of constant pressure added. We then have a complete graphical representation of the common properties for all of the phases from liquid to superheated vapor. Any problem which is capable of solution from the tables may be solved from a temperature-entropy diagram of this character. A completed T–S diagram is shown in Fig. (IX–2).

When the temperature-entropy diagram for steam in the superheated region is drawn on rectangular coördinates, there is apt to be difficulty in following the lines of constant pressure as distinct from the lines of constant volume. This difficulty can be minimized by means of a polar diagram, which has the tendency to open out the scale in the superheated regions. Such a diagram, due to Mr. E. M. Barber, is shown in Fig. (IX–3). It is a true temperature-entropy diagram.

IX–9. Mollier Diagram.—A temperature-entropy diagram, however, is not always a convenient one to read, particularly for heat content and volumes. A great deal of our work deals with adiabatic or throttling operations for both of which processes we wish to know the change in heat

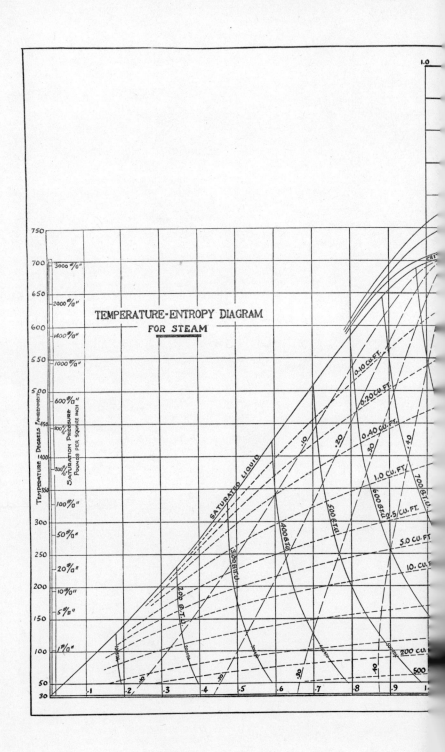

TEMPERATURE-ENTROPY DIAGRAM

FOR STEAM

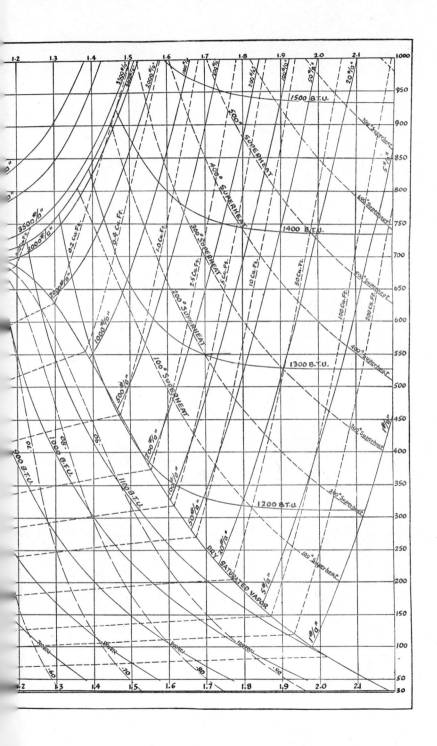

content and a diagram of properties using heat content and entropy for coördinate axes facilitates solution of problems of this sort. Such a chart is commonly called the Mollier diagram after the name of the originator, Professor Mollier of Dresden University, though diagrams on axes of heat content *vs.* pressure are also sometimes called by the same name.

A complete Mollier diagram from the liquid phase through the dry saturated and into the superheated region would be constructed in much

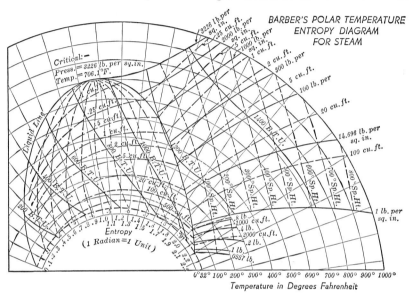

FIG. (IX–3). Polar Temperature-Entropy Diagram for Steam.

the same manner as that outlined for the entropy-temperature diagram, namely, for the liquid line successive values of heat content and entropy would give a curve representing the saturated liquid and a similar graph could be plotted for the dry saturated vapor. On each of these curves could be plotted points which correspond to certain pressures. Straight lines connecting the points of equal pressure would then represent the vaporization process from liquid to dry saturated vapor at constant pressure, as the increase in the heat content during vaporization is directly proportional to the increase in entropy. It is also of interest that the slope of these lines is equal to the saturation temperature for the given pressure.

$$\text{Slope} = \frac{dh}{ds} = \frac{dh}{\dfrac{dq}{T}}$$

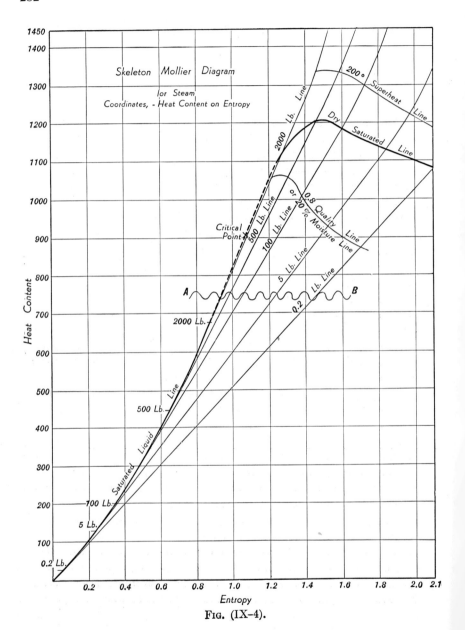

Fig. (IX-4).

but the heat added at constant pressure $(dq)_p$ is equal to the change in heat content (dh).

Therefore, $$\text{slope} = \frac{dh}{\dfrac{dh}{T}} = T.$$

The Mollier diagram permits ready solution of problems which deal with changes in heat content. For example, a reversible adiabatic expansion from one pressure to another is represented by a *vertical* line (constant entropy) from the initial state to the terminal pressure. The length of this represents the adiabatic heat drop while the lower end of it shows at a glance the final quality and heat content.

For a throttling process (during which the heat content remains constant) the process is shown by a *horizontal* line and the final state is clearly represented by the right hand termination of the line.

In order to facilitate accurate solution of problems, the Mollier diagrams commonly used do not extend to the liquid phase. Fig. (IX-4) shows a skeleton Mollier diagram for steam covering the complete range from saturated liquid through dry saturated vapor and into the superheat region. It is customary, however, to omit the section that lies below the line A–B solely for convenience and to permit a larger scale to be used without the diagram becoming unduly large. An abbreviated diagram of this sort is shown in Fig. (IX-5).

When dealing with vapors which pass through the stage of complete condensation, it is desirable to open out the scale in the lower temperature range. That is, instead of plotting the properties to rectangular coördinates, they are plotted on skewed coördinates. This has been done under the auspices of the British Institution of Mechanical Engineers by opening out the coördinate axes, as shown in Fig. (IX-6) for ammonia.*

IX-10. Determination of State After Various Changes.—For predicting the final state of a vapor after a change has taken place from some given initial state, the underlying method is the same as used for gases, but the working data differs. As before, we have an initial state of which we know all the properties and a definite route to a second state, such as a constant pressure change, constant volume, adiabatic or isothermal. We wish to predict the properties in the final state. Since any two independent properties definitely determine the state, this means that we must be able to determine two independent properties in the final state. When dealing

---

* In this diagram, ϕ is used to denote entropy and I to denote heat content. The basic thermal unit used is the centigrade thermal unit or the pound-calorie.

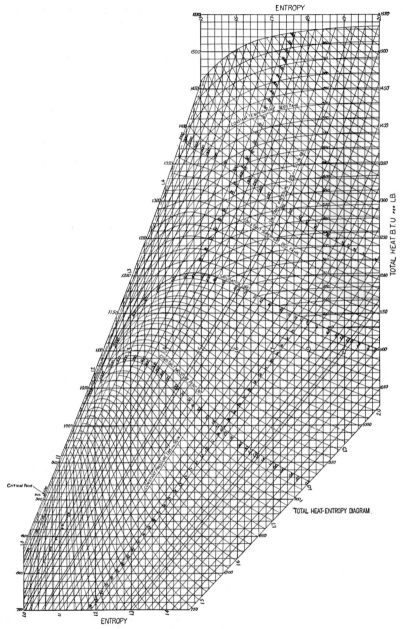

Fig. (IX-5).

with saturated vapors, pressure and temperature are not independent and the knowledge of one implies a knowledge of the other.

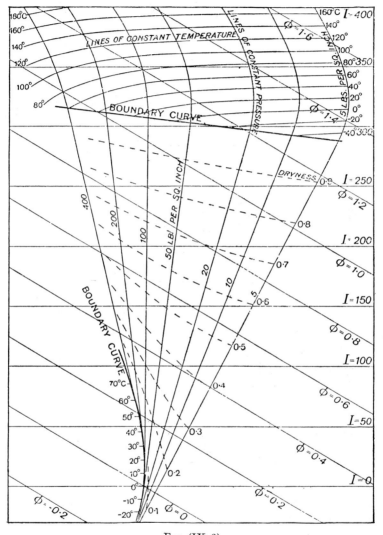

Fig. (IX–6).

For a constant pressure change, we have knowledge of the properties in the initial state p_1, v_1, h_1, x_1, etc. We have also information that the change is progressing at p_1 to a certain final volume or other property. Thus, in the final state we know the pressure and one other independent property. Take for example, the case of a change at *constant pressure* of 100 lbs. from a volume of .50 cu. ft. to a volume of 4.0 cu. ft. The final state is at 100 lbs. and 4.0 cu. ft. The specific volume of dry saturated steam at 100 lbs. is equal to 4.432. Therefore, the steam has a quality which can be determined after the expansion. Denoting the specific volume of the wet mixture by v_x,

$$v_x = v_f + xv_{fg} \quad \text{or} \quad v_{x\,100\,\text{lbs.}} = v_{f\,100\,\text{lbs.}} + xv_{fg\,100\,\text{lbs.}}$$

$$4.0 = 0.0177 + x4.414,$$

$$x = 3.9823 \div 4.414,$$

$$x = 0.902.$$

Now, since the final quality is known, the heat content and any of the other properties can be determined.

$$h_x = h_f + xh_{fg},$$

$$= 298.4 + .902(888.8) = 1100.1 \text{ B.t.u.}$$

Changes at *constant volume* are solved in practically the same manner as those at constant pressure.

For example, find the final properties after a constant volume change from $p_1 = 300$ lbs. per sq. in., $x_1 = 0.95$ to a final pressure (p_2) of 10 lbs. per sq. in.

$$v_1 = v_2 = v_{f\,300\,\text{lbs.}} + xv_{fg\,300\,\text{lbs.}} = .019 + .95(1.523) = 1.467,$$

$$1.467 = v_2 = v_{f\,10\,\text{lbs.}} + xv_{fg\,10\,\text{lbs.}} = .017 + x_2(38.40)$$

$$x_2 = .0377,$$

$$h_2 = h_{f\,10\,\text{lbs.}} + .0377\,h_{fg\,10\,\text{lbs.}} = 161.2 + .0377(982.1) = 198.1 \text{ B.t.u.}$$

The isothermal change is (in the saturated region) a change at constant pressure and our solution parallels that of a constant pressure change. In the superheated region a final temperature and pressure is known and these are independent variables, thus the solution for other final properties may be read directly from the superheat tables.

The determination of the quality after a reversible *adiabatic change* (isentropic) since the entropy has remained constant, is made by equating the expressions for the entropy before and after the change.

For example, required the quality after an adiabatic expansion from an initial condition of 100 lbs. and the quality of 0.9 to a final pressure of 2 lbs. The entropy in the first state is known and this is equated to the expression for the entropy after expansion. The initial entropy is

$$s_1 = s_f + x s_{fg} = s_{f\ 100\ \text{lbs.}} + 0.9 s_{fg\ 100\ \text{lbs.}}$$

$$= 0.4740 + 0.9(1.1286),$$

$$= 1.4894.$$

This is equal to the entropy in the second state, for which the expression is

$$s_2 = s_{f_2} + x_2\ s_{fg2}.$$

Thus,

$$1.4894 = 0.175 + x_2(1.7451),$$

or

$$x_2 = 0.753.$$

Thus a second independent property is obtained for the final state and the others are fixed and determinate.

$$h_2 = h_{f\ 2\ \text{lbs.}} + x_2 h_{fg\ 2\ \text{lbs.}} = 94.0 + 0.753(1022.2) = 863\ \text{B.t.u.}$$

$$v_2 = v_{f\ 2\ \text{lbs.}} + x_2 v_{fg\ 2\ \text{lbs.}} = 0.016 + 0.753(173.7) = 131\ \text{cu. ft.}$$

IX–11. Energy Changes for Various Processes.—As in the case of perfect gases, we are interested in the energy changes which take place when a vapor undergoes any of the orthodox changes. The fundamental energy equation, $dQ = dU + \dfrac{dW}{J}$, of course, applies, and the effect any change causes in each of the terms is of direct practical importance. It is essential that we know the heat supplied, the change of intrinsic energy, and the work done for the constant volume, constant pressure, isothermal, and adiabatic changes of saturated vapors.

The underlying methods of obtaining these are identical with those adopted for perfect gases, but instead of obtaining the properties from a characteristic equation we refer to the tables and there is an added property (quality) to be dealt with.

For a *change at constant volume* no work is done and the last term of the energy equation vanishes then,

$$(dQ)_v = dU \quad \text{or} \quad {}_1Q_2 = U_2 - U_1.$$

The property intrinsic energy is not separately listed in all tables, but heat content is always included, it is preferable, therefore, to operate with heat content and derive the intrinsic energy change from that, as follows:

$$H = U + APV \quad \text{or} \quad U = H - APV,$$

thus,

$$U_2 - U_1 = H_2 - H_1 - (AP_2V_2 - AP_1V_1),$$

but,

$$V = V,$$

and this becomes,

$$U_2 - U_1 = H_2 - H_1 - AV(P_2 - P_1). \tag{IX-1}$$

The problem then becomes one of finding the change in heat content and applying the corrective term, $AV(P_2 - P_1)$.

Let it be required to find, the heat supplied, the change of intrinsic energy, and the work done, for a change *at constant volume* of one pound of steam originally at a pressure of 40 lbs. per sq. in. abs. and quality of 0.20, to a final state of 200 lbs. per sq. in. abs.

The original heat content can be found, as the initial quality and pressure are known,

$$h_1 = h_{f\ 40\ \text{lbs.}} + x_1 h_{fg\ 40\ \text{lbs.}},$$

$$= 236.0 + 0.2(933.7),$$

$$= 422.7 \text{ B.t.u.}$$

To find the volume,

$$v_1 = v_{f\ 40\ \text{lbs.}} + x_1 v_{fg\ 40\ \text{lbs.}},$$

$$= 0.017 + 0.2(10.48),$$

$$= 2.113 \text{ cu. ft.}$$

In the final state, $p_2 = 200$ lbs. and $v_2 = v_1 = 2.113$ cu. ft. The final quality can be determined from this volume,

$$2.113 = v_2 = v_{f\ 200\ \text{lbs.}} + x_2 v_{fg\ 200\ \text{lbs.}},$$

$$= 0.0184 + x_2(2.270),$$

$$x_2 = 2.095 \div 2.270 = 0.923.$$

Thus the final heat content,

$$h_2 = h_{f\ 200\ \text{lbs.}} + 0.923 h_{fg\ 200\ \text{lbs.}},$$

$$= 355.3 + 0.923(843.0),$$

$$= 1133.3 \text{ B.t.u.}$$

The change of intrinsic energy is then (equation IX–1),

$$u_2 - u_1 = h_2 - h_1 - Av(P_2 - P_1),$$

$$= 1133.3 - 422.7 - \frac{2.113}{778} (200-40)144,$$

$$= 710.6 - 62.7,$$

$$= 647.9 \text{ B.t.u.}$$

To summarize, the heat supplied is 647.9 B.t.u., the change of intrinsic energy is 647.9 B.t.u. increase and the work done is zero.

For a *change at constant pressure,*

$$_1Q_2 = U_2 - U_1 + AP(V_2 - V_1),$$

$$= H_2 - H_1.$$

Thus the change in heat content measures the heat supplied. The change in intrinsic energy is obtained directly from the change in heat content as just illustrated. The work done is equal to the product of the pressure and the change of volume.

$$_1W_2 = \int_1^2 PdV = P(V_2 - V_1).$$

Consider the case of a change at constant pressure from an initial state of 50 lbs. per sq. in. abs. and 0.3 quality to a final state of 0.98 quality.

$$h_1 = h_{f\,50\,\text{lbs.}} + x_1 h_{fg\,50\,\text{lbs.}},$$

$$= 250.0 + 0.3(924.0),$$

$$= 527.1 \text{ B.t.u.},$$

$$h_2 = h_{f\,50\,\text{lbs.}} + x_2 h_{fg\,50\,\text{lbs.}},$$

$$= 250.0 + 0.98(924.0),$$

$$= 1155.5 \text{ B.t.u. per lb. of steam.}$$

The heat supplied is, $1155.5 - 527.1 = 628.4$ B.t.u.

The change of intrinsic energy is,

$$u_2 - u_1 = h_2 - h_1 - AP(v_2 - v_1),$$

$$v_1 = v_{f\,50\,\text{lbs.}} + x_1 v_{fg\,50\,\text{lbs.}},$$

$$= 0.017 + 0.3(8.508),$$

$$= 2.570,$$

$$v_2 = v_{f\ 50\ \text{lbs.}} + x_2 v_{fg\ 50\ \text{lbs.}},$$

$$= 0.017 + 0.98(8.508),$$

$$= 8.338,$$

$$u_2 - u_1 = 1155.5 - 527.1 - \frac{50 \times 144}{778}(8.338 - 2.570),$$

$$= 574.5 \text{ B.t.u. per lb. of steam.}$$

The work done is,

$$P(v_2 - v_1) = 50 \times 144(8.338 - 2.570),$$

$$= 41,600 \text{ ft. lbs. per lb. of steam.}$$

For an *isothermal change* we know that in the saturated region constant temperature means constant pressure, and therefore the energy changes for an isothermal are the same as those listed for constant pressure.

For an *adiabatic change*, the heat supplied is equal to 0 by definition and the work that is done has been done at the expense of the intrinsic energy.

It must be clearly borne in mind that the properties which we are dealing with now are the properties corresponding to the stated point of the substance, that when we speak of heat content, H, it is not the heat content of dry saturated steam, but it is the heat content of steam in the condition under which we are considering it. It is represented by the sum of the heat of the liquid plus x times the heat of vaporization, and, therefore, it is essential to know the quality before any of the properties in the wet vapor region can be determined.

IX–12. **Thermal Properties of Compressed Liquids.**—Thus far it has been assumed, in finding the properties of the liquid, that the liquid was a saturated one. In actual practice, properties of liquids, not at their boiling point, are desired. Fortunately, when pressures are low, various properties (such as heat content, specific volume, and entropy) are practically independent of pressure and depend only on temperature. In other words, the various properties of a liquid at low pressures and any given temperature may be taken to be the same as those properties of a saturated liquid at the same *temperature.*

The pressures used in modern power plant work are sufficiently high to cause some deviations between the properties of water entering the boiler and saturated water at the same temperature. This pressure has very little effect on either the specific volume or internal energy. Although there is no appreciable difference in volume between saturated and non-saturated water at a given temperature, the high pressures cause a difference in the APV term, and hence a difference in the heat content. The true differences in heat contents (heat content actual—heat content of saturated water for the same temperature) are given in a separate table (Table IV—Thermodynamic Properties of Steam by Keenan and Keyes). In this table the differences between the actual water and saturated water at the same temperature, are given for both specific volumes and entropies.

A temperature-entropy diagram for water is shown in Fig. (IX–7).* Here the constant pressure liquid lines are greatly distorted to show their divergencies from the saturated liquid line. If these lines were not distorted, they would fall practically on top of the liquid line. It is to be noted that there is a very slight increase in temperature as water is compressed isentropically.

IX–13. Temperature-Entropy Diagrams for Various Vapors.—Many common vapors have their vapor dome (i.e., their saturated liquid and vapor lines) on the temperature-entropy diagrams similar in shape to that of steam. Some such vapors are ammonia, carbon dioxide, sulphur dioxide, and mercury. There are, however, vapors (particularly many hydrocarbon vapors) that have a vapor dome materially different from that of steam. The difference, for the most part, is in the saturated vapor line. Temperature-entropy sketches of the vapor domes of seven interesting vapors are assembled in Fig. (IX–8). For some of these vapors, the entropy of the dry saturated vapor is materially less at low pressures than at high pressures.†

This being the case, an isentropic expansion of these vapors from the high pressure, high quality regions to regions of low pressure will superheat the vapor. This is a very desirable property, for some purposes. As will be pointed out later on, the increased moisture content of steam (due to expansion) in both steam engines and steam turbines presents a real problem due to loss of efficiency and mechanical difficulties. Hence it would be very desirable to have a vapor that superheated itself upon expansion. However, vapors that have this property usually have other undesirable properties that prevent their use in heat engines.

It is to be noted that an isentropic compression of such vapors from

---

* From "Thermal Properties of Compressed Water," by J. H. Keenan, Mechanical Eng'g, Feb. 1931.

† Taken largely from article by J. A. Ewing entitled "The Specific Heat of Saturated Vapor."—*Phil. Mag.*, Vol. 39.

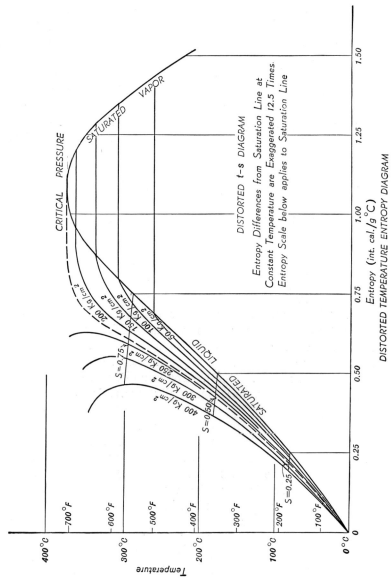

CRITICAL PRESSURE

SATURATED VAPOR

LIQUID

SATURATED

200 Kg/cm²
150 Kg/cm²
100 Kg/cm²
50 Kg/cm²

250 Kg/cm²
300 Kg/cm²
400 Kg/cm²

S=0.75

S=0.50

S=0.25

DISTORTED *t-s* DIAGRAM

Entropy Differences from Saturation Line at
Constant Temperature are Exaggerated 12.5 Times.
Entropy Scale below applies to Saturation Line

0.25   0.50   0.75   1.00   1.25   1.50
Entropy (int. cal./g °C)

DISTORTED TEMPERATURE ENTROPY DIAGRAM

FIG. (IX–7).

400 °C
300 °C
200 °C
100 °C
0 °C

—700 °F
—600 °F
—500 °F
—400 °F
—300 °F
—200 °F
—100 °F

Temperature

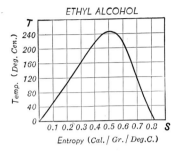

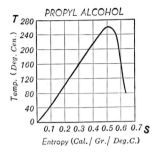

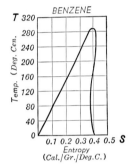

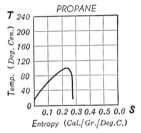

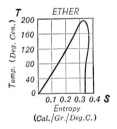

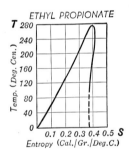

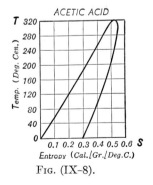

FIG. (IX–8).

either the dry saturated or slightly superheated state will cause the vapors to become wet. Such a process may conceivably take place as the fuel air mixture is compressed in an internal combustion engine or in the compressor of a refrigeration machine.

The vapor domes of several vapors are shown in Fig. (IX–8).

IX–14. Actual Gases and Superheated Vapors.—Of the substances we commonly call gases there is none but what can be brought into the liquid phase. A proper lowering of temperature coupled with sufficiently high pressure brings even that most intractable one, Helium, into liquid form. Thus, at some time during their career they each have passed through the state of a Saturated Vapor, and, accordingly, previously existed at a temperature in excess of their saturation temperatures, then conforming to our definition of a Superheated Vapor. Naturally the question arises, when should a substance be considered a gas and when a Superheated Vapor, to which probably the best reply would be, that nothing should ever be considered a perfect gas. It is only when a substance conforms with reasonable approximation to the very simple laws postulated for that mythical substance that there is the slightest excuse for calling it a gas, even then it must be borne in mind constantly that it can be so treated only within the relatively narrow range of pressures and temperatures covered by the original information. To illustrate, it is customary to call air a gas and assume that any third property may be determined from the equation $Pv = WRT$ when two of the properties are known. This is correct *when temperature and pressure are near common atmospheric conditions.* But if we wish to deal with air at say 6,000 lbs. per sq. in. absolute pressure the so-called *constant R* has changed to 67.6, even at the very moderate temperature of 70° F. (530° F. abs.). Similarly at atmospheric pressure but a temperature of 317° F. below zero, air becomes a *liquid* and the equation $Pv = WRT$ does not have the slightest value.

Obviously then, when reaching a decision as to the applicability of the gas laws, a great deal depends upon the proximity of the region in which the action is taking place to the region of saturation, and this has served after a fashion, to differentiate the so-called *gases* from the substances commonly listed as superheated vapors. Common practice is to term those substances *gases* which are far removed from the saturated vapor region whereas substances usually dealt with when in states bordering the saturation line are usually termed *superheated vapors.* The former are considered amenable to the gas laws but the latter are not. There is no rigid line of demarcation and sometimes the terminology appears inconsistent.

IX–15. Determination of Properties of Superheated Vapors.—For those substances usually dealt with in states remote from saturation, such as the gases nitrogen, hydrogen, oxygen, helium, etc., data as to the various properties are obtained from the characteristic equations in conjunction with equations for the specific heat-temperature relation, while for those close to the saturated region the properties are usually assembled in tabular form directly from experimental information obtained in the saturated and slightly superheated regions. These are usually issued in conjunction with the tables of the saturated properties, as in the cases of steam and the common refrigerants.

Provided the characteristic equation can be established for a superheated vapor, the customary thermodynamic properties can be computed for most of the common vapors. Attempts have been made to produce the characteristic equations for the superheated state, but in practically all cases, the equations are quite complex. They do not lend themselves readily to easy manipulation, and it is practically universal now to compile tabulations of the properties of the various vapors in the superheated phase as well as in the saturated phase. Such tabulations permit ready determinations of the common properties and lend themselves to the prediction of the various energy changes.

With steam, however, largely because of mental inertia, computations for adiabatic changes in the superheated region have frequently been handled by the perfect gas law:

$$PV^n = C,$$

and the adjustment necessary obtained by modification of the exponent, n. In the Keenan tables, there are values of n covering the various ranges in various pressures of the superheated region. However, these are of interest mainly as showing the magnitude of the departure from the perfect gas action which is actually displayed by the steam, ranging as they do, from values of 1.25 to 1.32.

IX–16. Steam Calorimeters.—It is frequently desirable to determine the quality of saturated steam, and, as pressure and temperature are the only observable properties under practical conditions, this determination must be contrived by the use of these properties only. Consider, for instance, steam flowing within a pipe. Its pressure and temperature may be directly observed, and, if these do not correspond according to the properties of steam, the temperature being above the boiling point for the pressure, then it is known at once that the vapor is in the superheated condition. If, on the other hand, the temperature and the pressure do correspond, it is known that the steam is saturated, but the state may be anything from a saturated liquid to dry and saturated steam. Under these conditions, the quality must first be determined before other properties can be found. The devices which aid in finding quality are misnamed calorimeters, of which there are several types, the throttling calorimeter being the most interesting from the thermodynamic standpoint.

The Throttling Calorimeter.—Pressure and temperature establish a state point for a vapor when the vapor is in the superheat region. This is not so in the saturated region. The throttling calorimeter operates upon the principle of transferring a sample of steam from the saturated region where pressure and temperature are not independent into the superheated region where they are independent and can be used to identify the state.

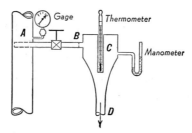

Fig. (IX–9).   Throttling Calorimeter.

The process used is the throttling process, from which the calorimeter takes its name, and the heat content remains constant while this change is taking place. The operation of the apparatus is shown by Fig. (IX–9). A small amount of steam flowing through the pipe *A* is removed, to be passed through the calorimeter, by a sampling tube, the function of which is to obtain a representative sample of the steam and water mixture within the pipe. The sample is conducted through a small and short pipe to the calorimeter which consists essentially of an orifice *B*, in which expansion takes place, followed by a chamber *C*, where, by means of turbulence and impact, the kinetic energy of the steam from the orifice is dissipated, thus producing overall a throttling action. In this chamber is inserted a thermometer well for the reading of temperature, and also a small tube leads from the chamber to be connected to a mercury manometer so that the pressure may be determined. The steam is discharged from the chamber to the atmosphere through the pipe *D*. If the steam is superheated at *C*, the pressure and temperature determine its state and the heat content may be found by reference to steam tables. But the heat content at *C* is the same as that at A, so that the latter is also known and this property, together with pressure or temperature, fixes the state in the saturated region. The process simply involves solving for the quality in the equation $h_x = h_f + x h_{fg}$ in which h is known and h_f and h_{fg} are taken from the tables for the pressure, or temperature, at A, thus,

$$x = \frac{h_x - h_f}{h_{fg}}.$$

This is illustrated in the following problem:

A throttling calorimeter takes steam from a main where the pressure is 146 lbs. gage. The calorimeter manometer shows a pressure of 2 in. Hg and the thermometer reads 260° F. The barometer reading is 28.5 in. Hg. Calculate the quality of steam in the main.

Abs. press. in main $= 146 + (.491)(28.5) = 160$ lbs. per sq. in.

Abs. press. in calorimeter $= (28.5 + 2.0)(.491) = 15$ lbs. per sq. in.

From superheat steam tables, the heat content in the calorimeter is 1173.7 B.t.u. Then the heat content in the main is also 1173.7. Hence,

$$1173.7 = h_f + x h_{fg},$$

or

$$x = \frac{1173.7 - 335.93}{859.2} = 97.5 \text{ per cent.}$$

Checking on the Mollier diagram by locating 15 lbs. per sq. in. abs. and 260° and then going horizontally to the left until the 160 lb. line is reached, a moisture content of 2.5 per cent is found. This corresponds to a quality of 97.5 per cent.

Obviously, this device will not work if the steam fails to attain superheat after throttling. Inspection of the constant heat content lines on the T–S or the Mollier diagram will show, therefore, that it is distinctly limited to the determination of initial qualities that are quite high, say above .95, the exact limit depending somewhat upon the initial pressure. The securing of a sample of steam from the main line which is truly representative of the average condition within the pipe is always open to question and is a fault which, by no means restricted to the throttling type, is common to all types of calorimeters. In the construction and operation of throttling calorimeters care should be exercised to ensure that they are well lagged throughout to minimize heat losses and that the kinetic energy of the steam after passing through the orifice is dissipated by baffles or equivalent device before reading the thermometer well where the temperature is to be read. The exhaust pipe should be proportioned so that the kinetic energy of the leaving stream is approximately equal to the entering stream.

The separating calorimeter depends upon the mechanical separation of water from the sample of steam, the dry steam being measured by means of an orifice so calibrated that the quantity flowing may at once be determined from the initial pressure. Knowing the amount of water taken from a known quantity of steam, the quality may be obtained. Unlike the throttling type, this device works best with a considerable amount of moisture present.

Another interesting, but rarely used, calorimeter is the barrel type. In its simplest form, this consists of a barrel of cool water to the bottom of which is conducted, by a pipe or hose, the steam sample of unknown quality, and this is condensed in bubbling up through. The weight and the temperature of the water in the barrel are taken before and after the sample is admitted. In this way, the weight of the steam condensed may be found and the problem becomes simply one of mechanical mixtures. The heat content of the steam per pound may thus be found, and the procedure is exactly similar to that for the throttling calorimeter. As the weight of the condensate is small compared to the total weight and the mean temperature difficult to ascertain accurately, the accuracy of quality determination is inferior to that of either of the above types.

CHAPTER X

FLOW OF VAPORS

X–1. Basic Equations.—In the discussion of flow of gases, Chapter VIII, the equations evolved from the fundamental laws of Continuity of Mass and Continuity of Energy were said to be general and not confined to any one substance. Thus, *for adiabatic flow*, which may be assumed for vapors as for other fluids through nozzles and orifices practically without error, the increase in the kinetic energy of the jet during an expansion is,

$$\frac{\text{Vel.}_2{}^2 - \text{Vel.}_1{}^2}{2gJ} = h_1 - h_2. \tag{X–1}$$

If the initial velocity is, or may be assumed to be, zero, the final velocity is,

$$\text{Vel.} = 224 \sqrt{h_1 - h_2}. \tag{X–2}$$

For calculation of nozzle dimensions, or for the amount of fluid passing, the equations,

$$a = \frac{Wv}{\text{Vel.}} \quad \text{and} \quad W = \frac{a(\text{Vel.})}{v}, \tag{X–3}$$

apply to any substance in the fluid state.

Similarly, the equation for the determination of the ratio of critical pressure to initial pressure,

$$p_t/p_1 = \left(\frac{2}{k+1}\right)^{\frac{k}{k-1}},$$

holds for vapors, but care must be exercised in its use, since the value of k for vapors is dependent upon several factors and does not remain constant in either the saturated or the superheated region. However, the use of an average k over the range in question will usually give sufficiently accurate results for most calculations, particularly within moderate pressure and temperature ranges. For steam, in the saturated region, and for equilibrium expansion, k may be taken as 1.135, with a corresponding value for p_t/p_1 of 0.58.   For steam at moderate pressures and superheat $k = 1.3$, and $p_t/p_1 = 0.545$.

X–2.   Change of State During Expansion.—Reference to a typical T–S diagram for a vapor, Fig. (X–1), shows immediately that the manner in which the condition of the vapor changes during an isentropic expansion depends largely upon where the expansion starts and the completeness with which it is carried out.   Thus an expansion, such as a–c, starting at the

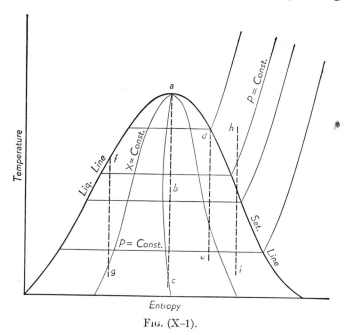

Fig. (X–1).

critical point, or as b–c, starting about midway in the saturated region, would produce but little change in quality.   That is, such an expansion would result neither in further evaporation nor in further condensation of the vapor to any extent.   An expansion, on the contrary, starting anywhere on the saturation line, well below the critical temperature, such as d–e, would result in condensation of part of the vapor and a decreasing quality as the expansion progressed.   With the liquid line as the starting point, f–g, an expansion produces a drying action, some of the liquid is vaporized, and the quality is increased.

Between the boundary curves, either of the effects mentioned above may be had, depending upon whether the expansion takes place in the very wet region, near the mid-section, or in the drier region of higher quality. An expansion might even be conceived which would result, first, in an increase, then in a decrease of quality as it crosses and recrosses a curved line of constant quality.

Adiabatic expansion starting in the superheat region will produce, first, a reduction in temperature as the pressures become successively lower, until the saturation line is reached. Any further expansion below this point would be similar to d–e and would produce constantly increasing moisture content. An example of such an expansion is h–i.

X-3. Equilibrium Expansion.—Expansion of a vapor through a nozzle, if taking place in a condition of equilibrium and without friction, is of the form of the reversible adiabatic and the fluid undergoes no change in entropy. Thus, with the initial conditions known, the final conditions, after any given pressure drop, may be found. If the expansion carries into the saturated region, the final quality, at some desired pressure, is essential in the determination of other final properties, specific volume and heat content, which are necessary for the solution of problems dealing with nozzles and orifices. The quality may be determined as follows, the pressure being known:

$$s_1 = s_2 = s_{f2} + x_2 s_{fg2}, \qquad x_2 = \frac{s_1 - s_{f2}}{s_{fg2}}. \tag{X-4}$$

Knowing the quality, other properties may be easily calculated, as,

$$h_2 = h_{f2} + x_2 h_{fg2} \quad \text{and} \quad v_2 = v_{f2} + x_2 v_{fg2}.$$

When the expansion terminates in the superheat region, it is only necessary to refer to the superheat tables at the pressure desired and the initial value of entropy in order to determine the properties.

Having found the properties at the second condition, the velocity of the jet, area required for a given quantity, or the quantity flowing through a given cross-sectional area, may be determined from the basic equations for flow.

Because of the fact that the practical nozzle is made with a uniform taper from throat to mouth and is simply rounded out at the entrance, the two controlling areas are that at the throat and that at the mouth, and the proper relationship between these two areas is of prime importance. These being correct, the rest of the nozzle, insofar as cross-sectional areas are concerned, takes care of itself. In design, therefore, these areas are usually the ones calculated unless the area at some other point is desired in a special case, as for the longitudinal cross-section of the theoretically correct nozzle.

Example.—A nozzle is to be designed to pass 1200 lbs. of steam per hour under the following conditions. Initial state of steam is 200 lbs. per sq. in. abs., 500° F. Final pressure (at mouth) is 2 lbs. abs. Calculate the throat and mouth areas required for equilibrium flow without friction.

Solution.—$s_1 = 1.6240$. $h_1 = 1268.9$ B.t.u. per lb.

Throat area: For superheated steam, $p_t/p_1 = 0.545$, and p_t in this case $= .545 (200) = 109$ lbs. abs.

$$s_t = s_1 = 1.6240.$$

$$t_t \text{ (by interpolation)} = 374° \text{ F.}$$

Interpolating further, $v_t = 4.349$ cu. ft. per lb.
and

$$h_t = 1211.8 \text{ B.t.u. per lb.}$$

$$\text{Vel.}_t = 224 \sqrt{1268.9 - 1211.8} = 224 \sqrt{57.1}$$

$$= 1694 \text{ ft. per sec.}$$

$$a_t = \frac{1200 \,(4.349)}{3600 \,(1694)} = .000856 \text{ sq. ft.} \quad \text{or} \quad 0.1232 \text{ sq. in.}$$

Mouth area: Obviously the state point will cross the saturation line before the pressure has dropped to 2 lbs. abs. In case of doubt, however, it may be seen that s_g at 2 lbs. exceeds s_1, thereby showing that the condition at the mouth lies to the left of the saturation line at 2 lbs. pressure.

$$x_2 = \frac{1.6240 - .1749}{1.7451} = \frac{1.4491}{1.7451} = .83 \quad \text{or} \quad 83 \text{ per cent.}$$

$$h_2 = 94 + .83 \,(1022.2) = 942 \text{ B.t.u.}$$

$$\text{Vel.}_2 = 224 \sqrt{1268.9 - 942} = 4050 \text{ ft. per sec.}$$

$$v_2 = .83 \,(173.73) = 144.2 \text{ cu. ft. per lb.}$$

$$a_2 = \frac{1200 \,(144.2)}{3600 \,(4050)} = .01188 \text{ sq. ft.} \quad \text{or} \quad 1.71 \text{ sq. in.}$$

If the problem is to find the quantity flowing through a certain area under given conditions, the required properties are determined as in the example, and the weight solved for instead of the area in the last equation.

X-4. Effect of Friction.—In the flow of a vapor through a nozzle, there is a frictional resistance to be overcome due to actual rubbing of the fluid over the walls of the nozzle and to the presence of some turbulence which will occur in all but a perfect nozzle under perfect conditions. No attempt is ordinarily made to distinguish between these two causes, since the results are the same in effect. The result of friction is the destruction of kinetic energy of the jet and its retransformation into heat. As heat, the kinetic energy, dissipated in overcoming friction, is taken up by the stream causing the fluid to be discharged with a heat content greater than would be the case with isentropic expansion. The T–S diagram, Fig. (X–2), shows the effect of friction on the final condition of the vapor. The line a–b shows adiabatic expansion without friction, and a–c shows adiabatic expansion with friction. Since the transformation of kinetic energy into heat is a purely irreversible process, and increase in entropy

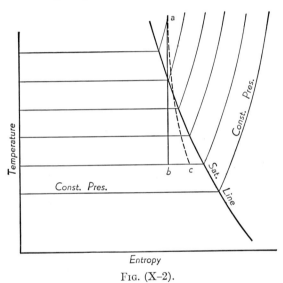

Fig. (X–2).

results. This has the effect of increasing the quality at the end of expansion in the wet region, or, if the terminal point is in the superheat region, of increasing the temperature. An initial state and final pressure might be selected, such that the isentropic expansion would terminate in the saturated region and the expansion with friction in the superheat region. The result of friction in the design of nozzles is to decrease the jet velocity and to increase the specific volume, both tending to produce an area larger than that required for frictionless flow. Conversely, the amount of fluid passing through a nozzle of given size will be reduced as the frictional effects are augmented. Frictional losses in a nozzle are expressed as the per cent of the originally available heat which has become unavailable through fric-

tion. When the function of a nozzle is thought of as being the transformation of heat into kinetic energy, the term " nozzle efficiency " may
be used to express the ratio of the kinetic energy actually developed to
the heat originally available. The loss in availability, that is, the kinetic
energy, which is reconverted into heat and is taken up by the fluid, is known
as " reheat," expressed directly in heat units.

Example.—Correct the example in the preceding article for a 10 per cent
friction loss (nozzle efficiency 90 per cent).

Solution.—Throat area:

$$p_t = 109 \text{ lbs. abs.}$$

$$\text{Vel.}_t = 224 \sqrt{.9 \ (57.1)} = 1608 \text{ ft. per sec.}$$

$$\text{Reheat to throat} = .1 \ (57.1) = 5.7 \text{ B.t.u. per lb.}$$

$$h_t = 1211.8 + 5.7 = 1217.5 \text{ B.t.u.}$$

$$v_t = 4.41 \text{ cu. ft. per lb.}$$

$$t_t = 384° \text{ F.}$$

$$a_t = \frac{1200 \ (4.41)}{3600 \ (1608)} = .000915 \text{ sq. ft.} \quad \text{or} \quad .132 \text{ sq. in.}$$

Mouth area:

$$\text{Vel.}_2 = 224 \sqrt{.9 \ (326.9)} = 3845 \text{ ft. per sec.}$$

$$\text{Reheat to mouth} = .1 \ (326.9) = 32.7 \text{ B.t.u. per lb.}$$

$$h_2 = 942 + 32.7 = 974.7 \text{ B.t.u.}$$

$$x_2 = \frac{974.7 - 94}{1022.2} = \frac{880.7}{1022.2} = .862 \quad \text{or} \quad 86.2\%.$$

$$v_2 = .862 \ (173.73) = 150 \text{ cu. ft. per lb.}$$

$$a_2 = \frac{1200 \ (150)}{3600 \ (3845)} = .013 \text{ sq. ft.} \quad \text{or} \quad 1.87 \text{ sq. in.}$$

That the effect of friction in such a calculation is appreciable, may be
seen in that the error, by the assumption of isentropic expansion, in computation of the throat area is 6.8 per cent, and for the mouth area is 8.6
per cent. Also, the nozzle designed neglecting friction would pass but
1118 lbs. per hour instead of the 1200 lbs. for which it was intended.

X-5. Non-equilibrium or Metastable Phenomena.—Under certain
conditions, a substance may exist, temporarily, in a state of instability
which may be chemical, physical, mechanical, or thermal. When
equilibrium is disturbed, nature always makes an effort to restore it, but

the process of rectification may consume time, and before and during the restoration process a metastable condition exists. States of this sort are common. Any force which is not opposed by an equal force produces, in the body upon which it is acting, a mechanical instability. A stone falling from a cliff is not in a state of equilibrium until it settles at the bottom. A chemically supersaturated solution may exist for a time in an unstable state if it happens to lack the means of starting precipitation. Under such circumstances, the slightest disturbance is likely to provide the means for letting nature restore equilibrium. Such is the nature, also, of explosives, some of which detonate very easily. It has been experimentally demonstrated that humid air may be cooled below the temperature at which condensation should occur without precipitation, provided there is a total absence of nuclei, such as dust particles, which may start the condensation process and a consequent return to the normal state.

In order to demonstrate the importance of time in some of these phenomena, it might be conceivable to *very suddenly* lower the temperature of water to below 32° F. and at standard atmospheric pressure without the immediate formation of ice. The quicker the cooling process could be carried out, the more pronounced would be the results. Then, after a certain necessary time had elapsed, the restoration process would take place and the sudden formation of ice would be the result. Much the same sort of thing actually does occur in the condensation of steam under certain conditions.

X–6. **Supersaturated Expansion.**—If steam be expanded isentropically in the cylinder of a steam engine so that the state point crosses the saturation line, condensation occurs as the expansion progresses to just the degree expected from knowledge of the properties of steam. The moisture content could be computed at any stage of the process, and, if the action were to be stopped at any point, and the adiabatic state maintained, there would be no physical or thermal change of the fluid within the cylinder. In other words, the expansion is taking place in complete equilibrium, the time element being sufficient to permit condensation to take place at the proper rate.

In expanding through a nozzle, however, the change is extremely rapid. For instance, if the nozzle in the example of the preceding article is assumed to be 6 ins. from throat to mouth, and the average velocity in that section be taken as 2700 ft. per sec., the steam will leave the mouth .000185 second after passing the throat. In this brief time, the pressure has dropped from 109 lbs. per sq. in. abs. to 2 lbs. abs., and the quality has supposedly changed from a small amount of superheat to 86.2 per cent. It is now known, however, that the quality has not changed to that extent, that condensation has not kept pace with the rate of expansion, and that the steam is much drier than is indicated in the solution where thermodynamic equilibrium is assumed to exist. Furthermore, observation would show the temperature to be lower than the saturation temperature for the pressure at any stage of the expansion following the passing of the saturation line. What has happened is that the steam has expanded in the superheat region, in the absence of moisture, very much as a perfect gas, has achieved

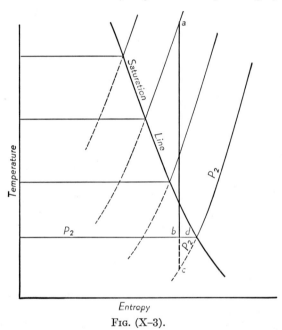

Fig. (X–3).

the saturation temperature, and entered what would ordinarily be the wet region. But the condensation which would, under equilibrium conditions, begin to take place at this point, takes time, and time is not allowed in the exceedingly rapid expansion which the vapor is undergoing. Therefore, the process still takes place *in the absence of moisture*, and approximates the action as a perfect gas. Accordingly, the saturation temperature has no significance, and the fluid will expand to the terminal pressure *as a gas*.

This action is shown in Fig. (X–3), the solid lines representing vapor in the equilibrium states, and the dotted lines isobaric states for a gas. Equilibrium expansion is shown by *a–b* with the normal condensation taking place. Metastable expansion is shown by a–c to the same terminal pressure, but the terminal point will be on the isobaric line representing that pressure for a gas. Both processes are shown, for simplicity, without frictional effects. It will be noted that point c lies well below the saturation temperature for the particular pressure, hence the term "supercooled," or "supersaturated" is applied to a vapor in this unstable state. If the expansion be carried sufficiently far, some condensation may occur, but always less than that stipulated by equilibrium conditions.

Following non-equilibrium expansion, comes a restoration to a state of stability. Time is the important element in this type of instability, and,

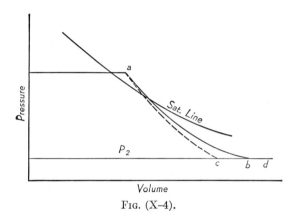

Fig. (X-4).

time being allowed, recovery takes place very suddenly. Goodenough states that, in order to produce a metastable condition, the time of expansion must be, approximately, less than 0.001 second. The restoration process consists of a rapid condensation, in quantity sufficient to return the vapor to the equilibrium quality, and, thereby, a sudden liberation of the latent heat of vaporization of those particles which condense. This is a reheating effect and an irreversible process which results in an increase in entropy. The final state of the vapor, after equilibrium has been restored, therefore, lies to the right (T–S diagram) of the terminal point for stable expansion. This point is shown as d in Fig. (X-3). The result is a loss of available energy, with a corresponding decrease of kinetic energy produced. The manner in which point d is reached from c, being irreversible in nature, is not shown on the T–S diagram in Fig. (X-3), since such a representation would serve no useful purpose. Fig. (X-4) shows the same process as Fig. (X-3), but on the P–V plane.

Since metastable expansion, in what would normally be the saturation region, takes place without the formation of moisture, the curve may be represented closely by applying the same exponent as is generally issued for superheated steam, that is, $pv^{1.3} = \text{Const.}$ Also the relation $p_t/p_1 = 0.545$ is correct for nonequilibrium expansion.

Based on the foregoing, the general equation for the weight discharged becomes: *

$$\frac{p}{p_1} < 0.545 \qquad wt. = 0.406\frac{ap_1}{\sqrt{T_1}}. \qquad (X\text{--}5)$$

$$\frac{p}{p_1} > 0.545 \qquad wt. = 1.795\frac{ap_1}{\sqrt{T_1}}\left[\left(\frac{p}{p_1}\right)^{1.54} - \left(\frac{p}{p_1}\right)^{1.77}\right]^{\frac{1}{2}} \qquad (X\text{--}6)$$

where, $wt.$ denotes the weight discharged in lbs. per sec.

a denotes the area of the opening in square inches

p_1 denotes the initial or upstream steam pressure in lbs. per sq. in.

p denotes the discharge or downstream pressure in lbs. per sq. in.

T denotes the absolute initial temp. Fahr. deg.

Equation (X–6) is easily applied if values of the term in parentheses are known. Below is given a tabulation of the values of this term for varying ratios of back to initial pressure.

Values of the term $\left[\left(\frac{p}{p_1}\right)^{1.54} - \left(\frac{p}{p_1}\right)^{1.77}\right]^{\frac{1}{2}}$ for various pressure ratios:

Ratio p/p	$\left[\left(\frac{p}{p_1}\right)^{1.54} - \left(\frac{p}{p_1}\right)^{1.77}\right]^{\frac{1}{2}}$
0.55	0.225
0.60	0.223
0.65	0.220
0.70	0.214
0.75	0.205
0.80	0.190
0.85	0.170
0.90	0.145
0.95	0.100
1.00	0.000

Although time is largely the controlling element in the supersaturation phenomenon, there also appears to be a limit to the extent to which the supersaturated condition may extend into what would normally be the

* "Some Suggested Errors in Nozzle Experiments." H. M. Martin, London, Eng., Jan. 10, 1913; also "A New Theory of the Steam Turbine." H. M. Martin, London, Eng., 1918.

saturated region. Experiments by Wilson and others have pretty definitely determined the conditions beyond which it is impossible to repress condensation. When plotted on property coördinates (the heat content-entropy plane), this line, representing the limit, is roughly parallel to the saturation line. This is sometimes referred to as the " Wilson Line " since much of the work in its determination was done by Wilson. For ordinary considerations with steam initially dry or slightly superheated, and with supersaturation considered to take place only to the throat of the nozzle, the limit need not be taken into account, as it is probably not reached under these conditions.

The degree of supersaturation is expressed as a ratio of the density of the supersaturated vapor to the density of saturated vapor in the equilibrium condition at the same temperature. This is practically the same as a ratio of the pressure of the supersaturated vapor to the pressure corresponding to its temperature for equilibrium condition. To illustrate, suppose a supercooled vapor to exist at a pressure of 40 lbs. abs. and a temperature of 190° F., the specific volume being 9.7 cu. ft. The specific volume of saturated steam at 190° is 41 cu. ft., and the degree of supersaturation is 41/9.7 = 4.23. The pressure corresponding to 190° F. is 9.34 lbs., which gives a degree of supersaturation of 40/9.34 = 4.28. The vapor in this case might also be said to be supercooled 267.24° − 190° = 77.24° F.

Example.—Find the area of a nozzle necessary to pass 1800 lbs. of steam per hour from an initial pressure of 160 lbs. per sq. in. abs., dry and saturated, to 90 lbs. abs. Consider the effect of metastable expansion throughout the nozzle.

Solution.—The throat pressure would be .545 (160) = 87.2 lbs. were the back pressure less than this or equal to it. With a discharge pressure of 90 lbs., however, this becomes the minimum pressure in the nozzle, and the nozzle is of the converging type.

For the calculation of the area, the weight flowing, specific volume, and velocity are required. The expansion being, in this case, as a gas without the formation of moisture, it is not necessary to calculate the final quality. The specific volume may be determined directly from the equation representing the path.

$$p_1 v_1^{1.3} = p_2 v_2^{1.3},$$

$$p_1 = 160 \text{ lbs. abs.,}$$

$$v_1 = 2.83 \text{ cu. ft. per lb.,}$$

$$p_2 = 90 \text{ lbs. abs.,}$$

$$v_2 = \sqrt[1.3]{\frac{160 \,(2.83)^{1.3}}{90}} = \sqrt[1.3]{6.88} = 4.41 \text{ cu. ft. per lb.}$$

The final kinetic energy, $\dfrac{\text{Vel.}^2}{2g}$, is equal to the work done by the expanding fluid, which is

$$\int_{p_1}^{p_2} vdP = \frac{n}{n-1}(P_1v_1 - P_2v_2)$$

$$= \frac{1.3}{.3}(144)[160\,(2.83) - 90\,(4.41)] = 624\,(56)$$

$$= 34{,}940 \text{ ft.-lbs.}$$

$$\text{Vel.}_2 = \sqrt{64.4\,(34{,}940)} = 1500 \text{ ft. per sec.}$$

$$\text{Area} = \frac{1800\,(4.41)}{3600\,(1500)} = .00147 \text{ sq. ft.} \quad \text{or} \quad .2118 \text{ sq. in.}$$

Example.—A convergent-divergent nozzle of circular cross-section has a throat diameter of 0.3 in. Initial steam pressure is 180 lbs. per sq. in. abs., dry and saturated. Discharge pressure 1 lb. abs.

Calculate the quantity of steam discharged per hour, considering (a) Equilibrium expansion; (b) Metastable expansion. Neglect friction in both cases.

Solution.—Since the throat conditions govern the quantity of fluid discharged, calculations should be for this point. Owing to the different relation of critical to initial pressure in each case, the throat pressures will be different.

$$\text{Throat area} = \frac{\pi(.3)^2}{4\,(144)} = .000491 \text{ sq. ft.}$$

(a) Equilibrium condition:

$$h_1 = 1196.9 \text{ B.t.u.}$$

$$s_1 = 1.5542 = s_2$$

$$p_t = .58\,(180) = 104.4 \text{ lb. abs.}$$

$$x_t = \frac{1.5542 - .4782}{1.1209} = .96$$

$$h_t = 301.7 + .96\,(886.2) = 1151 \text{ B.t.u.}$$

$$\text{Vel.}_t = 224\sqrt{1196.9 - 1151} = 1517 \text{ ft. per sec.}$$

$$v_t = .96\,(4.25) = 4.08 \text{ cu. ft. per lb.}$$

$$wt. = \frac{3600\,(.000491)(1517)}{4.08} = 657 \text{ lbs. per hr.}$$

(b) Metastable condition:

$$p_t = .545\,(180) = 98.1 \text{ lbs. abs.}$$

$$v_1 = 2.532 \text{ cu. ft. per lb.}$$

$$v_t = \sqrt[1.3]{\frac{180(2.532)^{1.3}}{98.1}} = \sqrt[1.3]{6.14} = 4.04 \text{ cu. ft. per lb.}$$

$$\frac{\text{Vel.}^2}{2g} = \frac{1.3}{.3}(144)[180 \times 2.532 - 98.1 \times 4.04] = 36,800 \text{ ft.-lbs. or } 47.3 \text{ B.t.u.}$$

$$\text{Vel.} = \sqrt{64.4\,(36,800)} = 1540 \text{ ft. per sec.}$$

$$\text{Weight} = \frac{3600\,(.000491)(1540)}{4.04} = 674 \text{ lbs. per hr.}$$

X–7. Effect of Moisture in the Steam.—An additional loss is encountered in the flow of steam through nozzles when the vapor is initially wet or expands to a considerable degree of wetness. The small droplets, originally present or formed in the course of the expansion, having a comparatively great concentration of mass and possessing no means of providing for their own acceleration, constitute inert bodies which must be carried along by the vapor stream. The inertia of the droplets prevents their acceleration to anything like the velocity attained by the jet, the result being a tendency to retard the flow in much the same manner as rocks in a swift flowing stream have a damming effect. This is a frictional and impact loss, but is distinctly different in nature to the frictional loss previously discussed and is dependent largely upon the moisture content of the expanding steam. Experimental evidence shows that, on the average, the velocity of the water particles is from .08 to .2 times the steam velocity. The final results of this particular loss are a reduction in the final jet velocity and a slight increase in specific volume due to reheat, both tending to decrease the quantity of fluid discharged from the nozzle.

X–8. Summary of Nozzle Losses.—Nozzle losses fall into two separate classes: that due to the supersaturation phenomenon, and that due to friction of one kind or another. The latter may be subdivided into: friction caused by the passing of the stream over the nozzle wall and general turbulence; and friction, impact, and turbulence caused by droplet lag.

Friction with the nozzle walls is present, irrespective of the conditions under which the expansion takes place, and the percent loss is almost independent of steam conditions.

Of the other sources of loss, supersaturation and droplet lag, the following may be said in general. With highly superheated steam neither occurs. With initially dry and saturated or slightly superheated steam, since the moisture content will be small, only supersaturation need be considered. With steam possessing a large amount of moisture, super-saturation is negligible but the drag due to water particles is comparatively large.

The table given below will serve to illustrate the variation in losses with different initial moisture contents.

STEAM NOZZLE LOSSES WITH VARYING INITIAL MOISTURE CONTENTS

(Expressed as per cent of available energy)

Initial moisture	0	0.04	0.08	0.12	0.16
Nozzle friction	3.17	3.17	3.17	3.17	3.17
Supersaturation	2.16	2.21	2.20	1.93	1.37
Droplet lag	0	0.51	1.06	1.65	2.29
Total loss	5.33	5.89	6.43	6.75	6.83

The above table is taken from Part II of a paper on " Supersaturation and the Flow of Wet Steam," by G. A. Goodenough, appearing in *Power*, Oct. 4, 1927.

X-9. Flow Through Orifices.—The function of a nozzle may be considered the development of kinetic energy in the issuing jet, while that of an orifice is simply to pass fluid from a region of higher pressure to a lower pressure. Usually an orifice is used to pass a given amount of fluid or to provide the means of metering an unknown quantity of fluid. An orifice may consist simply of a cylindrical hole drilled in a plate or may be rather elaborately formed, but, in any case, its length to diameter ratio is usually much smaller than that of a nozzle and it never possesses a divergent section which is so important in order that the nozzle may fulfill its function.

The theory underlying flow through orifices does not differ fundamentally from that for nozzles. The orifice is, in effect, the throat of a nozzle alone or with a rounded approach, but, due to its form and construction, the orifice requires corrections in addition to those which were applied to nozzle calculations. If the stream flowing through an orifice could be seen in profile, its outline would be somewhat similar to that shown in Fig. (X-5), and it immediately becomes apparent that, in addition to the ordinary losses encountered in the nozzle, there is undoubtedly more friction in the square-edged type of orifice and an effective area somewhat less than the actual area provided. The latter is due to the natural formation by the fluid stream of a longitudinal contour somewhat resembling that of the theoretically correct nozzle. It may be seen that the vena contracta or part of smallest cross-section does not actually occur at the orifice itself but a little beyond it. It is at this point that the critical pressure exists when the back pressure is less than critical, and it is the area of the vena contracta, not the orifice itself, that directly controls the quantity of fluid passing. Since the vena contracta is smaller than the orifice, the result of this phenomenon is to reduce the quantity that will be discharged.

There is usually no effort made to evaluate the various losses in the orifice. Instead of this, actual quantities discharged from a given orifice

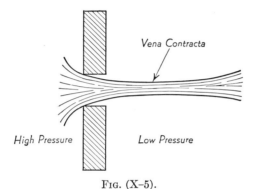

Fig. (X–5).

under certain conditions are experimentally determined and a coefficient of discharge applied to the theoretical determinations in order to predict the amount of fluid which a given orifice will discharge or in order to design an orifice to deliver a certain quantity. The coefficient of discharge, experimentally found, is the ratio of the actual discharge to the theoretical discharge, as determined in a manner similar to that for a nozzle. The rather wide discrepancies between actual quantities passed and theoretical quantities, and the great variety of losses, have led to the use of empirical formulae largely in the calculations for orifices. Such formulae have been evolved for the flow of steam by Grashoff and others. Grashoff equation is

$$wt = 0.0165ap^{0.97}.$$

wt is flow in pounds per second,

a is area in square inches,

p is absolute pressure in pounds per square inch.

In general, however, it will be found advisable to make calculations from the fundamental equations, correcting, as any equation must be corrected, by the application of a coefficient of discharge. Much work was done by Rateau on the flow of steam. His results show that the Grashoff equation may be used to calculate the amount of flow if the following coefficients are used.

Ratio of back pressure to initial pressure	Ratio of actual to computed discharge	
	Converging orifice	Orifice in thin plates
0.95	0.45	0.30
.90	.62	.42
.85	.73	.51
.80	.82	.58
.75	.89	.64
.70	.94	.69
.65	.97	.73
.60	.99	.77
.55	....	.80
.45	....	.82
.40	....	.83

Example.—How much steam will be discharged through a ¼-inch orifice in a plate from an initial pressure of 200 lbs. abs., dry and saturated, to: (a) 130 lbs. abs., coefficient = 0.73; (b) 80 lbs. abs., coefficient = 0.83; (c) atmospheric pressure, coefficient = 0.83. Coefficients of discharge apply to frictionless equilibrium expansion.

Solution.—

$$wt. = \frac{Ca(\text{Vel.})}{v}$$

$$a = \frac{\pi(.25)^2}{4\,(144)} = .000341 \text{ sq. ft.}$$

$$h_1 = 1198.4 \text{ B.t.u.}$$

$$s_1 = 1.5453$$

$$p_t = .58\,(200) = 116 \text{ lbs. abs.}$$

(a)

$$x_2 = \frac{1.5453 - .4995}{1.0817} = .967$$

$$h_2 = 318.8 + .967\,(872.9) = 1163 \text{ B.t.u.}$$

$$v_2 = .967\,(3.455) = 3.335 \text{ cu. ft. per lb.}$$

$$\text{Vel.} = 224\sqrt{35.5} = 1335 \text{ ft. per sec.}$$

$$wt. = \frac{3600\ (.000341)(1335)(.73)}{3.335} = 359 \text{ lbs. per hr.}$$

(b)
$$x_2 = \frac{1.5453 - .4883}{1.1022} = .959 \text{ (at } P_t)$$

$$h_2 = 309.8 + .959\ (880) = 1154 \text{ B.t.u.}$$

$$v_2 = .959\ (3.85) = 3.69 \text{ cu. ft. per lb.}$$

$$\text{Vel.} = 224\ \sqrt{44.4} = 1494 \text{ ft. per sec.}$$

$$wt. = \frac{3600\ (.83)(.000341)(1494)}{3.69} = 412 \text{ lbs. per hr.}$$

(c) Since the expansion was to the critical pressure in part (b), there will be no increase in the quantity discharged in this case, the coefficient remaining the same.

It should be remembered in connection with the use of the orifice as a metering device, that the expression $h_1 - h_t$ represents the increase in kinetic energy and not the final kinetic energy, except in the case where the initial velocity has been assumed to be zero. When an orifice has been placed in a pipe line for measuring flow, the velocity of approach is never zero and serious errors may result from assuming it so unless the coefficient of discharge has been so determined as to take care of this.

Orifices are frequently used as permanent metering fixtures in service lines and when so installed necessarily operate with a small pressure differential between the two sides. Under such conditions, the difference in enthalpy is so slight as to be incapable of precise determination and recourse is had to actual calibration to determine coefficients of discharge.

Such coefficients are usually reported in terms of Reynolds Number, pipe size, and ratio of diameter of orifice to pipe diameter. Much work has been done along this line and a comprehensive report has been issued by the Special Research Committee on Fluid Meters of the American Society of Mechanical Engineers (4th Edition, 1937). The action of such low head metering orifices has little thermodynamic interest and is more properly discussed from the general fluid dynamics viewpoint. Hence details will not be further discussed here except to state that in general over a rather wide range of pipe sizes (2″ to 14″) and orifice ratios (0.15 to 0.70) the coefficient ranges from .62 to .67 at low Reynolds numbers and averages about .62 for Reynolds numbers above 200,000. For an excellent survey of this field and graphical data on constants, see Fluid Flow Measurement by Head Type Metering Elements by F. C. Stewart and J. S. Doolittle, The Instruments Publishing Company, Pittsburgh, Pennsylvania.

CHAPTER XI

ENGINEERING DEVICES USING VAPORS

XI-1. Classification.—Devices which use compressible fluids for producing useful work are customarily classified into two groups: (1) those using gases by which is meant, substances conforming to the perfect gas formulation, and (2) those using vapors by which is meant, substances most commonly in the saturated vapor region. Obviously, such a classification is artificial, as neither medium remains true to its classification in its behavior, but each overlaps into the realm of the other. We may have, for example, air compressors or air engines operating over ranges of pressure and temperature sufficient to bring the working substance close to or even within the saturated region; and conversely, we may operate a steam plant with such degrees of superheat that the steam behaves as much like a perfect gas as air at ordinary temperatures and pressures. Nevertheless, precedence is so strong that the classification still persists, even though for the group which uses vapors for motive fluids, we must qualify the term by stating whether it is a saturated or a superheated vapor that we are dealing with.

Devices Using Steam.—Although many vapors are in use for various devices, by far the most common medium is steam, and the most common utilizers for the production of power are the reciprocating steam engine and the steam turbine. Thermodynamically there is practically no difference in the series of events which constitute the operative cycle of these two engines. Each consists of a source of heat (the boiler), a utilizer, a receiver of rejected heat and a condenser (or atmosphere, if non-condensing). The simple fact that the utilizer in one case is a reciprocating unit, and in the other case a rotating element makes not the slightest difference in the general analysis of the heat cycle, even though the manner by which the heat supplied to the steam is transformed into useful work may differ. Any steam plant should be considered in its entirety as a heat engine and the series of events or cycle by which the heat supply from some external source is transformed into useful work should proceed from boiler back to boiler.

XI-2. Simple Steam Engine.—The oldest and most widely used device for the production of power by heat is undoubtedly the simple reciprocating steam engine. Dating back to Newcomen's atmospheric engine in 1705, its history has been one of consistent improvement, both mechanically and thermodynamically to the present time. Mechanically it has progressed through an era of low-pressure, slow-speed, ill-fitting pistons up to the modern ball-bearing, high-speed unit with mechanical fits of micrometer dimensions. Thermodynamically it has progressed from the stage of the early atmospheric type of Newcomen where the pressure of the piston was obtained by condensation, due to injecting a spray of water in the volume of steam under the piston, to the modern high-pressure type, using superheated steam and operating condensing or non-condensing

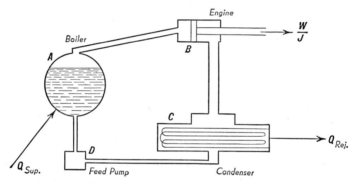

Fig. (XI-1).   Simple Steam Engine.

as the character of its service demands. Thermodynamically speaking, we rarely isolate the steam engine itself from the entire plant of boiler, engine cylinder, condenser and feed pump which constitute the ensemble of the heat engine, though mechanically we frequently isolate the engine mechanism for descriptive convenience. It is preferable, however, in thinking of the steam engine, to consider the actual engine mechanism as but an item in the entire heat engine set-up. Fig. (XI-1) gives a diagrammatic sketch of a simple steam engine.

From a thermodynamic point of view, it consists of a source of heat (A), the boiler at which the heat supply ($Q_{sup.}$) is received by the steam; engine cylinder (B), in which the steam with its supply of heat energy pushes out the piston and does the useful work at the expense of its own intrinsic energy; the condenser (C), to which the steam next passes and in which the heat ($Q_{rej.}$) is given to the cooling water and ultimately to the atmosphere; and the feed pump (D), which returns the condensed steam to the boiler for its next trip around the circuit. Regardless of the type of individual units, this is the basic set-up and holds for all steam plants. We may, if we wish, operate non-condensing, in which case, the steam is delivered directly to the atmosphere, the heat rejected ($Q_{rej.}$) goes directly to the atmosphere, but the only difference is that the mechanical unit (the condenser) disappears, for after the steam has been condensed, it becomes water and ultimately is taken by the feed pump and returned to the boiler.

Similarly, we may in place of the reciprocating steam engine substitute a steam turbine in which the steam is first expanded and the kinetic energy of the issuing jet is absorbed by the turbine rotor and transmitted as useful work, or the boiler may be of the external fire or internal fire, fire-tube type, or of the water tube or flash type, the fundamental conception is the same and the thermal efficiency is always

$$\frac{\text{Work done}}{\text{Heat supplied}} = \frac{Q_{sup.} - Q_{rej.}}{Q_{sup.}}.$$

The heat supplied, since the process of heating the feed water and converting it into steam is one of constant pressure, is equal to the difference in the heat content of the steam leaving and the heat content of the feed water coming in. Similarly, the heat rejected, whether it be to the condenser or to the atmosphere, is also a constant pressure process, and is equal to the difference between the heat content of the exhaust steam and the water fed to the boiler. For the ideal case, feed water temperature would be the same as the temperature at which the exhaust steam is condensed and the work done is equal to the difference between the heat supplied and the heat rejected minus the feed pump work. Similarly, the heat supplied is equal to the increase in heat content of the water coming to the feed pump and leaving the boiler, minus the work spent on the water to deliver it into the boiler.

High spots of mechanical development are roughly as follows: beginning with Newcomen's atmospheric engine, Watt produced an engine which operated from a boiler delivering steam at more than atmospheric pressure. This was a single-acting engine, its steam force was exerted on one side of the piston only. The next step was to make the engine double-acting, steam acting alternately on each side of the piston. After this followed the use of the D slide valve instead of the early poppet type, lagging of the cylinders to reduce radiation and conduction losses, increased rotative speeds, and the adoption of multiple expansion and higher boiler pressures all contributing to increased output and improved efficiency.

XI–3. Ideal Cycles.—Considering the operation of a normal steam plant from boiler back to boiler, the major events consist of (1) the reception of heat by the motive fluid at constant pressure corresponding to the formation of a pound of steam by the boiler; (2) the expansion to lower pressure doing useful work which may be in the cylinder of a reciprocating engine or in the nozzle and blades of a steam turbine; (3) withdrawal of heat at this lower pressure until the substance becomes liquefied, this corresponds to the action which takes place in the condenser; (4) an increase of pressure at nearly constant volume which corresponds to the action of the liquid from the condenser through the feed pump back and into the boiler ready to again receive heat and repeat its circuit.

Any ideal cycle to serve as a criterion for the measuring of actual performance must have for its individual events, processes similar to those actually occurring, but idealized to represent optimum conditions. In the earliest days of the steam engine, it was proposed to use Carnot's Cycle for the yardstick by which actual performance might be compared. Carnot's Cycle for a saturated vapor when drawn on a $P–V$ plane is not much different in appearance from the indicator diagram returned from the cylinder of a reciprocating steam engine, but this similarity is deceptive and the cycle is not a good approximation to that outlined above. It differs in two major respects; first, in the Carnot Cycle it is specified that heat is received at constant temperature, in the actual plant the heat is always received at constant pressure. It is true in the saturated region that these two are interdependent variables, but in the superheated region they are independent. If, for example, we were to specify that a steam plant using superheated steam were to operate on the Carnot's Cycle, it would mean that all the heat should be supplied from the higher temperature, which in turn would require that the latter portion of the heat supplying process would have to be at a series of lower pressures. This is clearly shown in Fig. (XI–2).

The second major point by which the Carnot Cycle diverges from the actual operating conditions is in the heat-rejection processes. In the Carnot Cycle, heat is rejected at the lower temperature until the vapor reaches such a quality that adiabatic compression from that point to the initial temperature will result in the vapor being compressed into a liquid. A glance at the temperature-entropy diagram will show that the adiabatic compression of vapor which has but little moisture in it will result in drying out the vapor, while adiabatic compression of a very wet vapor will result in making it wetter. Thus, for the adiabatic compression of the Carnot Cycle, wet steam would be withdrawn from the condenser and passed through a large compressor during which compression, it would become liquefied and delivered to the boiler. This is radically different from what actually takes place in the steam plant, as there the condensation is carried to completion and the liquid returned to the boiler pressure by the feed pump.

Rankine was one of the early writers who felt keenly the impropriety of using the Carnot Cycle and in place of it, proposed a cycle in which heat should be supplied and rejected at constant pressure and the condensation carried to completion. Such a cycle was given his name and

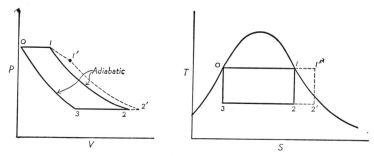

Fig. (XI–2).   Carnot Cycle for Saturated Steam.

constitutes our best ideal cycle for any modern power plant using a vapor or vapors for its motive fluid.

XI–4. The Rankine Cycle.—The cycle as proposed by Rankine consisted of heat being supplied at constant pressure, thus simulating the actual condition, and an adiabatic expansion to the lower pressure; heat was next rejected at constant pressure until the vapor was completely condensed to liquid form, thus again following the actual practice; and the cycle was completed by forcing the liquid into the boiler. For the moment, neglecting the feed pump work, we may then define the Rankine Cycle as the cycle of an ideal engine using a vapor as the working medium and consisting of the reception of heat at constant pressure, followed by adiabatic expansion, followed by the rejection of heat at constant pressure, and the cycle closed by a process of approximately constant volume. Such a cycle is shown both in the PV and the TS planes in Fig. (XI–3). From 0 to 1 represents supplying of heat at constant pressure which corresponds to the heating of the incoming water first up to the boiling temperature and then boiling it off into saturated steam. From 1 to 2 represents the adiabatic expansion.

From 2 to 3 represents the rejection of heat at constant pressure wherein the vapor is condensed to a liquid.

From 3 to 0 represents the passage through the feed pump and back into the boiler at high pressure.

The line 0 to 0′ on the temperature-entropy diagram represents the heating of the liquid after it is in the boiler. The point 0, 3, on the temper-

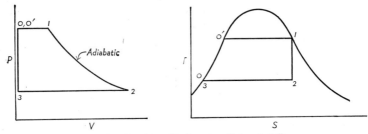

FIG. (XI–3). Rankine Cycle using Saturated Steam.

ature-entropy diagram is really two points corresponding to the passage of the water through the feed pump, but without appreciable rise in temperature corresponding to the line 3–0 on the PV plane. Similarly the line 0–0′, on the TS plane becomes practically a single point on the PV plane, as the increase of volume of the water is trivial, except at very high pressures.

XI–5. Characteristics of the Rankine Cycle.—The expression for efficiency of any heat engine is

$$\text{Eff.} = \frac{Q_{\text{sup.}} - Q_{\text{rej.}}}{Q_{\text{sup.}}}.$$

As the supply and rejection of heat are at constant pressure, the change in the heat content during these two processes will evaluate the heat supplied and rejected. Thus the efficiency of the Rankine Cycle (Eff._R):

$$\text{Eff.}_R = \frac{(h_1 - h_3) - (h_2 - h_3)}{h_1 - h_3} = \frac{h_1 - h_2}{h_1 - h_3},$$

where $(h_1 - h_2)$ represents the adiabatic heat-drop from initial to final pressure and h_3 denotes the heat of the liquid at the lower pressure. As h_3 is equal to h_{f2} it is more convenient to write the equation,

$$\text{Eff.}_R = \frac{h_1 - h_2}{h_1 - h_{f2}},$$

where the subscripts 1 and 2 refer to the initial and final pressures respectively.

In solving this equation the initial state is known and hence h_1 and s_1. The adiabatic expansion is at constant entropy, thus $s_1 = s_2$ and knowing s_2 and the final pressure, the heat content after adiabatic expansion can be computed. (See Chapter IX.) The value of h_{f2} can be obtained directly from the steam tables for the terminal pressure. Thus the only thermodynamic computation which is entailed is that for determining h_2, the heat content after adiabatic expansion.

The solution of problems is simplified by using the Mollier diagram of heat content on entropy from which the value of h_2 can be read directly. Using this, from the initial state, a vertical (constant entropy) path is followed until the lower pressure is reached. This intersection is the state point after expansion and h_2 can be read directly. Arranged in the following form the calculation can be made in less than two minutes.

$$p_1 = 200 \text{ lbs. dry} \qquad\qquad\qquad p_2 = 20 \text{ lbs.}$$

$$\begin{array}{ll} h_1 = 1198.5 & h_1 = 1198.5 \\ h_2 = 1028.5 & h_{f2} = 196.2 \\ \hline 170.0 \div & \phantom{h_{f2} = }1002.3 = 16.97 = \text{Eff.}_R. \end{array}$$

If the efficiency be computed for a series of back pressures, it is possible to construct a curve which will give directly the efficiency to any back pressure for any one initial pressure. By building up a family of such curves, J. S. Doolittle has evolved a chart, Fig. (XI–5), from which the efficiency of the Rankine Cycle can be directly read for any range of conditions normally encountered. Referring to this, the solution of the above problem is read directly as 16.9.*

The pounds of steam per Hp.-hr. for the Rankine Cycle will be equal to the thermal equivalent of one Hp.-hr. divided by the heat equivalent of the work done per pound of steam, or the adiabatic heat drop. Thus,

$$\text{Lbs. Steam per Hp. hr.} = \frac{2544}{h_1 - h_2}.$$

Similarly, the B.t.u. per Hp. per minute will be equal to the thermal equivalent of the Hp. divided by efficiency of conversion or B.t.u. per

$$\text{Hp. per min.} = \frac{42.4}{E_R}.$$

* If the steam is not originally dry and saturated a correction, shown in the upper right-hand corner of the figure, is to be added directly to the efficiency obtained for dry saturated steam.

The performance of any actual engine may be gaged by checking it against the performance of the ideal engine operating between the same limits. The Rankine cycle is the accepted ideal for any steam engine and the ratio of the thermal efficiency of any actual engine to the thermal efficiency of the Rankine cycle between the same initial and back pressures becomes the best gage of the *effectiveness of performance* of actual engines. Such a ratio is termed the Rankine Cycle Ratio (R.C.R.).

$$\text{Rankine Cycle Ratio} = \frac{\text{Thermal Effic. (actual engine)}}{\text{Thermal Effic. (Rankine Cycle)}}.$$

As the thermal efficiency is equal to $\dfrac{42.42}{\text{Btu/Hp/min}}$ this is equivalent to:

$$\text{Rankine Cycle Ratio (R. C. R.)} = \frac{\text{B.t.u. per Hp. per min. (R. Cycle)}}{\text{B.t.u. per Hp. per min. (Actual)}}.$$

So far, we have treated the Rankine Cycle only in its most simple form, namely, neglecting feed pump work and confining its range to the saturated region. If the supply of heat produces steam which is superheated, then the cycle partakes of the following character (See Fig.

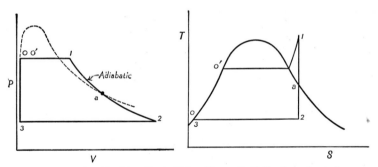

FIG. (XI–4). Rankine Cycle Using Steam Initially Superheated.

(XI–4)). The expansion commences in the superheated region and later passes into the saturated region at pressure (*a*). The character of the two expansions differs slightly but not enough to show an appreciable point of inflection at (*a*) in the PV graph. Strictly speaking, the heat supplied ($Q_{sup.}$) is the simple difference between the heat content of the steam leaving the boiler and the feed water entering *the boiler* and not between the heat content of the steam leaving the boiler and the heat content of the feed water entering the *feed pump*. Thus, $Q_{sup.} = h_1 - h_0$ and $h_0 = h_3 +$ Feed

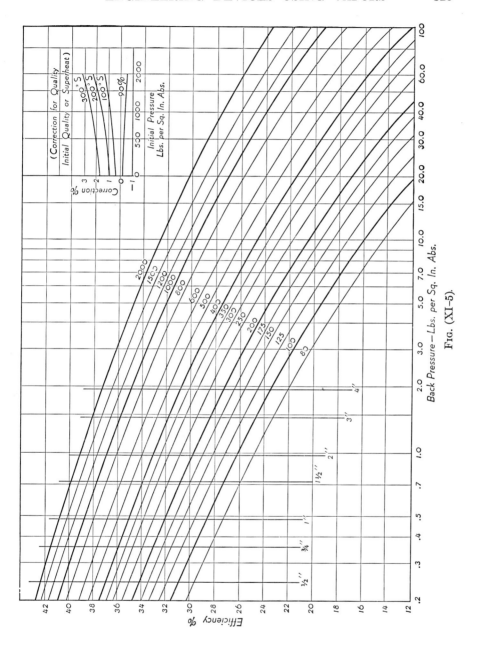

Fig. (XI-5).

Pump Work $= h_3 + A(P_0 - P_3)V_f$. Thus the accurate expression for efficiency becomes

$$\frac{h_1 - h_2 - A(P_0 - P_3)v_f}{h_1 - h_3 - A(P_0 - P_3)v_f} \quad \text{or} \quad \frac{(h_1 - h_2) - (h_0 - h_3)}{(h_1 - h_0)}.$$

An idea of the amount of this ideal boiler feed pump work is given by the following example: Water at 300° F., 100 lbs. per sq. in. abs., is pumped into a boiler against a pressure of 1500 lbs. per sq. in. abs. The work is

$$144(1500 - 100)(.0174) = 3510 \text{ ft.-lbs. or } 4.51 \text{ B.t.u.}$$

The feed pump term is so small and its effect on efficiency so slight that, except for high-pressure ranges or unusually refined work, it is usually omitted and the approximate form of equation used.

The Rankine Cycle operates between *pressure* limits, whereas the Carnot Cycle operates between *temperature* limits. If the comparison be confined to the saturated region, the extreme limits of both may be considered the same. However, since the heat supplied in the Rankine Cycle for heating the feed water up to the boiler temperature is supplied at a series of temperatures increasing from the lowest to the highest, the efficiency of this cycle will be inferior to that of the Carnot, in which all of the heat is supplied at the highest temperature. The Carnot Cycle is a reversible cycle by definition, and if the heat supplied to heating the feed water in the Rankine Cycle be considered as having been supplied by a series of units with temperatures varying from lowest to highest, we may also consider that this heat has been applied reversibly. Thus the Rankine is also a reversible cycle, but as already mentioned, a reversible cycle operating for part of its duration through a temperature range distinctly inferior to that of a comparable Carnot Cycle.

XI–6. Conditions Affecting the Efficiency of the Rankine Cycle.— Anything which tends to increase the pressure range through which the Rankine Cycle operates will obviously increase its efficiency. This can be accomplished by,

1. Increasing the initial pressure.
2. Decreasing the back pressure.
3. Superheating.

Each of these, obviously, increases the net or effective working area on the temperature-entropy plane, as shown by the hatched area, on Fig. (XI–6), and each produces a gain in efficiency as may be seen in Fig. (XI–7), which shows graphically the successive efficiencies. In this latter the heat available for useful work $(Q_{sup.} - Q_{rej.})$ is shown above the heavy line and the heat supplied $(Q_{sup.})$ below, thus giving a graphical representation of the fraction,

$$\frac{Q_{sup.} - Q_{rej.}}{Q_{sup.}}.$$

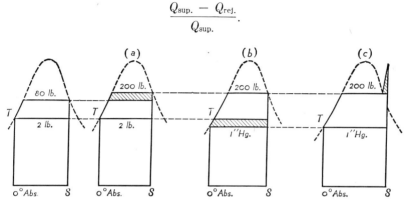

FIG. (XI–6). Graphical Illustration of Gain to Rankine Cycle from Increasing (a) Initial Pressure, (b) Back Pressure and (c) Superheating.

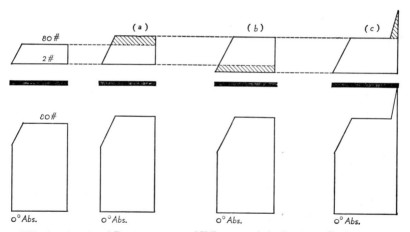

FIG. (XI–7). Graphical Representation of Efficiency of the Rankine Cycle as Affected by Increasing the Range of Pressure (a) (b) and by Superheating (c). The Heavy Line Represents the Dividing Line of the Fraction.

In addition to these rather obvious means for increasing efficiency, there are those of resuperheating and regenerative feed-water heating which apply particularly to turbine installations and which deserve special mention, and will be dealt with later.

XI–7. Divergence of Actual Performance from Ideal.—The test returns from actual engines show appreciable divergence from the performance predicted for the ideal Rankine Cycle operating between the same range. This ratio (Rankine Cycle Ratio) ranges from 35 per cent (or even less) to 85 per cent, and it is interesting to note the items to which this divergence is mainly due.

Considering first the reciprocating steam engine, the major losses consist of:

1. Effect of cylinder walls (initial condensation and subsequent re-evaporation).
2. Incomplete expansion.
3. Wire drawing (throttling) in admission and exhaust passages.
4. Radiation and convection.

Of these by far the most important is the first one. Heat will flow whenever there is a temperature difference, and in the case of the reciprocating steam engine, as the piston passes out on the working stroke, the steam which comes into the cylinder encounters the walls which have attained approximately the temperature of the low pressure and low temperature steam leaving on the previous exhaust stroke. Immediately heat flows from the steam warming the walls and cooling the steam, with the result that a film of condensate is deposited on the walls of the cylinder. As the piston travels further during the expansion stroke, its pressure and thus its temperature begin to fall and soon reach a temperature below the temperature of the cylinder walls which have just been warmed by the incoming steam. The result is, from there on, the re-evaporation of the moisture condensed on the cylinder walls as the heat flows back from the cylinder walls into the steam. This action is clearly shown on the T–S plane in Fig. (XI–8). The net result of this process is that an appreciable amount of heat is short-circuited from doing useful work during the expansion stroke. It went out to the cylinder walls at the beginning of the stroke at high temperature and availability, and was returned to the steam at the end of the stroke degraded, to a lower temperature and less available state. The net effect of this action is to materially reduce the thermal efficiency. It may, dependent upon type and construction, reduce the thermal efficiency to $3/4$ or even $1/2$ of the ideal. Obviously, it is minimized by anything which minimizes the temperature differential between the steam and the cylinder walls. If, for example, the range of pressures were reduced, the range of temperature fluctuation in the steam would be reduced and the corresponding heat transfer to and from the walls would be reduced. Also, since condensation and re-evaporation will require an appreciable time interval for their consummation, the quicker the operation of the engine, the less will be the condensation and re-evaporation.

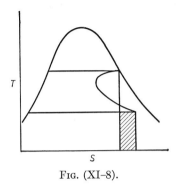

FIG. (XI–8).

Incomplete Expansion.—Incomplete expansion occurs when an engine releases at the end of its stroke at a pressure which is higher than the back pressure. Obviously, such an event simply discharges steam into the exhaust passage which might have been used for useful work, thus the term "incomplete expansion." Extreme instances of this sort occur in the case of steam pumps by which the steam is admitted at high pressure throughout the entire stroke and no expansion occurs in the cylinder at all. The effect is clearly shown in the accompanying figure.

The PV diagram shows a constant volume drop in pressure at the end of the stroke. This is commonly taken as representing a cooling at constant volume. What actually occurs is a throttling at release to atmospheric or back pressure with a subsequent cooling at constant pressure. From a thermodynamic point of view the two events are nearly equivalent, as it can be shown that the heat removed at constant pressure after the throttling process is nearly the same as that which would be removed were the volume to remain constant. It is a convenient assumption and materially simplifies the discussion.

In Fig. (XI–9), process 1–2′ represents a constant volume cooling, and thus area 0′–1–2′–3 is equivalent to the work done in the cylinder. The actual process—expansion throttling into the exhaust pipe—is shown as 1–2″. The loss of available energy by such a process is area, 2–2″–5′–4, which is equivalent to the loss of energy incurred by a constant volume cooling in the engine cylinder and represented by area 1–2–2′.

Wire drawing is the reduction in pressure which the steam undergoes in flowing through the rough and tortuous passages into and out from the cylinder. There is appreciable energy degradation by virtue of the friction and turbulence created.

Mechanical friction and leakage past imperfectly fitted parts, together

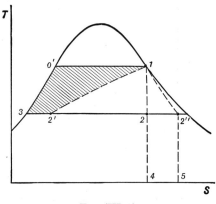

Fig. (XI-9).

with radiation losses, also cause considerable departure from the ideal efficiency.

XI-8. Multiple Expansion and Other Aids to Economy.—When expansion is arranged to take place in two cylinders, each doing approximately half the total work, it is possible to reduce the temperature fluctuations in each cylinder without affecting the total expansion ratio; such a device is called "compounding." It is resorted to solely to minimize cylinder condensation and is the most effective means for accomplishing this.

The same principle may be carried further and the total expansion divided into three or even four parts with accompanying decrease in cylinder condensation. When the total expansion is divided into three steps, it is customary to call the engine a "triple expansion engine," and where the expansion is carried out in four stages, "quadruple expansion." The prime objective in all cases is the same, namely, minimizing the loss due to initial condensation on the cylinder walls.

The minimizing effect of multiple expansion on the loss due to multiple expansion is graphically shown in Fig. (XI-10). Figs. *a*, *b*, and *c* represent respectively a simple, compound, and triple-expansion engine all operating through the same range of processes and starting with steam in the same initial state. Obviously the compound has less loss than the single, and the triple effects a still further gain.

There are many arrangements of cranks and cylinders for each of these general types, but the ultimate objective is the same. Obviously the higher the range of pressures, the more feasible does multiple expansion become.

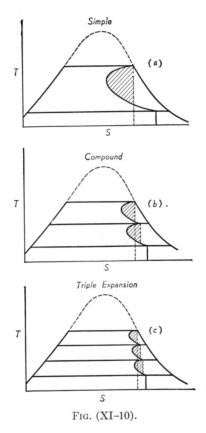

Fig. (XI-10).

Up to throttle pressures of 150 lbs., the expansion is usually split into two stages (compound engine); from 150 lbs. to 250 lbs., three stages of expansion (triple-expansion engines) are common and for pressures in excess of that, quadruple engines are frequently built, though the gain of the quadruple over the triple is materially less than that of the triple over the compound, as may be seen from the accompanying table.

RELATIVE GAIN FROM MULTIPLE EXPANSION

Simple	Compound	Triple
1.00	1.25	1.28
....	1.00	1.07

While the main objective of multiple expansion in successive cylinders is to minimize the evil effect of cylinder condensation, there is an attendant gain of increase in the expansion ratio which is practically obtainable.

In addition to the foregoing, the superficial wall area for the compound engine is about $\frac{3}{4}$ of the superficial area of the equivalent single-cylinder engine, which is another helpful influence.

Beside the use of multiple expansion, the following developments have contributed toward improving the economy of the modern steam engine, the use of superheated steam, higher rotative speeds, steam jacketing, the use of reheaters and the uniflow type of engine. All of these are in the nature of mechanical improvements as they do not strictly come within the category of improvements to the thermodynamic cycle.

Use of Superheated Steam.—The use of superheated steam is primarily beneficial in that it appreciably minimizes initial condensation. The thermal conductivity of superheated steam is not high and heat transfer from the body of the superheated steam to the cylinder walls is not rapid. However, the steam near the walls exerts an appreciable heating effect before it is cooled to saturation temperature. It is not definitely known which of these effects predominate, but tests indicate an appreciable reduction in initial condensation by the use of superheated steam.

Use of Higher Rotative Speeds.—By increasing the rotative speeds it is possible to so shorten the time of one stroke that there is insufficient time for the condensation film to take place as completely as at lower speeds. The change of phase of the steam requires a certain time for its completion and condensation loss is materially lessened at very high revolutions.

Use of Reheaters.—Reheating is frequently adopted for multiple-expansion engines and consists of passing the steam after leaving the first cylinder, through a reheating device where additional heat is taken on. From here the steam passes to the next cylinder and repeats for later stages. Any gain in thermal efficiency by reheating is slight, although the capacity of the engine may be increased.

Use of the Uniflow Engine.—The uniflow engine was a sincere attempt to design a steam engine which should operate in such a manner that the condensation losses should be minimized. In its essence it consists of making the cylinder longer than the normal engine and supplying the live steam at the end of the cylinder with the exhaust ports at the middle of the cylinder. Figure XI–11 shows a sketch of a uniflow engine. If the piston is also made long, we have in effect two single-acting cylinders with pistons placed in each end, in each of which the steam enters at one end of the cylinder and leaves at the other. With such a device there is built up a more stable temperature region between the admission ports and the

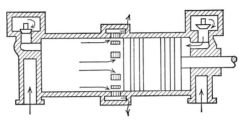

Fig. (XI–11). Uniflow Engine.

exhaust ports than with the ordinary type. Such engines, particularly for fairly large expansion ratios, have shown decided improvements in economy and are in current use.

XI–9. Other Types of Steam Engine.—Beside the orthodox reciprocating steam engine, there are the rotary steam engine and the steam turbine. The rotary steam engine in its essence consists of a unit by which the steam acts expansively upon some rotating member to drive it by direct pressure.

Innumerable forms have been proposed, but almost without exception, they have been failures from the thermodynamic point of view, as might be expected by examination of their operative cycles. They offer nothing in the way of improved cyclical performance, and their only claim to consideration lies in the substitution of the rotary motion for the orthodox reciprocating motion of the piston. Thus, thermodynamically, there is no gain and mechanically the simple substitution of a rotating prime mover for a reciprocating one offers no gain.

The other type of prime mover, namely, the steam turbine, offers a very real gain for the following reasons: using steam expansively behind a piston, where the pressure that is pushing the piston out is continually decreasing, there is soon reached a limit at which the force pushing the piston is no greater than necessary to overcome the rubbing friction of the piston in the cylinder. Expansion may be carried to this point, but no further, and as the volume of the steam increases tremendously at the lower pressures, and the frictional resistances build up rapidly. In the steam turbine, the large volumes corresponding to the very low pressures may be readily handled without excessive frictional losses, and it thus becomes possible for a steam turbine to utilize a lower back pressure, thus increasing the operative pressure range of the cycle and there results a radical improvement in the cycle efficiency and corresponding efficiency of the actual unit. Were it not for the fact that the steam turbine can capitalize this extremely low-pressure region, there would be no particular thermodynamic gain in building it; or stated differently, the efficiency of

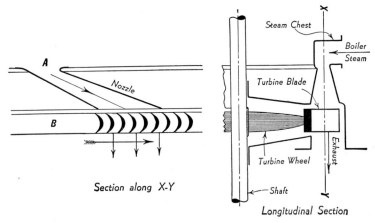

FIG. (XI–12).   Simple Impulse Turbine.

a steam reciprocating engine and that of a steam turbine, each operating between initial pressure and atmospheric, would be very little different, which accounts for the fact that we practically never see non-condensing steam turbines in use where thermal efficiency is an important objective.

In its simplest form the steam turbine consists of a nozzle through which steam is expanded and from which it issues at high velocity and a device for decelerating this jet, and by this deceleration transmitting an impulse which is passed on as useful work. The turbine of the DeLaval type, as shown in Fig. (XI–12) is an excellent typical example: steam enters nozzle A, expands to back pressure and leaves the mouth with high velocity. In passing through the vanes (B), it is slowed down so that it leaves theoretically with no velocity at right angles to the shaft axis (velocity of whirl).

This slowing down of the jet has resulted in a force on the blade tending to drive the rotor. The conversion into useful work has been accomplished in a manner slightly different from the reciprocating engine in that the heat content of the steam has been utilized in, (1) producing the high velocity of the issuing jet, and (2) the kinetic energy of the issuing jet is transformed into useful work.

Thus the consideration of the performance of the steam turbine requires a scrutiny of the thermodynamic means by which the jet may be produced and then the vapordynamics of its utilization. Expansion through the nozzle is so quick that it is practically adiabatic and the effective energy is the adiabatic heat drop from initial to terminal pressure. In this action the available heat $(H_1 - H_2)$ has been converted into kinetic energy of the jet. (See Chapter X.)

XI-10. **Vapordynamics of the Simple Steam Turbine.**—It is essential, in steam turbine work, to be able to analyze the steam velocities and their variations, and particularly to be able to predict the result of steam of a certain velocity acting upon blades which move with a different speed, and to determine the proper angle to which the blades should be formed in order that the steam may enter the blade passage smoothly and without shock or impact. In this work, the use of vectors provides the easiest and most facile means of solution. Vectors are capable of representing magnitude and direction of velocities. Velocities are always relative. It is customary, however, to call the velocities with respect to stationary objects *absolute* velocities, while those relative to the moving blades are called *relative* velocities. Fig. (XI-13) is a vector diagram for a row of blades moving in the direction indicated at a speed of V_b ft. per sec., V_1 represents the spouting velocity of the steam from the nozzles making an angle with the plane of rotation of α, called the nozzle angle. Laying out V_b in relation to V_1, as shown, and closing the triangle, V_{r1} is obtained. This is the velocity of the steam from the nozzles entering the blades, expressed with reference to the blade. Also the angle β is determined, which is the true angle at which the steam enters the blades. The blades, then, should be designed to conform to this angle, and β is known as the blade entrance angle. If, now, the steam in the blade passage encounters no frictional resistance, it will leave, relative to the blade, at the same speed at which it entered. And if, further, the blade exit angle, γ, be made the same as the entrance angle, β, the vector, V_{r2}, showing the magnitude and direction of the relative velocity leaving the blade, may be laid out. Again using V_b and closing the diagram, V_2 is obtained and also the angle δ. These are, respectively, the absolute velocity and the angle at which the steam leaves the plane of rotation.

As previously mentioned, work is done upon the blades by reducing the absolute velocity and hence kinetic energy of the steam jet. To accomplish this, the absolute velocity of the steam must be less when it emerges than when it enters the blades. Reference to Fig. (XI–13) will show that this is so, V_2 being less than V_1. The kinetic energy which has left the jet is $\dfrac{V_1{}^2 - V_2{}^2}{2gJ}$ B.t.u. per lb. of steam, and, *with no friction*, this represents the work done on the blades. However, *with friction*, as in all actual cases, some of the kinetic energy has been transformed into work and the rest into heat.

The velocity diagram shown in Fig. (XI–13) is not so easy to use as the modification shown in Fig. (XI–14), which is laid out to the same scale

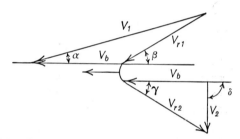

Fig. (XI–13).   Velocity Diagram for Simple Turbine
(Symmetrical Blades and No Friction).

and notation. The latter is less bulky, easier to lay out, and is geometrically and trigonometrically simpler. Work is done on the blades of a turbine by a force acting through a definite distance. The force is produced by changing the direction of motion of the jet of steam which is issuing from the nozzles. Since this is done by the blades, the force is impressed upon the blades. The distance through which that force acts is, therefore, the distance that the blades travel in one minute, if foot-pounds per minute are desired, or one second for foot-pounds per second. The force necessary to accelerate, or decelerate, a given mass a known amount is easily determined from the relationship $f = ma$. Thus, the force exerted by one pound of steam per second in being brought from V_1 to rest would be $f = \dfrac{V_1}{g}$. Unfortunately, this force cannot be fully utilized since it would be exerted at an angle α to the direction in which the blades are moving. In other words, the changes in velocity, which provide useful forces, are only those which occur in the rotational plane. This useful change in velocity is called the change in velocity of whirl, V_w, which may be found by resolving the velocities involved into their components, which are parallel to the plane of rotation. Thus, the entrance velocity of whirl is the horizontal component of V_1, or $V_1 \cos \alpha$, and the exit velocity of whirl is $V_2 \cos \delta$. The latter value may be positive or negative or zero, depending upon whether δ is less than or equal to or greater than 90°, but the total change velocity of whirl is the algebraic sum of the two. Obviously, V_w is also

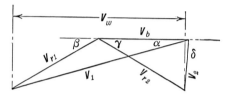

FIG. (XI–14). Velocity Diagram for a Simple Impulse Turbine (Symmetrical Blades and No Friction).

equal to the sum of the horizontal components of the relative velocities, thus,

$$V_w = V_1 \cos \alpha + V_2 \cos \delta = V_{r1} \cos \beta + V_{r2} \cos \gamma.$$

The force exerted by W pounds of steam per second,

$$F = \frac{WV_w}{g} = \frac{W(V_1 \cos \alpha + V_2 \cos \delta)}{g} = \frac{W}{g}(V_{r1} \cos \beta + V_{r2} \cos \gamma).$$

And the work done by W pounds of steam per second,

$$\text{Work} = \frac{WV_wV_b}{g} = \frac{W}{g}(V_b)(V_{r1} \cos \beta + V_{r2} \cos \gamma).$$

The relation between blade speed and jet velocity has an important bearing upon the work done. If the blade velocity were zero, for instance, there would obviously be no work done because there would be no distance displaced. If the blade speed were equal to the steam speed, there would also be no work done because the steam could not catch up to and enter the blades to exert a force. Between these two extremes there must be an optimum velocity of the blades with respect to the spouting velocity of the steam, which may be found as follows, assuming the conditions to exist as in the velocity diagram, Fig. (XI–14).

$$V_w = 2V_{r1} \cos \beta = 2(V_1 \cos \alpha - V_b),$$

$$W = \frac{2V_b(V_1 \cos \alpha - V_b)}{g} \text{ per lb. of steam per second,}$$

W will be a maximum when the first derivative of W with respect to V_b is zero and the second derivative is negative. Differentiating,

$$\frac{dW}{dV_b} = \frac{2V_1 \cos \alpha - 4V_b}{g} = 0 \quad \text{and} \quad \frac{d^2W}{dV_b^2} = -\frac{4}{g}.$$

$$V_b = \frac{V_1 \cos \alpha}{2} \quad \text{or} \quad \frac{V_b}{V_1} = \rho = \frac{\cos \alpha}{2}.$$

The same expression may be shown to hold when friction and nonsymmetrical blades are considered.

The simplest form of impulse blade is that made from a piece of sheet metal bent to the correct curvature for inlet and outlet angles as shown

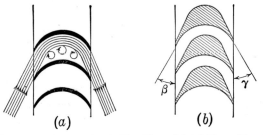

(a)   (b)

Fig. (XI–15). Impulse Blading of (a) The Sheet Metal Type Showing Possibilities of Eddy Losses and (b) The Conventionial Type.

in Fig. (XI–15) (a). A blade of this type, however, provides a passage of non-uniform width, increasing from entrance to half through the blade and decreasing to exit. In addition to this, due to the violent deflection which takes place in the blade passage, a compression of the fluid occurs, resulting in an actual decrease in the stream width, as illustrated. The blade passage desired, then, is one with a slight constriction at the midpoint. The sheet metal vanes have just the opposite, the result being a cavity in which swirling and turbulence may take place with consequent loss. Therefore, the blades are formed as shown in Fig. (XI–15) (b), the cavity being filled by metal. It should be noted that the blade entrance and exit angles

are very clearly defined in this type of blade. An additional advantage
to be gained by thus forming the blades is further stiffness which will help
to reduce the vibrations which are likely to occur.

XI-11. **Turbine Losses and Their Effects.**—There are four important
losses in the steam turbine: Fluid friction, steam leakage, radiation, and
mechanical friction, named in the order of their magnitude for the average
case.

Fluid Friction.—The turbine being a kinetic device, it is natural that it
should be subject to the losses which ordinarily affect a fluid in motion.
These losses are almost entirely frictional, that is, due to contact of the
fluid with surfaces and to turbulence, but a small proportion is due to
impact and supersaturation. However, the result is the same in either

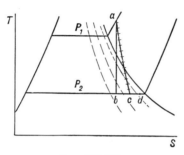

Fig. (XI-16).

case and no attempt will be made to distinguish between them in general.
The immediate effect of these losses is the dissipation of kinetic energy
and its subsequent transformation into heat. The action is very much
akin to throttling, and, as such, results in the loss of availability. The
expansion is still approximately adiabatic, but is not isentropic, the partially irreversible action resulting in an entropy increase. This departure
from the isentropic is shown graphically in Fig. (XI-16). a–b represents
a reversible adiabatic expansion from P_1 to P_2, while a–c–d shows the
actual path in passing through a stage of an impulse turbine. This curve
may be divided into two distinct parts: a–c showing the effect of nozzle
friction, during the drop in pressure, and c–d representing the frictional
effect in transit through the blades at constant pressure.

With the retransformation of kinetic energy into heat, this heat is
immediately added to the steam as additional unavailable energy and, as
a result, the final specific volume and heat content of the steam are increased
over their values, following a reversible adiabatic expansion. This, together

with the fact that the velocities are reduced, must be considered in the design of nozzle and blade passages. The quantity of energy so reconverted into heat is called reheat and may definitely be expressed in B.t.u. per pound of steam. Nozzle loss has been discussed in a previous chapter, and it will be recalled that the means of determining the reheat was from the efficiency, expressed as the percentage of available energy converted into kinetic energy. In the case of blading, it is customary to use a velocity coefficient which is the ratio of the exit to the entering relative velocity. This affects the velocity diagram directly. Windage losses, due to the resistance offered to rapidly rotating parts in an atmosphere of steam, account for most of the remainder of this class of losses.

Steam Leakage.—This divides itself into two classes: atmospheric gland leakage, and interstage leakage in the case of compounding. The former is due to the leakage of steam from the casing around the shaft as it emerges, while the latter arises when steam passes from one stage to the next, either around the shaft or over the tips of the blades without doing work. The total loss from leakage probably does not exceed 2 per cent of the steam flowing in the average case, but this is dependent upon the steam conditions, number of stages, type of turbine, and design.

Radiation.—This is proportional to the area of the casing and to the temperature difference involved. Since the areas are small relative to the enormous amount of steam passing through the turbine and the average casing temperature is much less than the maximum, this loss is comparatively small. The calculation of the magnitude of the radiation loss is difficult to carry through with a high degree of accuracy, but existing data seem to indicate that it is approximately 1 per cent of the heat supplied. Effort is usually made to keep this loss to a minimum by covering the high and intermediate pressure cylinders of turbines.

Mechanical Losses.—These losses do not all come under the head of direct friction of mechanical parts. Shaft bearings produce frictional resistance, and the work required to operate oil pumps, governors, and other auxiliary apparatus accounts for the remainder of the losses in this class. Results differ widely with different units, but again a rough estimate may be placed at between 1 per cent and 2 per cent of the shaft work.

XI-12. Need for Compounding in Steam Turbines.—It has been seen, in the consideration of the simple impulse turbine, that the mean blade velocity, for best diagram efficiency, should be a certain proportion of the spouting velocity of the steam jet from the nozzles.

Thus the blade speed should be $\dfrac{\cos \alpha}{2} \times$ steam speed for the simple turbine where α is the angle made by the nozzles with the plane of rotation. Since the nozzle angle is always small, this ratio is roughly $\frac{1}{2}$. The heat available per pound of steam in the modern steam plant is such as to give very high jet velocities from the nozzles when the steam is expanded throughout the entire range in one step, which would, in turn, necessitate extreme peripheral speeds of the rotor. This is undesirable because it involves either high rotative speeds which cannot be conveniently used or prohibitive stresses beyond the ability of engineering materials to with-stand. The earlier de Laval turbines were of the simple type, with small rotors and rotative speeds of from 20,000 to 40,000 revolutions per minute. These could be built in small sizes only and were soon replaced by types in which some form of compounding was used. The reduction in periph-eral velocity can be accomplished by two methods: (1) by subdividing the total pressure drop into several stages for each of which the nozzle exit velocity is correspondingly reduced, and (2) by retaining full range pressure drop with subsequent excessive exit velocity and absorbing this velocity in several rows of vanes, each utilizing a portion of the kinetic energy. The first is called pressure compounding and the second velocity compounding. All modern turbines are compounded in one way or another, and it is only through compounding that large units in use today have been made possible.

XI-13. Velocity Compounding.—In this method, only one set of nozzles is employed to expand the steam from initial conditions to the exist-ing back pressure as in the simple turbine. The jet velocity is, therefore, the same as for the simple type for the same steam conditions. However, in transforming the kinetic energy of the steam into mechanical energy at the shaft, more than one set of vanes is used as shown diagrammatically in Fig. (XI-17). Stationary guide blades, as shown, must be interposed between the moving rows in order to redirect the steam for proper entry into the succeeding row of blades. Unlike the simple machine, the first row of vanes, in this case, need not reduce the steam velocity to a minimum since that which escapes the first row may be picked up by the second. Thus the blade velocity may be considerably reduced, the result being an increased carry-over velocity from the first row, which would be wasted in the case of the simple turbine, but which, in this case, would be taken care of by the second row of blading. It may be shown that, for best diagram efficiency, the ratio of blade speed to steam speed for the velocity compounded turbine should be $\dfrac{\cos \alpha}{2n}$ where n is the number of moving rows of vanes. Thus, by the use of two velocity rows instead of one, the blade velocity may be halved; by the use of three or four rows, the blade speed will be one third or one fourth that for a single row, etc. It would seem that the blade velocity might be reduced in this manner to any desired value, but inspection of the velocity diagrams for this type of

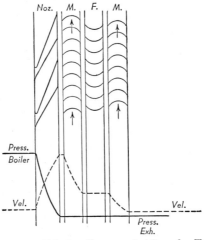

Fig. (XI–17).   Velocity Compounded Impulse Turbine.

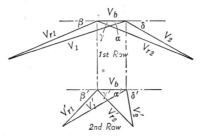

Fig. (XI–18).   Velocity Diagram for Two Row Velocity Compounded Stage
(Symmetrical Blades, No Friction).

turbine, Fig. (XI–18), shows that the work done by the steam in successive blade rows becomes less and less until it is no longer practicable to add more rows. The following table shows approximately the proportion of the total work done by each blade row in stages of two, three, four, and five rows of rotating blades. For this reason, more than two rows of blades are seldom used per stage in American practice, and, if further reduction in blade speed is desired, other means are resorted to.

WORK PROPORTIONS OF VARIOUS ROWS IN VELOCITY COMPOUNDING

Blade Rows	Work—Per cent of Total				
	1st Row	2nd Row	3rd Row	4th Row	5th Row
2 Rows.....	75	25			
3 Rows.....	56	33	11		
4 Rows.....	44	31	19	6	
5 Rows.....	36	28	20	12	4

XI-14. Pressure Compounding.—A reduction in blade velocity to within reasonable limits might be effected in the simple turbine by reducing the range of expansion across the turbine to the point where the available energy for that expansion is sufficiently small to give the desired spouting velocity. As was seen in the discussion of the Rankine Cycle, this reduction in heat available may not be brought about by changing the steam conditions of the plant without impairing the theoretical efficiency, but it may be achieved by placing a number of simple turbines in series in such a way that each expands the steam only through the desired range. In such a case, the turbines might all be mounted upon the same shaft and contained within the same casing and considered as one machine which is pressure compounded, that is, the expansion of the steam has itself been split up into a number of parts. In this case, the turbine, as a whole, is made up of a number of pressure stages, each stage being composed essentially of a set of nozzles with its succeeding blades. This arrangement is illustrated diagrammatically in Fig. (XI-19). A turbine of this type would be known as a four-stage impulse turbine. In the illustration, because of the small number of stages, the expansion in each set of nozzles would be to a pressure well below the critical and the nozzles would have divergent sections as shown. Actually, however, the number of stages would be such as to give expansions which would require convergent nozzles throughout.

Velocity diagrams for a turbine of this type would be drawn for each individual stage and so would consist of a series of diagrams exactly similar to those for simple turbines.

In practice, all large impulse turbines are pressure compounded since this method lends itself readily to the accommodation of any desired blade velocity and stages may be made to do equal work or any other proportions that might be desirable. This method has the additional advantage over velocity compounding of considerably better efficiencies in practice. The principal disadvantage is the increased bulk of the machine over that which is purely velocity compounded for the same power output under identical steam conditions. Thus, many of the smaller turbines, such as might be used to drive auxiliaries, are simply velocity compounded because small size is more important than high economy,

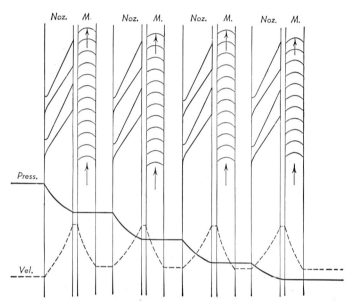

Fɪɢ. (XI–19).   Pressure Compounded Impulse Turbine.

whereas the main turbines of a plant, where economy is important, would invariably be pressure staged.

XI–15. Combination of Pressure and Velocity Compounding.—It is obvious that a combination of the two methods of compounding just discussed might be used in such a way as to retain most of the advantages of both. Figure (XI–20) shows the arrangement of nozzles and blade rows in a turbine in which the two systems have been combined throughout. This would be known technically as a three-stage impulse turbine, each stage velocity compounded. A turbine such as this would give better efficiencies than with pure velocity compounding and will be of smaller size than if purely pressure staged for the same power. The velocity diagrams would consist of a series similar to that shown in Fig. (XI–18), one for each stage.

In practice, most large turbines, in addition to being pressure compounded, have the first stage velocity compounded. The velocity rows

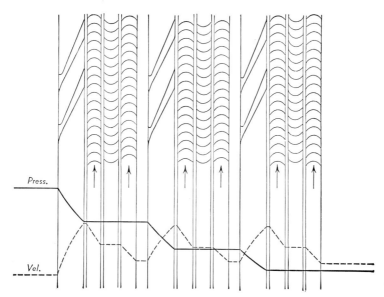

Fig. (XI–20).   Pressure and Velocity Compounded Impulse Turbine.

in such machines, besides serving to reduce size, are important from the standpoint of other practical considerations.

XI–16.   Reaction Turbines.—The driving force in the impulse turbine results from the kinetic energy of the steam which has been shot at high velocity from the nozzles into the blades and there decelerated. However, the acceleration of the steam in the nozzles has also produced a recoil or reaction, a force acting in a direction opposite to the steam flow. The impulse turbine, by holding the nozzles stationary and permitting the blades to move, utilizes for the purpose of doing work only the *impulse* force of the steam. The reaction turbine, by allowing the nozzles to rotate, utilizes the *reaction* force provided by the acceleration of the steam. The nozzles for expanding the steam in this type of turbine are made up of vanes shaped in such a way as to provide the proper section for steam flow and are ordinarily called blades, since they resemble rather closely the blades used in impulse turbines and not at all the conventional nozzle

of the de Laval type. Fig. (XI–21) shows reaction blade sections which
are typical. It will be noticed that these blades or vanes form convergent

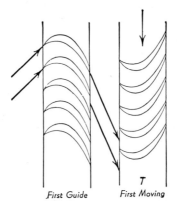

First Guide   First Moving

FIG. (XI–21). Reaction Blading.

nozzles in section. The reason for this is that a large number of stages are
used in reaction turbines, with the result that each individual expansion

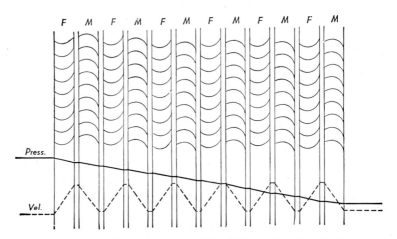

FIG. (XI–22). Blade Arrangement for 6 Stage Reaction Turbine.

is to a pressure well above the critical and therefore requires a nozzle
passage of the convergent type.

The diagrammatic arrangement of blades in the reaction turbine is
shown in Fig. (XI–22). The function of the fixed blading is two-fold:

first to act as a guide for the reversal of the direction of flow before entering the next moving row; and, second, to expand the steam sufficiently so that it may attain the velocity required to overtake and enter the moving row which follows. Therefore, a set of moving blades must always be accompanied by a set of fixed blades, and the combination constitutes what is known as a stage in a reaction turbine. Practically, the fixed and moving blades in any one stage or group of stages are so designed as to expand through the same heat drops and are identical in form but simply reversed in curvature. Because an expansion takes place in the blades, there is a pressure drop of the steam as it passes through each set from entrance to exit as shown in Fig. (XI–22). In analyzing the velocity curve, it must be remembered that this is a curve of absolute velocities. Due to expansion, the steam velocity relative to the blade row in question is always greater at exit than at entrance as reference to the velocity diagram in Fig. (XI–21) will show, but this diagram will also show that, while the *absolute* velocity leaving the fixed rows is greater than that entering, just the reverse is true of the moving blades. This results in a curve as in Fig. (XI–22) for the velocity.

The velocity diagram Fig. (XI–23), for the reaction turbine may be laid out in a manner similar to that for the impulse, but is somewhat simpler because of the similarity of the velocity triangles. In fact, for blading within small groups, these triangles are not only similar but are equal. This is due to the fact, before mentioned, that fixed and moving blades within a stage or small group are alike except for the direction in which they guide the steam. In this diagram, all absolute velocities and the angles made by their vectors refer to fixed blading, while all relative velocity vectors with their angles refer to moving blading. For best diagram efficiency, the blade speed to steam speed ratio should be, for the reaction turbine, cos α. It will be noted that this ratio is just twice that for the simple impulse turbine, but, due to the large number of stages used, the steam velocity remains comparatively low, resulting in reasonable rotor speeds.

The blade speed-steam speed ratios which have been given from time to time are for best diagram efficiency, but there are other considerations to be taken into account in the actual machine. The result is that the ratios used are invariably less than those given here. In the case of the reaction turbine, a ratio for maximum diagram efficiency would result in a diagram such as is shown in Fig. (XI–23) closed by the dotted lines. The blade entrance angles would be 90°, and thus the steam, in coming to the blades would enter axially and could not exert an impulse force in the

direction of rotation.   This would be a pure reaction turbine.   Actually,
however, due to the reduced speed ratio, the diagram is as shown with
blade entrance angles less than 90°, which results in some impulse force
in the rotative plane as the steam enters the blade.   The conventional

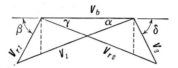

FIG. (XI–23).   Velocity Diagram for Reaction Blade.

reaction turbine, therefore, is not a pure reaction machine, but, since
by far the greater proportion of the driving force is due to reaction, this
type is known as a reaction turbine.

XI–17.   Combined Impulse and Reaction Turbines.—It was noted in
the discussion of impulse turbines that pressure compounded machines
are frequently preceded by a velocity compounded stage for practical
reasons.   The same reasons apply to the reaction type, and, in addition,

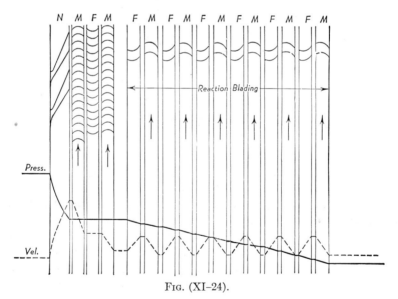

FIG. (XI–24).

is the fact that reaction turbines are more efficient in the low-pressure
regions than in the high.   It is common practice, therefore, in reaction
turbines which handle the steam throughout the full range to precede the

reaction blading by a velocity compounded impulse stage in which a considerable expansion takes place. This reduces the pressure and the temperature of the steam quickly before entering the casing and relieves the latter of stresses attendant upon high pressures and temperatures, as well as acting to reduce the pressure before the reaction blading is reached. Machines of this type are very common in the field of large reaction turbines.

XI–18. Stage Efficiency, and Reheat Factor.—The stage efficiency is the ratio of the work output of a turbine stage to the heat available if that particular expansion, between the same pressure limits, were conducted isentropically.   In other words, this is the efficiency ratio for each stage and is more comprehensive than diagram efficiency, although the latter is useful for certain analyses.

The effect of reheat in a compound turbine is shown in Figs. (XI–25) and (XI–26) on T–S and H–S diagrams respectively. Heat available is, of

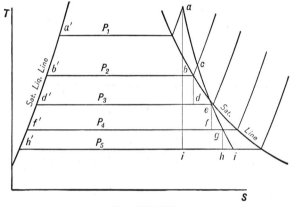

FIG. (XI–25).

course, represented in Fig. (XI–25) as an area, and in Fig. (XI–26) as an ordinate.   In the following discussion, the T–S diagram in Fig. (XI–25) will be referred to, but similar notation has been used in Fig. (XI–26) so that no difficulty should be experienced in following that diagram also. The heat available over the entire range of expansion of the turbine is the area $a'ajh'$.   Consider first the case of isentropic expansion with equal allocation of work amongst the four stages.   Then the heat available per stage is in each case the area to the left of the line aj between the pressure limits for each particular stage, and these areas will be equal.   With reheat, however, the actual expansion in the first stage

follows the curve a–c, the second stage follows c–e, the third stage
follows e–g, etc. Now it will be noted that the state of the steam
at entrance to the second stage is shown as point c and that the heat
available in the second stage is represented by the area $b'cdd'$ which is an
increase in the heat originally available with isentropic expansion. The
same is true for all succeeding stages, each having its available heat augmented over its predecessor by virtue of part of the reheat in one stage
becoming available for doing work in the next. As a consequence, two
things have happened: first, assuming equal or nearly equal stage effi-

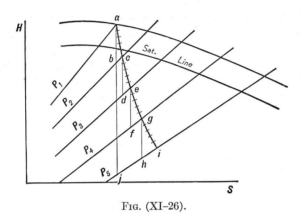

Fig. (XI–26).

ciencies, the division of work has been upset in such a way that the low
pressure stages are doing more than their share, and, second, the summation of the stage isentropic heat drops exceeds that which was originally
available. In turbine design, then, if it is desired to equalize the work
between stages or to proportion it in some other way, something must be
known concerning the effects of reheat from stage to stage. A convenient
expression for use in this connection is a ratio of the summation of the
available heats per stage to the available heat with a single isentropic
expansion, that is,

$$\frac{\Sigma \text{ heat available per stage}}{\text{Heat available in one expansion}}.$$

This ratio is called reheat factor. It must be greater than unity, and usually
varies from 1.03 to 1.15. As may be seen, its value is a function of the
number of stages and of the amount of reheat for each stage. It might be
thought, from the general appearance of the diagrams and the fact that

more heat is available with than without losses, that the amount of work done by the actual turbine would be greater than that performed by the theoretical. Such an impression is entirely erroneous. This becomes evident when it is considered that the additional available energy in any one stage is due to, *but is only a part of*, the losses in the preceding stage. As an example, suppose the reheat in one stage to be 20 B.t.u. per lb. of steam. Only a part of this, perhaps 5 B.t.u., becomes available to the following stages, the remaining 15 B.t.u. being entirely unavailable and passing to the exhaust. By means of losing 20 B.t.u., 5 B.t.u. have been gained, the net result still being a loss which is irrecoverable.

XI–19. Rankine Cycle with Regenerative Feed Heating.—If the Rankin Cycle be restricted to operation entirely within the saturated region, it is possible to raise its efficiency to almost that of the Carnot Cycle by progressively heating the feed water, using for that purpose heat taken in inverse progression from the steam as it undergoes adiabatic expansion. To illustrate from the *T–S* plane, Fig. (XI–27). If after the

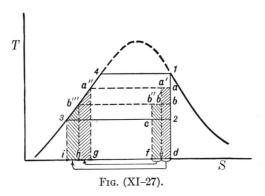

Fig. (XI–27).

steam had expanded from 1 to *a*, a small amount of heat were withdrawn and applied to heating the feed water, it would provide this heating effect with a minimum of energy degradation as the heat would be transferred to previously heated water of nearly the same temperature. At the end of the next step, the steam would be at pressure *b*. At this pressure, heat would again be removed sufficient in this case to heat the feed from 3 to *b'''* and the transfer would be nearly a reversible one (i.e., at the same temperature). The original adiabatic expansion would now be modified into the line 1, *a'*, *b''*, *c*, which begins to simulate the liquid line 3–4. By increasing the steps indefinitely the transfers of heat would approach the reversible limit of constant temperature and the expansion line a curve exactly similar to the liquid line, Fig. (XI–28). For such a limiting case the efficiency would be raised to the same value as the Carnot Cycle as the area representing the heat equivalent of the work done would be $(T_1 - T_2) \times (S_1 - S_4)$ [or $(S_2 - S_3)$] and the heat supplied *from external sources* would be $(T_1) \times (S_1 - S_4)$. This latter is true as the heat for heating the feed has only been *transferred* from the expansion process and did not come from outside the system.

The same result might have been obtained if instead of abstracting *small amounts of heat* from *all the steam*; *all the heat* back to condensation had been extracted from *small amounts of steam* taken at successively lower processes. This is the method actually used, as it can be accomplished by

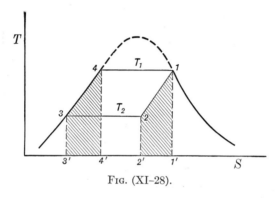

FIG. (XI–28).

bleeding steam from successive stages of the turbine directly to the feed heaters.

The method is ingenious, sound and practically applicable to turbine installation. It cannot be applied to reciprocating engines. As above developed, it is restricted to the saturated region and when so used the gain is greatest. However, most turbines operate mainly in the superheated region and there the gain, while appreciable, is not so great proportionally, because the reversible feed heating does not apply above the temperature of steam generation, i.e., the saturation temperature of the boiler pressure.

XI–20. Rankine Cycle with Resuperheating.—A basic principle for all heat engines, enunciated by Carnot, is, that for best efficiency all the heat received should be supplied at the highest operative temperature and all the heat rejected should go out at the lowest temperature. In an attempt to fulfill the former, steam turbines, which of necessity operate largely in the superheated region, have revived the reheating modification of the multiple expansion reciprocating engine by passing the steam after partial expansion back through superheaters. Such a method is illustrated in Fig. XI–(29). The steam begins its expansion at a and after adiabatic expansion to b, leaves the turbine and is passed through a superheater until it again is heated to its original temperature (c). From the resuperheater it passes back to the turbine and completes its expansion. As shown, the steam undergoes one reheating but this may be repeated as desired.

The gain is a three-fold one, (1) usually a slight increase in cycle efficiency, (2) an increase in output per pound of steam, and (3) a reduction

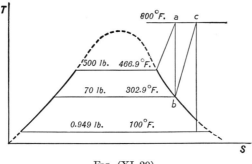

FIG. (XI–29).

in the moisture content of the steam in the low process stages of the turbine. This last is largely a maintenance gain as moisture droplets have a serious effect on blade deterioration.

An illustrative problem follows:

Example.—A steam turbine receives steam at 600 lbs. per sq. in. abs., 700° F. The reheating pressure is 100 lbs. per sq. in. abs. and the exhaust is at 1 lb. per sq. in. abs. Reheating temperature is 600° F. Calculate per pound for isentropic expansion, (a) the work done, (b) the heat added in the boiler, (c) the heat added in the reheater, (d) efficiency. Also determine (e) the work in the straight Rankine Cycle and (f) Rankine Cycle efficiency.

(a)   1351 − 1175 = 176   B.t.u. work, 1st expansion
     1329.0 − 982.5 = 346.5 B.t.u. work, 2nd expansion

        Total work,   522.5 B.t.u.

(b)   1351 − 69.7 = 1281.3 B.t.u. added in boiler

(c)   1329 − 1175 = 154 B.t.u. added in reheater

(d) $\text{Eff.} = \dfrac{522.5}{1281.3 + 154} = 36.4 \text{ per cent.}$

(e)   1351 − 885 = 446 B.t.u. work − Rankine

(f) $\text{Eff.} = \dfrac{466}{1281.3} = 36.3 \text{ per cent}$

The above calculations are made for the ideal case only.

XI–21. Binary Cycles.—Cycles using more than one fluid have been experimented with from early history. The basic objective is to increase the operative temperature range. Using steam, it was found that by the time the expansion had progressed to about 3 lbs. abs., the specific volume of the steam had become so large (118 cu. ft.) that it was too feeble per unit of volume to overcome the piston friction. If now there were some fluid whose boiling temperatures lay considerably below the range of those for water it might be possible to discharge the steam after it had reached its lower effective limit of pressure and use it to boil off this other liquid. Such vaporization of the second liquid would be accompanied by a converse process (condensation) of the steam. The new vapor would be at nearly the same temperature as the exhaust steam, but at a pressure sufficiently high to produce additional work in a companion cylinder. Many such secondary vapors exist and engines were actually built to utilize them. They were called binary engines (because using two fluids) and were successfully operated. The secondary vapors used were mainly chloroform, ether and sulfur dioxide. The approximate saturation pressures for these for the temperature corresponding to the condensation temperature of steam at 3 lbs. abs. are chloroform 15 lbs., ether 35 lbs. and sulfur dioxide over 160 lbs.

Mainly because of their mechanical complexity they were not commercially successful. Moreover, it should be noted that these were all attempts to utilize the low pressure region of the Rankine Cycle, and with the advent of the steam turbine this region was made almost completely available and further need for such vanished. With further low-pressure possibilities exhausted, attention was directed to increasing the upper range of the cycle. Similar reasoning to that just used holds for this region except that the limit in upward trend is at present definitely fixed by metallurgical limitations to temperatures lying from 800° F. to 1000° F. With this in mind, if a vapor which had a condensing temperature at low pressure of about 500° F. were available, it might be possible to use it as a primary fluid and steam as a secondary. Only one such fluid has been seriously proposed; mercury. It has a saturation pressure of 180 lbs. at 1000° F. and at 30 lbs. and 1 lb., saturation temperatures of 750° F. and 458° F. respectively. With such a fluid it becomes possible to vaporize at high temperature and reasonable pressure, to expand to a lower pressure, doing work, and still have the exhaust (at low pressure) sufficiently hot to generate steam at high pressure and temperature for the regular cycle. Figure (XI-30) illustrates this.

Such a development as outlined has been sponsored by the General Electric Company and successful stations using this system are now in operation. Economies are reported as low as 9000 B.t.u. per kw. hour.

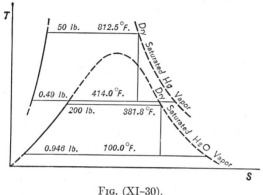

Fig. (XI-30).

XI-22. Injectors and Ejectors.—Injectors and ejectors belong to a group of engineering devices which rely upon the principle of a small jet with high-energy content mingling with a larger mass of less energy content and producing by the mixing a resultant jet of sufficient velocity to attain the desired objective. This objective varies all the way from forcing feed water into boilers at high pressure to pumping liquid through a few feet of elevation. Any motivating fluid may be used, but the most effective are condensible vapors as they acquire higher jet velocities due to the vacuum formed in the combining tube. Those used to feed liquids into pressure vessels are usually classed as injectors while those used to withdraw liquids or gases from non-pressure compartments are called ejectors.

The most familiar form is the steam injector used to pump feed water into a boiler by means of a jet of steam drawn from the same boiler. Figure (XI-31) shows a longitudinal section though a simple form of one. It consists of three essential parts, the steam-nozzle (a), the combining tube (b), and the delivery tube (c). Steam comes to the injector directly from the boiler through the pipe (a) and water is drawn from the feed supply tank through the water supply pipe. Both fluids mingle in the combining tube (b) and the resulting jet has sufficient velocity at the delivery tube (c) to force itself into the boiler against the existing pressure.

For simplicity a non-lifting type has been shown, i.e., one which has the feed water supplied to it from a slight head. When the injector is operating, steam expands through the nozzle and meets the water from the feed tank in the combining tube. This mingling results in condensation suffi-

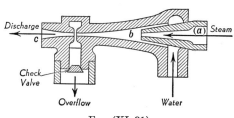

FIG. (XI–31).

cient to maintain a vacuum at the exit end of the steam nozzle and a high velocity is imparted to the combined jet.

Considering the action of the entire unit as adiabatic and applying the principle of conservation of energy the total energy brought in by the feed water must equal the total energy possessed by the water leaving the combining tube, hence

$$(JH + KE)_{steam} + y(JH + KE)_{water} = (1 + y)(JH + KE)_{mixture},$$

where y denotes the pounds of water drawn in per pound of steam. In this expression the various kinetic energies are so small as compared with the energies represented by the various heat contents that they may be omitted without affecting the results by one per cent. If this is done the equation simplifies to

$$H_{steam} + yH_{water} = (1 + y)H_{mixture} \qquad (2)$$

Similarly, equating the momenta there results:

$$\text{Vel.}_{steam} + y\,\text{Vel.}_{water} = (1 + y)\,\text{Vel.}_{mixture} \qquad (3)$$

By means of (3) it is possible to calculate any velocity provided the other two can be determined independently. The value of the exit velocity of the steam can readily be calculated knowing the boiler pressure and the back pressure. The back pressure or nozzle exit pressure may be taken as atmospheric though actually appreciably lower. The velocity of the water in the combining tube where it mixes with the steam jet ranges from 20 to 40 ft., dependent upon the vacuum.

An illustrative example will emphasize some of the foregoing facts.

Example.—An injector, receiving dry steam at 150 lbs. per sq. in. abs. is to deliver 10,000 lbs. of water per hour. Calculate the pounds of steam per hour and the percentage of available energy utilized.

Assuming water velocity of 25 ft. per sec. coming into the injector, the head of water to cause this velocity is

$$\frac{25^2}{2g} = 9.87 \text{ ft. or } 4.28 \text{ lbs. per sq. in.}$$

The absolute pressure at exit of steam may then be assumed to be 10 p.s.i.

Assume maximum discharge pressure at injector outlet is 185 p.s.i. per sq. in. abs. The pressure rise is 185 − 10 = 175 p.s.i.

$$175 \text{ lbs. } = 404 \text{ ft. head of water.}$$

Velocity necessary to set up this head, no friction,

$$= \sqrt{2g \times 404} = 161.5 \text{ ft. per sec.}$$

Actual velocity with velocity coefficient of 80 per cent

$$= \frac{161.5}{.80} = 202 \text{ ft. per sec.}$$

The adiabatic heat drop in the steam nozzle is

$$1194 - 1001 = 193 \text{ B.t.u.}$$

Using a nozzle efficiency of 90 per cent, the steam velocity at the nozzle exit is $224 \sqrt{193 \times .9} = 2950$.

From equation (3)

$$2950 + y\,(25) = (1 + y)(202),$$

$$y = 15.5 \text{ lbs. water per lb. steam,}$$

$$\frac{10,000}{15.5} = 645 \text{ lbs. steam per hour.}$$

The efficiency of the injector in transforming available energy into work is

$$\frac{(15.5 + 1)\left(\dfrac{404}{778}\right)}{193} = 4.44 \text{ per cent.}$$

Sometimes air is used as the motivating fluid, in which case the action is much the same as above described, only there is no vacuum formed at the nozzle exit, and the mixture passing out consists of both gas and water with correspondingly less density. Such devices are called ejectors and are used for pumping in inaccessible spaces or where steam is not available. They usually operate only against a small head and are even less efficient than injectors. Ejectors using water or other fluids are also occasionally used as in Fig. (XI–32) (*A*) to raise a similar fluid against a small head. The basic treatment is the same.

Sometimes steam is used but not to return a liquid to a boiler but to exhaust a bulky gas from an enclosed space Fig. (XI–32) (*B*). When used

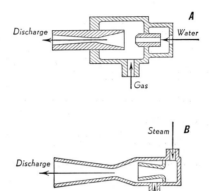

Fɪɢ. (XI–32).

for such *ejection* purposes they are also called ejectors. An example of such is the so-called air ejector frequently used with marine turbine installations, where it is used to exhaust the very low pressure and very bulky gas from the condenser.

CHAPTER XII

MIXTURES OF GASES AND VAPORS

XII-1. Basic Equations Similar to Mixtures of Gases.—The treatment of a mixture of gases and vapors does not differ fundamentally from that for a gaseous mixture alone. Dalton's principle of partial pressures holds to a sufficiently close approximation, as do also the basic assumptions set forth in Chapter VII regarding the relationship between properties of the mixture and properties of the individual constituents. So long as the vapor constituent remains well in the superheated state, and particularly at low pressures, the method of solution of ordinary problems may follow exactly that for mixtures of gases alone insofar as the determination of density, specific volume, apparent molecular weight, apparent gas constant, and specific heat of the mixture is concerned. The calculation of intrinsic energy, heat content, and entropy for the mixture, however, are more readily carried out in conjunction with tables of the properties of the vapor or vapors concerned.

In cases where the vapor in the mixture is saturated or has only a small amount of superheat, difficulties are introduced due to the fact that the vapor does not even approximately conform to gas laws, and such terms as apparent molecular weight and apparent gas constant lose their significance. Under these conditions, also, the specific heat of the vapor is infinite and any withdrawal of heat will produce a partial condensation of the vapor which will result in a change in the weight ratio of the constituents and a change in their respective partial pressures.

XII-2. Properties of Mixtures of Gases and Vapors.—Any one of the true properties of a mixture is simply the summation of the properties of its individual constituents. When a vapor constitutes a part of the mixture, its properties are best found by reference to tables dealing with those properties, while those of the gaseous constituents may be found in the usual way. The following example, using a simple mixture, will serve to illustrate.

Example.—A mixture consists of nitrogen = 60 per cent and water vapor = 40 per cent by volume. The pressure and temperature of the mixture are

20 lbs. per sq. in. abs. and 200° F. respectively. (For these conditions the vapor is superheated.)

Calculate: (a) Analysis by weight; (b) apparent molecular weight; (c) apparent gas constant; (d) volume per mol and per pound; (e) partial pressures of constituents; (f) molal specific heats, Mc_p and Mc_v; (g) specific heats per pound, c_p and c_v; (h) intrinsic energy per mol and per pound; (i) heat content per mol and per pound. (Instantaneous specific heats; energies based upon 32° F.)

Solution.—(a)

Constituent	Mols per Mol of Mixture		Molec. Wt.		Lbs. per Mol of Mixture		Mix. Molec. Wt.		Lbs. per Lb. of Mixture		Wt. Analysis
N_2	.60	×	28	=	16.8	÷	24	=	.70	=	70 per cent
H_2O	.40	×	18	=	7.2	÷	24	=	.30	=	30 per cent
	1.00 mol.				24 lbs. per mol.				1.00 lbs.		

(b) Appar. molecular wt. = 24.

(c) Appar. gas constant = $\frac{1545}{24}$ = 64.3.

(d) Vol. per mol = $\frac{1545\,(660)}{20\,(144)}$ = 354 cu. ft.

Vol. per lb. = $\frac{354}{24}$ = $\frac{64.3\,(660)}{20\,(144)}$ = 14.75 cu. ft.

(e) The partial volumes, if both constituents existed at 20 lbs., would be as given in the volumetric analysis. Therefore the partial pressures are:

$$P_{N_2} = .6\,(20) = 12 \text{ lbs. abs.}, \quad P_{H_2O} = .4\,(20) = 8 \text{ lbs. abs.}$$

(f) Instant. Mc_p for $N_2 = 6.93 + .12\,(10^{-6})T^2 = 6.93 + \frac{.12\,(660)^2}{1,000,000}$

$$= 6.93 + .052 = 6.982 \text{ B.t.u. per mol per deg. F.}$$

$$Mc_v = 6.982 - 1.985 = 4.997.$$

For H_2O, $Mc_p = 8.33 - \frac{.276T}{1000} + \frac{.423T^2}{1,000,000} = 8.33 - .182 + .184$

$$= 8.332 \text{ B.t.u. per mol per deg.}$$

$$Mc_v = 8.332 - 1.985 = 6.347 \text{ B.t.u.}$$

For mixture:

$$Mc_p = .6\,(6.982) + .4\,(8.332) = 7.522 \text{ B.t.u. per mol per deg.}$$

$$Mc_v = .6\,(4.997) + .4\,(6.347) = 5.537.$$

(g) $c_p = \frac{7.522}{24} = .313$ $\quad$ $c_v = \frac{5.537}{24} = .23$

MIXTURES OF GASES AND VAPORS

(h) U for N_2 per mol (above 32° F.) $= 4.945\ (660 - 492) + .12\ \dfrac{(\overline{660}^3 - \overline{492}^3)}{3,000,000}$

$$= 830 + 6.75 = 836.75 \text{ B.t.u. per mol.}$$

For steam at 8 lbs., 200° F. (from Tables), $h = 1147$.

$$u = 1147.5 - \frac{8\,(144)(48.7)}{778.3} = 1147.5 - 72.2 = 1075.3 \text{ B.t.u. per lb.}$$

For mixture, $U = .6\ (836.75) + .4\ (18)(1075) = 502 + 7740 = 8242$ B.t.u. per mol (on 32°).

$$u = \frac{8242}{24} = 343 \text{ B.t.u. per lb.}$$

(i) $h = 8242 + \dfrac{20\,(144)(354)}{778.1} = 8242 + 1310 = 9552$ B.t.u. per mol

$$h = \frac{9552}{24} = 398 \text{ B.t.u. per lb.}$$

In the above problem, the vapor was in the superheated state and the analysis was given much as for a mixture of gases. It will be noted that the treatment of each constituent is carried out just as though it occupied the space alone at its partial pressure but at the temperature of the mixture which is also the true temperature, of each of the gases or vapors making up the whole. When the vapor in a mixture is known to be saturated, as is frequently the case, the solution is somewhat simplified when no change of state of the mixture is concerned. The temperature of the mixture is a direct index to the partial pressure of the saturated vapor present because pressure and temperature are related in the saturated region for equilibrium conditions. In case of two or more gases being present, their volumetric relation must be known in order to determine their partial pressures. This might be accomplished by drying the mixture and making a volumetric analysis.

Example.—A cold boiler contains water with air above it. In the process of raising steam, before any outlet is opened, a mixture of air and water vapor exists in equilibrium. When the boiler pressure is 35 lbs. per sq. in. abs., the temperature of the contents is 228° F.

Calculate: (a) Partial pressures of the constituents; (b) volumetric analysis; (c) analysis by weight; (d) specific volume.

Intrinsic energy and heat content of the mixture would be calculated in a manner similar to that in the preceding example. Apparent molecular weight and gas constant have but little significance when one of the principal constituents is a saturated vapor. The instantaneous specific heat is infinite since it is so for a saturated vapor.

Solution.—(*a*) Pressure of water vapor 20 lbs. abs. (from tables). Pressure of air $35 - 20 = 15$ lbs. abs. Since air is 21 per cent oxygen and 79 per cent nitrogen by volume, pressure of oxygen $.21\ (15) = 3.15$ lbs., pressure of nitrogen $.79\ (15) = 11.85$ lbs.

(*b*) Vol. analysis:

$$O_2 = \frac{3.15}{35} = .09 \quad \text{or} \quad 9.0 \text{ per cent}$$

$$N_2 = \frac{11.85}{35} = .338 \quad \text{or} \quad 33.8 \text{ per cent}$$

$$H_2O = \frac{20}{35} = \underline{.572} \quad \text{or} \quad \underline{57.2 \text{ per cent}}$$

$$1.000 \qquad 100.0$$

(*c*) Analysis by weight:

O_2...................... $.09 \times 32 = 2.88 \div 22.64 = .127$ or 12.7 per cent
N_2...................... $.338 \times 28 = 9.47 \div 22.64 = .418$ or 41.8 per cent
H_2O.................. $.572 \times 18 = \underline{10.29} \div 22.64 = .455$ or 45.5 per cent

$$22.64$$

A more accurate method, since H_2O is saturated, might be to assume one pound of water vapor and calculate the corresponding weight of air in the mixture, thus:

Volume of 1 lb. of steam, saturated at 228° F. $= 20.07$ cu. ft.

Wt. of air in 20.07 cu. ft. $= \dfrac{15\ (144)(20.07)}{53.35\ (688)} = 1.182$ lbs.

Wt. of mixture $= 1.0 + 1.182 = 2.182$ lbs.

H_2O by weight $= \dfrac{1}{2.182} = .457$ or 45.7 per cent.

(*d*) The specific volume of the mixture is the volume of .127 lb. of O_2, .417 lb. of N_2, .544 lb. of air, or of .455 lb. water vapor, each at its partial pressure, because all occupy the same space at the same time.

$$\text{Vol. } O_2 = \frac{.127\ (48.2)(688)}{3.15\ (144)} = 9.27 \text{ cu. ft.}$$

$$\text{Vol. } N_2 = \frac{.418\ (54.9)(688)}{11.85\ (144)} = 9.27 \text{ cu. ft.}$$

$$\text{Vol. air} = \frac{.545\ (53.35)(688)}{15\ (144)} = 9.26 \text{ cu. ft.}$$

$$\text{Vol. } H_2O = .455\ (20.07) = 9.13 \text{ cu. ft.}$$

The discrepancy of the specific volume of the water vapor is due to its failure to follow the perfect gas laws.

XII-3. Property Relations for Various Changes of State.—When a gas-vapor mixture undergoes a change of state the behavior of each may be entirely different or may be similar, depending upon whether or not the vapor is brought to the saturated condition during the process. In any event, the conception is rendered much clearer when the gas and the vapor are separately considered. Suppose a simple mixture of a gas and a vapor to exist at a certain pressure and a certain temperature, and that the volumetric analysis is known. As has been seen, the last is equivalent to knowing the partial pressures. Figure (XII–1) shows two T–S

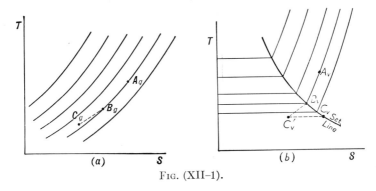

Fig. (XII–1).

plots, (a) for the gas, and (b) for the vapor. Constant pressure lines are shown on both, and, in addition, the saturation curve is shown on the diagram for the vapor. Let A_g and A_v represent the initial condition of each of the constituents of the mixture at the initial state specified.

Consider first a withdrawal of heat without change in total pressure. The number of mols of each constituent will remain the same; therefore, the partial pressures will bear the same relation to each other as before and will not change so long as the vapor is not partially removed by condensation. The process will move the state points in Fig. (XII–1) down their respective lines with a constantly decreasing temperature until the temperature is reached corresponding to the saturation pressure of the vapor; that is, until point A_v has reached the saturation line at B_v. From this point down to any lower temperature, the pressure exerted by the vapor will be that corresponding to the temperature of the mixture and will be constantly decreasing as cooling takes place, with corresponding progressive condensation of the vapor until zero pressure is reached, at which point there would be no vapor remaining. Considering the total quantity of moisture present, the state point would move to C'_v in the wet region, but, since the vapor remaining is all that concerns us—the condensate being no longer mixed with air—the condition of the vapor in the air is shown by point C_v on the saturation line. The effect on the gas of a decreasing vapor pressure with the total pressure remaining constant is to increase its partial pressure until, the vapor pressure becoming zero, the partial pressure of the gas is equal to the total pressure. Such a change as this is shown in Fig. (XII–1) (a) and (b) by the path ABC.

An isothermal compression from point A would result in moving the state point horizontally to the left in both diagrams crossing successively higher pressure lines. The relation between the partial pressures would not change until the saturation line was reached in diagram (b). Any further compression after this point is reached will result in an increased pressure of the gas only because the vapor, being saturated, is bound to the pressure corresponding to the constant temperature at which compression is taking place. Condensation will occur as the process is carried on into the saturated region of the vapor.

For an adiabatic compression, higher and higher temperatures are attained by each constituent. The vapor becomes more superheated and there is no change in the molal relationships.

XII–4. Humidity.—Humidity deals with the particular mixture of gases and vapors encountered in the atmosphere; that is, principally air and water vapor. Since this concerns human comfort and, in a good many cases, industrial production, there has naturally been a great amount of work done on this particular mixture, and, from this study have grown certain terminologies peculiar to humidity work. For instance, the saturation temperature corresponding to the partial pressure of the water vapor is called the *dew point*. That is, it is the temperature at which, were a sample of atmospheric air cooled at constant pressure, condensation of the moisture would begin. *Saturated air* is air at the dew point, the vapor in the air being saturated. *Absolute humidity* is the actual weight of water vapor in grains per cu. ft. of atmosphere. This may also be expressed as grains of moisture per pound of dry air, and is of somewhat more practical use in this form. *Relative humidity* is the ratio of the actual absolute humidity to the absolute humidity when saturated at the same temperature. This is usually expressed in per cent, the saturated air being 100 per cent. *Dry bulb temperature* is the ordinary temperature taken with the ordinary type of thermometer and is used to differentiate from *wet bulb temperature* which is obtained with a thermometer whose bulb is kept moist by wrapping with moist gauze. This will produce temperatures lower than the dry bulb when evaporation takes place around the bulb, the difference being known as *wet bulb depression*. This is roughly proportional to the dryness of the air. Figure (XII–2) is a low-pressure-superheated section of a T–S diagram, illustrating how dew point is reached (process A–C).

The properties of air and water vapor must, largely, be calculated from observations of merely pressure and temperature. However, pressure and temperature alone tell us nothing concerning the mixture unless supplemented by some indication of the degree of humidity that exists.

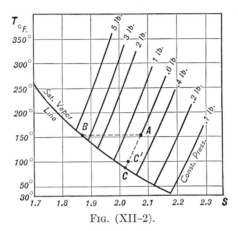

FIG. (XII–2).

XII–5. Dew Point.—Dew point is the temperature at which condensation starts when air is cooled at constant pressure. The dew point may be experimentally determined by cooling a given amount of air, decreasing its volume as it is being cooled to keep its pressure constant, until condensation starts. A simpler way to determine the dew point is to progressively cool a nickel-plated container until a film of moisture appears on its polished surface. The temperature of the container at which the film first commences to form is the dew point.

If the dew point of water vapor in air is known, the corresponding saturation pressure is the partial pressure of the water vapor. When the partial pressure of the water vapor is known, the properties of both the air and water vapor, and also of the mixture become determinable as $P_{at.} = P_{air} + P_{water}$ and $P_{at.}$ (the pressure of the atmosphere) is given by the barometer.

Each of the ingredients, air and water vapor, constituting the mixture can then be completely identified because two independent properties (pressure and temperature) are known for each and the perfect gas equation holds with sufficient precision.

For air the gas constant is,

$$\frac{1544}{29} = 53.35,$$

and for water vapor $1544 \div 18 = 85.8$.

It will be readily appreciated that the determination of the dew point or its companion property, the vapor partial pressure, is the key which unlocks the problem of the characteristic properties of the mixture. Accordingly, its determination either directly or indirectly is essential. One of the commonest methods is by means of an expression giving the vapor partial pressure in terms of wet and dry bulb temperatures.

XII–6. Wet Bulb Temperature.—The wet bulb temperature is the evaporating temperature of water into a given atmosphere. If the atmosphere is completely saturated, no evaporation takes place and the wet and dry bulb temperatures are the same. If the atmosphere surrounding the wet bulb is not completely saturated, then because of evaporation, the wet bulb temperature is less. If the wet bulb temperature coincided with the dew point the determination of the water vapor partial pressure would be simply a matter of reading the corresponding saturation pressure from the steam tables. However, the wet bulb temperature is not quite as low as the dew point; moreover, it is not a direct function of the dew point. Accordingly, it is necessary to evolve a relation by which the readily determined wet bulb temperature, together with the dry bulb temperature and barometric pressure can be used to determine the partial pressure of the water vapor. Several such equations have been developed, one of the most widely used being that of Carrier which was developed in accordance with the following reasoning.

As heat is required to vaporize the water on the wet bulb, and as water is at equilibrium temperature, and hence can supply no heat, the required heat must come from the air passing over the wet bulb. Neglecting radiation, the equation representing this heat exchange is

$$W(h - h')_{\text{air}} + W'(h - h')_{\text{vapor}} = W''h_{fg},$$

or

$$Wc_a(t - t') + W'c_w(t - t') = W''h_{fg}. \qquad \text{(XII–1)}$$

Where

W = weight of air passing over the wet bulb

h = heat content at dry bulb temperature, t

h' = heat content at wet bulb temperature, t'

W' = weight of water vapor in air passing over the wet bulb

c_a = specific heat of air at constant pressure
c_v = specific heat of vapor at constant pressure
W'' = weight of water vapor evaporated
h_{fg} = latent heat of evaporating water.

As the heat is exchanged by direct contact, the air giving up heat must come in contact with the wet bulb and hence it leaves the wet bulb completely saturated. Thus the above equation is written only for that extremely thin layer of air coming in contact with the wet bulb. This process is called by Carrier *adiabatic saturation*. This fundamental concept of adiabatic saturation will be used later in dealing with drying problems.

Carrier's equation is given below. Certain precautions are essential in determining wet bulb temperatures, the chief of which is to have a good air velocity by the bulb when the reading is taken. Also the bulb should be well wetted. Variations in the air velocity above a minimum value do not change the true wet bulb temperature.

$$p_s = p_s' - \frac{(p_b - p_s')(t - t')}{2755 - 1.28t'} \qquad \text{(XII–2)}$$

in which p_s = partial pressure of the vapor in the mixture—pounds per square inch absolute

p_s' = pressure corresponding to temperature t' for steam—pounds per square inch absolute

p_b = barometric pressure—pounds per square inch

t = dry bulb temperature—degrees F.

t' = wet bulb temperature—degrees F.

With the vapor pressure known, everything else may be calculated if the assumption be made that very low-pressure vapor acts as a perfect gas— an assumption which appears to be very nearly correct. The dew point may be found immediately from the steam tables as the temperature corresponding to the vapor pressure. The partial pressure of the air, the difference between the total and the vapor pressure, and the temperature will permit the density to be found by application of perfect gas law. In a similar manner, the vapor density can be found. This may also be calculated for the saturated vapor at the dry bulb temperature. and a ratio of the two gives the relative humidity while the actual steam density, expressed in grains, is the absolute humidity. If grains of moisture per pound of dry air is desired, it is only necessary to find weight of vapor in a volume equal to the specific volume of the dry air.

Example.—Barometer = 29.5 in. Dry bulb temperature = 90° F. Wet bulb temperature = 78° F. Find: (a) Vapor pressure; (b) dew point; (c) relative humidity; (d) absolute humidity; (e) grains of moisture per pound of dry air.

Solution.—

(a) $p_b = 29.5 \,(.491) = 14.5$ lbs. per sq. in.

$$p_s = 0.4744 - \frac{(14.5 - .4744)(90 - 78)}{2755 - 1.28 \,(78)} = .4744 - \frac{168.3}{2655.2}$$

$\qquad\qquad = 0.4109$ lbs. per sq. in. abs.

$p.p.$ air $= 14.0891$ lbs. abs.

) $D.P.$ (from steam tables) $= 73°$ F.

(c) Act. density $= \dfrac{PV}{RT} = \dfrac{0.4109 \,(144)}{85.8 \,(550)} = .001253$ lb. per cu. ft.

Density at 90°, sat. $= .00214$ lb. per cu. ft.

$$\text{Rel. humidity} = \frac{.001253 \times 100}{.00214} = 58.5 \text{ per cent}$$

(d) Abs. humidity $= .001253 \,(7000) = 8.771$ grains per cu. ft.

(e) Spec. vol. of air $= \dfrac{53.35 \,(550)}{14.0891 \,(144)} = 14.5$ cu. ft. per lb.

Grains per lb. dry air $= 14.5 \,(.001253)(7000) = 127.2$ grains.

Part (e) of the preceding example, grains of moisture per pound of dry air, is probably more usuable for the solution of practical problems than is the absolute humidity of part (d) because, in dealing with changes, the absolute humidity will change with varying temperature or pressure, while the moisture per pound of dry air changes only when water vapor is added or taken from the mixture. Another property of the mixture which is valuable in the determination of heat quantities is heat content or total heat. This is expressed, not in B.t.u. per pound of mixture, but in B.t.u. per pound of dry air. This may be based upon any desired temperature, but 32° F. is usually chosen as the zero point for convenience. As before stated, the total heat of the mixture would be the sum of the heat contents of the constituents.

XII–7. Air Conditioning.—Air conditioning deals with the deliberate change of state of atmospheric air to suit certain desired conditions. The usual processes are heating, cooling, humidifying, and dehumidifying. The last two usually involve heating or cooling processes as incidentals. That is, if it is desired to remove moisture from air, it must be cooled sufficiently to precipitate out the required amount, and then reheated to the temperature called for in the final state. Or, if moisture is to be added, the air may be heated in order to receive the vapor more easily. Air conditioning is so important in providing comfort to people and in controlling the temperature and humidity in certain industrial processes, that it has in itself grown to an industry within the last few years.

Example.—100,000 cu. ft. per hour of the air in the preceding example are to be conditioned to 70° F. and 40 per cent relative humidity. Find: (a) The temperature to which the air must be cooled; (b) the amount of moisture to be removed per hour; (c) the heat to be removed from the air—B.t.u. per hour.

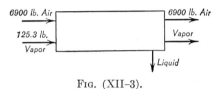

FIG. (XII–3).

Solution.—(See Fig. (XII–3.))

$$\frac{100,000}{14.5} = 6900 \text{ lbs. air per hr.}$$

$$100,000 \times .001253 = 125.3 \text{ lbs. water vapor per hr.}$$

At 70° F.

Density of water vapor, $70° = \frac{1}{869} \times .4 = .00046$ lb. per cu. ft.

$$P.P. = \frac{(.00046)(85.8)(530)}{1\,(144)} = .1453 \text{ lb. per sq. in. abs. water vapor pressure.}$$

Dew point = 44.6° F.

At the dew point

$$(P.P.)_{\text{air}} = 14.5 - .14 = 14.36$$

$$(\text{Sp. vol.})_{\text{air}} = \frac{(53.35)(504.6)}{(14.36)(144)} = 13.00$$

$$\text{Lbs. H}_2\text{O per lb. air} = \frac{13.00}{2063} = .00631 \text{ lb.}$$

Total weight of water vapor = $(6900)(.00631) = 43.5$ lbs.

Weight of vapor condensed = $125.3 - 43.5 = 81.8$ lbs.

Original heat content (above 32° F. as a datum plane)

Air = (6900)(.24)(90−32) = 96,000 B.t.u.

Water vapor* = (125.3)(1099.8) = 137,900

Total,   234,900 B.t.u.

Heat content at dew point

Air = (6900)(.24)(44.6 − 32) = 20,800 B.t.u.

Water vapor = (43.5)(1079.5) = 47,000

Condensed water = (81.8)(12.65) = 1,040

Total,   68,840 B.t.u.

Heat removed,   166,060 B.t.u.

XII–8. Physical Comfort.—Atmospheric air is rarely exactly at the correct conditions to satisfy human beings. Air conditioning for comfort is the adjusting the conditions of the atmosphere to meet the requirements of physical comfort. The scope of the subject of physical comfort is a large one and offers many problems not yet settled. Some items that must be considered are:

1. Air temperature.
2. Humidity.
3. Air velocity.
4. Individual physical activity.
5. Individual taste.
6. Kinds of clothing worn.
7. Outside temperature.
8. Temperature of the surrounding objects.

With this large number of variables, it is almost impossible to state desirable air conditions. There are, however, only three variables, controllable by the engineer. These are temperature, humidity and velocity. All of these influence the rate of heat loss from the body, which is the determining factor of physical comfort. The desirable figure for any one of these variables depends on the magnitude of the other variables. In general, however, high air velocities, recognized as " drafts," are objectionable and should be avoided. A draft may be defined as a current of air which carries away bodily heat faster than it is generated. About the maximum allowable air velocity striking a person is 50 ft. per minute.

* The heat content of very low pressure superheated steam may be taken as the heat content of saturated steam at the same temperature in absence of other data.

Some authorities state that the minimum allowable relative humidity (for comfort) in winter is 40 per cent and the maximum in summer is 65 per cent.

Considerable work has been done in the laboratory of the American Society of Heating and Ventilating Engineers (A.S.H.V.E.) on this subject.

A so-called "Comfort Chart" published by them gives the ranges of temperature and humidity for bodily comfort in still air (velocities less than 25 ft. per min.). This chart is reproduced in abbreviated form in Fig. (XII–4).

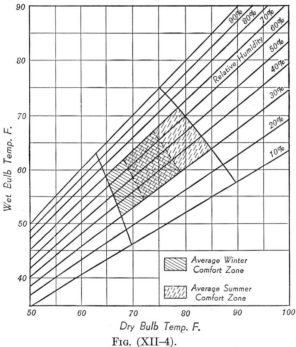

FIG. (XII–4).

XII–9. Methods of Obtaining Correct Humidity.—In the summer, air is normally too humid for comfort and water must be removed from it. In winter, on the other hand, water vapor must be added to air to make it comfortable.

The easiest way to remove water vapor from a large quantity of air is to chill it to below its dew point and condense the required amount of vapor. The air is then reheated to desirable temperature. This method is followed in the example in paragraph XII–7. The most convenient method of cooling the air is to chill water by use of a refrigerating machine (if a natural supply of cool water is not available), and to spray this water into the air. The spray droplets provide the very large surface necessary for the heat transfer from the air to the water.

Such a process, however, requires a large amount of refrigeration and also a very appreciable amount of heat to heat the air after the removal of the water vapor. Thermodynamically, both of these requirements may be minimized by use of a counter current heat exchanger in which the cool air coming from the dehumidifier cools down warm air on its way to the dehumidifier and is itself heated. However, the exhange from air to air through metal walls requires such a large surface that such a heat exchanger is not practical.

A desirable method is the so-called by-pass system. In this system, a portion of the hot, humid air, that is to be conditioned, passes to the dehumidifier where it is cooled to a somewhat lower temperature than when the entire amount of air is chilled. This air of low relative humidity mixes with the remainder of the hot, humid air, producing the correct final temperature with little or no addition of heat. A further gain can be made by recirculation of air and using only a small amount of make-up air.

The simplest way to add large quantities of water to air is to warm the water and then spray it into the air in such a way that it is well atomized. It is preferable to spray water into warm air as it will be vaporized more readily. If there is normal infiltration into a room on a cold day, the amount of water that should be added to give the desired humidity is large and cannot be supplied by open pans of water unless heat is added to the pans.

XII–10. Carburetted Mixtures.—Although an air-water vapor mixture is by far the most common gas-vapor mixture encountered in practice, others should be mentioned, particularly carburetted mixtures. The strict definition of carburetted is "charged with a volatile carbon compound." Such mixtures are encountered in internal combustion engines.

The mixture leaving the carburetor of an automotive engine consists of air, fuel vapor and particles of liquid fuel. As heat is required for vaporization, there is a drop in temperature of the air to supply this heat. If there is sufficient time, the mixture will come to some equilibrium temperature and a definite percentage of the fuel will be vaporized. In passing through the intake manifold, the mixture receives heat, tending to vaporize the fuel. Assuming complete vaporization, the heat required is found as in the following example.

Gasoline and air, each at 100° F., enter a carburetor and leave the intake manifold at 175° F. (c_p)-liquid and vapor = 0.5; latent heat

= 140 B.t.u. per lb.; air fuel ratio, 15 to 1.   Calculate the heat added per
pound of fuel.

$$\text{Heat for air} = 15 \times .24(175 - 100) = 270.0 \text{ B.t.u.}$$
$$\text{Latent heat} = 1 \times 140 \qquad = 140.0$$
$$\text{Sensible heat to vapor} = 1 \times .5(175 - 100) = 37.5$$

$$\text{Heat added, total,} \quad 447.5 \text{ B.t.u.}$$

Actually, however, the fuel is seldom completely vaporized as it leaves
the intake.   The percentage vaporized must be known to calculate the heat
added.   The determination of the percentage fuel vaporized is difficult, as
the liquid and vapor are not in an equilibrium condition, and will not
be discussed here.

XII–11.   Adiabatic Saturation: Its Application.—In the commercial
problems of drying; warm dry air is passed over the material to be dried.
After sufficient time for equilibrium to be established has elapsed, the
material reaches the wet bulb temperature of the entering air.   Furthermore, the wet bulb temperature of the air throughout the dry chamber is
constant.   This is true because, for adiabatic saturation, it makes no difference, as far as the evaporating temperature is concerned, whether the
process of heat exchange between the air and water is carried on in one
spot, as on the wet bulb, or spread out over a large surface as in the drying
chamber.   In other words, when a given sample of air comes in contact
with water, there is a given temperature at which the air will be saturated
and this temperature is definite and does not change as the air approaches
saturation.

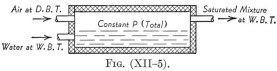

Fig. (XII–5).

The nearness to saturation of the air leaving the drying chamber
depends on the amount of surface for heat transfer and the degree of turbulence within the chamber.   Generally the air is not completely saturated
upon leaving.   If the wet and dry bulb temperatures of the entering and
leaving air are known, the problem of determining the air flow to remove
water at a given rate is a simple one.   If the temperature and relative
humidity of the incoming air is known, together with the exit temperature,
an application of the law, that the heat given up by the air and its vapor is
equal to the heat received by the water, will aid in determining the correct
air flow.

CHAPTER XIII

REFRIGERATION (Heat Pumps)

XIII-1. General.—By refrigeration is meant the production of a cooling effect—the lowering of the temperature of a body or a substance and the maintenance of the temperature below that of its surroundings. The idea of a heat pump immediately suggests itself when the fact is appreciated that a body existing at a temperature below that of its surroundings is subjected to an inflow of heat from without which must be removed as fast as it leaks in if the particular temperature is to be maintained.

XIII-2. Reversed Heat Engine or Heat Pump.—In the heat engine the transformation of *heat into work* was accomplished by means of a reversible expansion taking place in a cylinder. The concept of a reversed heat engine implies the reversal of this into a reversible *work to heat* transformation. Such can be effected if the same mechanism be modified to operate as a compressor.

It has already been shown in Chapter III that a heat engine when operated reversed, will have as energy input, the heat equivalent of the

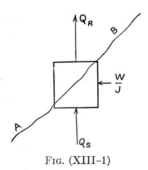

Fig. (XIII-1)

work done on the gas and the heat taken in at the lower temperature. The sum of these two constitute the energy output which is the heat delivered at the higher temperature. See Fig. (XIII-1).

Thus there is accomplished by aid of work from an external source, the elevation of a quantity of heat from a low temperature level to a higher one *plus* the heat equivalent of the external work of compression. Hence the heat delivered at the higher temperature will always be greater than that taken in at the lower temperature. The energy balance for a reversed heat engine is shown diagrammatically in Fig. (XIII–1) in which the energy vectors balance about the irregular line A–B. It should be borne in mind that the heat quantities Q_S and Q_R are at different temperature levels.

The useful application of a reversed heat engine may be for either of two purposes, (1) to abstract heat from some low-temperature region or (2) to supply heat to some high-temperature region. The first constitutes *refrigeration* as commonly understood, and the second comprises the rapidly developing field of *mechanical heating*.

In a heat engine the best efficiency is obtained by the use of a cycle composed entirely of reversible processes, so in the heat pump the best

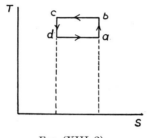

Fɪɢ. (XIII–2).

performance will be had by the use of a heat-engine cycle which is thermodynamically reversible. If Carnot's cycle, reversed, be represented on the T–S diagram, Fig. (XIII–2), a–b becomes an adiabatic compression, b–c an isothermal rejection of heat at the higher temperature, c–d an adiabatic expansion, and d–a an isothermal absorption of heat at the lower temperature. The areas involved on this diagram representing energies supplied to or rejected from the system are three in number. The area beneath d–a shows the heat taken up by the system at low temperature from the cold body, known as the *refrigerating effect*, and the area beneath b–c represents the quantity of heat rejected from the system at higher temperature. The difference in these heat quantities is the heat equivalent of the work done in operating the cycle, and is shown in Fig. (XIII–2) as the rectangular area $abcd$.

XIII–3. Coefficient of Performance (Ideal).—When discussing heat engines it was pointed out that the effective performance expressed in terms of heat energy supplied, constituted a coefficient of performance though termed efficiency. While the term " efficiency " as applied to heat engines was numerically always less than unity, this expression may exceed unity when used to denote the excellence of a reversed heat engine. Since we are not dealing with the transformation of heat into mechanical energy in the refrigeration system, there should be no confusion due to the fact that an energy ratio, which we choose to call " efficiency " or " coefficient of performance," may be greater than unity. A heat pump may have either of two objects; the abstraction of heat from a cold body; that is, *refrigeration*, with the rejection of heat at the higher temperature as an incidental process; or the supplying of heat to a warm body, that is, *heating*, the abstraction of heat from the cold body being incidental. In the first case, the heat quantity of most importance is the heat *absorbed* by the system; in the second, the heat *rejected* from the system. Thus what might be called the *useful output* of the machine depends upon the *purpose* for which it is intended. Coefficient of Performance may be defined as a ratio of the useful performance to the heat equivalent of the work required to produce that effect. Referring to Figure (XIII–1) the coefficient of performance would be, for a refrigeration system $\dfrac{Q_s}{AW}$;

for a heating system, it would be $\dfrac{Q_R}{AW}$. This applies to any heat-pump system, in general, whether ideal or practical.

For the reversed Carnot Cycle, Fig. (XIII–2), the coefficient of performance will be $\dfrac{T_a}{T_b - T_a}$ for refrigeration, and $\dfrac{T_b}{T_b - T_a}$ for heating. It may be seen from these expressions that the smaller the temperature range in the system, the higher will be the coefficient of performance. This is shown graphically in Fig. (XIII–3). In each of these cases the temperature at which heat is rejected from the system is the same, and the work input to the system is the same. The temperature at which heat is absorbed by the system is changed in each diagram, being highest in (a) and lowest in (c). Inspection shows that the refrigerating effect and the heat rejected become smaller as the range of temperatures is increased. With the work remaining the same, this results in a reduced coefficient of performance. In the refrigeration machine, the upper temperature is fixed by the natural means at hand for cooling, such as the temperature of air or cooling water, while the lower temperature is that desired for refrigeration which for best performance should be no lower than necessary.

XIII–4. Unit of Refrigeration.—The unit of refrigeration is the *ton of refrigeration*, the expression dating from the time when most cooling was accomplished by the use of ice. By a *ton of refrigeration* is meant the withdrawal from the substance being cooled of a quantity of heat every 24 hours equal to that which would be withdrawn by the melting of a ton of ice at 32° F. to water *at the same temperature*. Since the latent heat of fusion per pound of ice is 144 B.t.u., a ton of refrigeration is equivalent to the withdrawal of $144 \times 2,000 = 288,000$ B.t.u. per 24 hours from the

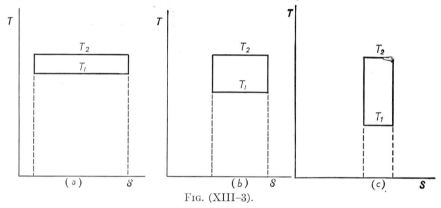

Fig. (XIII–3).

refrigerated substance. This is the unit used in denoting the *capacity* of a given refrigerating unit.

XIII–5. Evolution of the Compression System.—Probably the earliest type of mechanical refrigerating plants were those using air for the working fluid. A brief description of such has already been given in Chapter VI, but a recapitulation of its salient features may be helpful. Starting from atmospheric conditions the work of compression immediately brings the air to high pressure and high temperature. At this high pressure it is cooled by circulating water to approximately atmospheric temperature. The air then at high pressure and moderate temperature is ready to enter the expander cylinder. In the expander it undergoes an expansion, the converse of its earlier compression, and experiences a drop in temperature directly comparable with the rise in temperature experienced in the compressor cylinder. However, this drop in temperature *begins* at the temperature of the cooling water and the air becomes very cold. It then passes on to accomplish its refrigeration. In such a plant the work of the expander cylinder is used to minimize the work supplied to the compressor cylinder and only the difference or net work has to be supplied from outside sources.

The bulk of any refrigerating plant per ton of refrigeration must be largely affected by the thermal capacity per cubic foot of the fluid used. The greater the thermal capacity the smaller the plant. Gases are notoriously low in thermal capacity, liquids are much higher but are only slightly compressible, but the thermal capacity, " par excellence," occurs when a substance undergoes a change of phase, as from the vapor to the liquid or conversely. To illustrate, one pound of air takes on only one-quarter of a B.t.u. with one degree rise in temperature, whereas if it were chilled to the point of condensation, it would require approximately 65 B.t.u. simply to condense it. Similarly, water as superheated steam has a specific heat

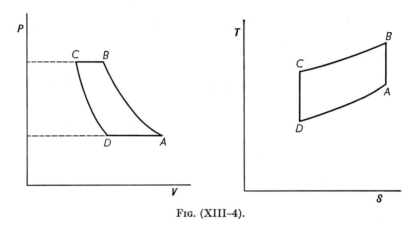

FIG. (XIII–4).

of about one-half a B.t.u., whereas the heat of vaporization is around one thousand. Theoretically, any compressible substance may serve as a refrigerating fluid, but in practice, if it is possible to use one which undergoes a change of phase, advantage can be taken of the enormous heat absorptive phenomenon incidental to such a change, the latent heat of vaporization.

To illustrate this, imagine it possible to so extend the operative range of the foregoing air refrigerating unit as to bring its operation to temperatures below the critical and establish a comparison. The P–V and T–S diagrams for normal operation are shown in Fig. (XIII–4). The refrigerating effect is represented by the area under D–A on T–S diagram and the heat rejected from the system by the area under B–C.

Suppose, now, that the substance, instead of merely being cooled as a gas to point C, were to be cooled below its critical temperature and to a degree where condensation occurs. The heat then rejected from the system would be the area beneath 2–3–4 on T–S diagram, Fig. (XIII–5).

This is much more per unit weight of the fluid than before, due to the removal of the latent heat of vaporization. If, with the refrigerant in the liquid phase, it were expanded to the lower pressure and then allowed to take up heat, the capacity of the machine would be enormously increased, the refrigerating effect being represented by the area under 5–6–1. The new cycle, which now would be a *vapor* cycle, would become more like that shown in Fig. (XIII–7).

Obviously, the use of air, with its very low temperature of condensation, would be impossible in the ordinary machine, but a number of vapors exist which have boiling points in the range suitable for practical use. With gas as a refrigerating fluid, the work of expansion plays an important part,

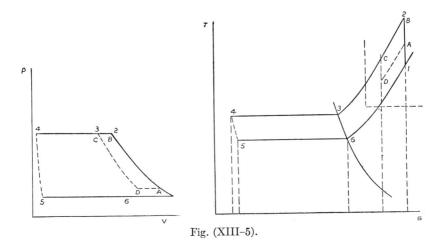

Fig. (XIII–5).

but with vapor, the change of phase predominates to such an extent as to make the heat equivalent of the work of expansion negligible. Thus throttling may be substituted in the vapor machine without materially reducing the efficiency of the system.

XIII–6. **Refrigerating Fluids Used.**—Although any substance in any phase might conceivably be used as the working substance in a refrigerating system, solids and liquids are practically unfitted for it, due to their slight volumetric changes within moderate pressure ranges. The Carnot Cycle and the fundamentals of reversed heat engines do not stipulate the working substance which shall be used, but only gases or vapors are well adapted.

The use of gases (air) for refrigerating machines was mentioned in

Chapter VI. In this type of system the cooling was accomplished by utilizing the decrease in temperature resulting from adiabatic expansion. No change of phase was involved. Air systems, however, have the distinct disadvantages over vapor systems of greater bulk for the same capacity, more complexity, lower coefficient of performance, and frosting difficulties, due to the water vapor in the air. On the other hand, the air machine has the advantage of using a cheap and innocuous fluid as a refrigerant.

The use of vapors as a refrigerant depends primarily upon the heat quantities involved in a change of phase and the relation between saturation pressure and temperature. In general, it may be said that vapors suitable for use as refrigerants must be capable of existing in the vapor phase at reasonable pressures when at temperatures suitable for refrigeration. A list of those commonly used comprises, Ammonia (NH_3), Carbon dioxide (CO_2), Sulfur dioxide (SO_2), Methyl chloride (CH_2Cl_2), Ethyl chloride (C_2H_5Cl), and a number of other proprietary compounds or mixtures.

XIII-7. Cycles.—In dealing with refrigeration devices there are two important limits which must be observed, (1) the temperature of the refrigerated space, and (2) the temperature of the supply of water used for the absorption of the heat withdrawn. These temperatures form limits outside of which the operation of actual units must lie. Fig. (XIII-5a) shows the cycle of operations of (a) a

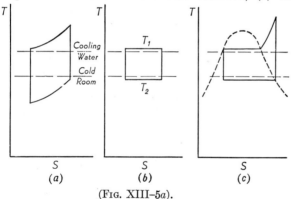

(Fig. XIII-5a).

machine using a non-condensable gas, as air, (b) one using a condensable vapor with the compression taking place entirely in the saturated region, and (c) a machine also using a condensable vapor, but with the compression carried out entirely in the superheated vapor region.

For these cycles adiabatic compression and expansion are shown, though actually neither compression nor expansion are adiabatic. The assumption of adiabatic action, however, simplifies the present discussion. Accepting this the optimum cycle is obviously the reversed Carnot operating between the limiting temperatures just mentioned. For such the coefficient of performance is,

for refrigerating machines, $T_2 \div (T_1 - T_2)$,

for heat pumps, $T_1 \div (T_1 - T_2)$.

Frequently the ratio of the coefficient of performance of the actual plant to that of the reversed Carnot Cycle is called the efficiency of the plant but the term is not universally accepted. Another method for expressing the performance of actual plants is in horsepower per ton of refrigeration which is Hp. $\times 2544 \div \dfrac{288,000}{24}$. Using this, relative performance can be expressed as the ratio of the actual to the idealized cycle. In Fig. (XIII–6) is shown diagrammatically the mechanical layout of a refrigerating plant using a condensable vapor. Except when using water vapor, plants of this type always operate as closed systems in order to conserve the operating fluid. They consist essentially of a compressor, condenser, expander, and evaporator. In the first the vapor is compressed to a hot high-pressure vapor, whence it passes to the con-

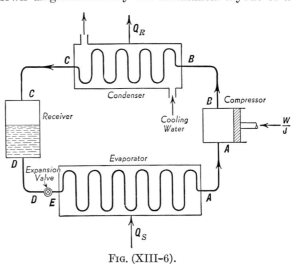

FIG. (XIII–6).

denser and becomes liquefied by the cooling water. From here it goes to the expander, which may be either a cylinder or more commonly a simple pressure reducing valve, after which it passes as a low-pressure boiling mixture of liquid and vapor to the evaporator where it completes its vaporization by taking on the heat Q_2 from the space to be refrigerated.

The thermodynamic action during the circuit may be seen from Fig. (XIII–7). The notation corresponds in all diagrams of Figs. (XIII–6) and (XIII–7). Optional compression lines, A–B and A'–B', are shown.

A–B, taking place in the superheat region would be known as *dry compression*, while *A'–B'*, taking place in the saturated region, would be called *wet compression*.   Compression lines are represented as taking place at constant entropy which is not far from the actual, the heat removed by the water jackets being comparatively small, unless two stages are resorted to when the actual compression varies rather widely from the isentropic. *B–C* represents the heat rejection process in the condenser resulting first in the removal of superheat, *B–B'*, and then condensation, *B'–C*, the state point moving over to the liquid line.   The receiver, *C–D*, has no thermodynamic significance.   The flow of the refrigerant through the

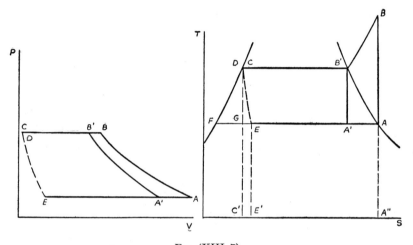

Fig. (XIII–7).

expansion valve is shown by *D–E*.   This is a throttling action and, consequently, takes place at constant heat content.   This expansion results in partial evaporation of the liquid to a state represented by *E* and takes the place of the reversible adiabatic expansion which is a part of Carnot's reversed cycle.   This substitution is made for mechanical simplicity as the small amount of work to be realized from expansion of the fluid from the liquid state is not worth the added complexity involved in its utilization.   Also careful regulation of the amount of liquid passing is required, and this is best accomplished by means of a valve.   The next process in the cycle is the refrigeration process involving the absorption of heat from the cold body, *E–A* (or *E–A'*).   Like the condensation process, this takes place at constant pressure, the refrigerant being more or less completely evaporated, and sometimes slightly superheated, as it leaves the evaporator to enter the compressor and repeat the cycle.

The energy quantities are represented in Fig. (XIII-7) as follows: The refrigerating effect is the area beneath the line representing the refrigerating process, that is, $EAA''E'$. Since EA is a constant-pressure process, the refrigerating effect is numerically equal to $h_A - h_E$. Likewise, the heat rejected in the condenser is the area $A''BCC'$ or $h_B - h_C$. The work of the cycle, on the $P-V$ plane, is the area lying to the left of the compression line AB, that is, $\int_{P_A}^{P_B} V dP$. The heat equivalent of the work done in compressing the vapor is represented on the $T-S$ diagram by the area $ABCFA$. This may be shown in the following manner:

$$AW = Q_{sup.} - Q_{rej.} = A''BCC' - A''AEE' = E'EABCC'.$$

In order for this to be equivalent to $ABCFA$, $E'EGC'$ must be proven equal to CFG:

$$CFG = (h_C - h_F) - (h_G - h_F) = h_C - h_F - h_G + h_F = h_C - h_G,$$

$E'EGC' = h_E - h_G$, which, since $h_E = h_C$, is equal to $h_C - h_G$.
Thus,
$$CFG = E'EGC' \quad \text{and} \quad AW = ABCFA.$$

The heat equivalent of the work may further be shown to be numerically equal to $h_B - h_A$ as follows:

$$AW = (h_B - h_C) - (h_A - h_E) = h_B - h_C - h_A + h_E = h_B - h_A.$$

This expression applies, of course, only to adiabatic compression.

The actual vapor cycle diverges from that shown in Fig. (XIII-7), notably in four ways: (1) Non-adiabatic compression due to cooling during the process; (2) heat rejected from or taken on by the various inter-connecting pipe lines and apparatus; (3) departure from true constant-pressure processes during condensation and evaporation; and (4) sub-cooling of the liquid before throttling.

By subcooling is meant the reduction of the temperature of the liquid below its saturation temperature corresponding to its pressure. Figure (XIII-8) shows the effect of subcooling from D to D'. The vapor leaving the expansion valve and entering the evaporator is of lower quality and is, therefore, capable of absorbing more heat before being taken to the compressor. This is a pure gain in refrigerating effect, represented by the shaded area, without in any way affecting the work done, which results in an increased coefficient of performance. It may be seen that, if the liquid could be cooled to the temperature corresponding to the evaporator pressure, all of the latent heat of evaporation could be utilized. This temperature is impossible of attainment, however, since the cooling must be carried on by the natural means available.

The fact that the coefficient of performance is inversely related to the temperature range for all mechanical refrigerating systems makes it desirable to keep the condenser pressure as low and the evaporator pressure as high as possible. The minimum range in temperature, however, is fixed by nature in that the condenser pressure must be high enough to produce liquefaction and the evaporator pressure low enough to give a temperature conducive to the preservation of the commodities cooled. The problem of heat transfer also enters into the question adversely because a temperature gradient must be maintained in all heat exchangers. This makes it necessary to have the refrigerant at a temperature higher than that of the cooling water in the condenser and lower than that of the cold room in the evaporator.

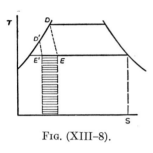

Fig. (XIII–8).

XIII–8. Illustrative Problem on Design.

—A 15-ton ammonia refrigerating machine using dry isentropic compression operates between pressures of 160 lbs. per sq. in. abs. and 30 lbs. per sq. in. abs. (Use cycle as represented in Fig. (XIII–7)).

Find: (a) Heat content at each point $ABCE$; (b) refrigerating effect per pound of NH_3 circulated; (c) pounds of NH_3 to be circulated per minute; (d) temperature of NH_3 leaving compressor; (e) work of compressor per pound of NH_3[3] and per minute .... B.t.u.; (f) heat rejected from condenser per pound of ammonia and per minute; (g) pounds of condenser cooling water required per minute, allowing a 15° temperature rise; (h) quality of vapor after throttling; (i) compressor I.Hp.; (j) coefficient of performance; (k) piston displacement of compressor .... cu. ft. per minute.

Solution.—(a) $h_A = 611.6$; $h_B = 716$; $h_C = h_D = h_E = 135$.

(b) Refrigerating effect per pound of ammonia $= 611.6 - 135 = 476.6$ B.t.u.

(c) Ammonia per minute $= \dfrac{15\,(200)}{476.6} = 6.3$ lbs.

(d) Ammonia temperature leaving compressor $= 213°$ F.

(e) Work of compression per pound of ammonia $= 716 - 611.6 = 104.4$ B.t.u.
Work of compression per minute $= 104.4 (6.3) = 657$ B.t.u.

(f) Heat rejected in condenser per pound of ammonia $= 716 - 135 = 581$ B.t.u.
Heat rejected per minute $= 581 (6.3) = 3660$ B.t.u.

(g) Cooling water per minute $= \dfrac{3660}{15} = 244$ lbs.

(h) Quality after throttling (point E) $= \dfrac{135 - 42.3}{569.3} = \dfrac{92.7}{569.3} = 0.163.$

(i) Compressor I.Hp. $= \dfrac{657}{42.4} = 15.5.$

(j) Coefficient of performance $= \dfrac{476.6}{104.4} = 4.57.$

(k) Specific volume of ammonia vapor at compressor entrance $= 9.236$ cu. ft.
Theoretical piston displacement required $= 9.236 (6.3) = 53.2$ cu. ft. per min.

XIII–9. Illustrative Problem on Test Analysis.—Let the following represent data from the test of an ammonia compression system:

Pressures

Condenser $= 136$ lbs. per sq. in. gage.
Evaporator $= 25$ lbs. per sq. in. gage.
Barometer $= 28.5$ in. of mercury.

Temperatures

Leaving compressor $= 209°$ F.
Entering condenser $= 190°$ F.
Leaving condenser $= 65°$ F.
Entering expansion valve $= 70°$ F.
Leaving evaporator $= 20°$ F.
Entering compressor $= 30°$ F.

Ammonia circulated per hour $= 192$ lbs.

Calculate: (a) Refrigerating effect per pound of ammonia, and the capacity of the plant in tons per 24 hours; (b) heat rejected by ammonia in condenser.... B.t.u. per hour; (c) work per pound of ammonia compressed and I.Hp. of compressor; (d) coefficient of performance; (e) heat losses and gains in pipe lines and receiver per pound NH_3; (f) heat balance of system per pound of ammonia.

Solution.—(a) Barometer $= 28.5 (.491) = 14$ lbs. per sq. in. Condenser pressure $= 136 + 14 = 150$ lbs. abs.; evaporator pressure $= 25 + 14 = 39$ lbs. abs.; h leaving evaporator (39 lbs., $20°$) $= 620.7$ B.t.u.; h entering evaporator (liquid at 70°) = 120.5; refrigerating effect per pound of ammonia = 620.7 −

120.5 = 500.2 B.t.u.; ref. eff. per minute = $\dfrac{192\,(500.2)}{60}$ = 1600 B.t.u.; tons per 24 hours = $\dfrac{1600}{200}$ = 8 tons.

(b) h entering condenser (150 lbs., 190°) = 702.9; h leaving condenser (liquid at 65°) = 114.8; heat rejected per pound = 702.9 − 114.8 = 588.1 B.t.u.; heat rejected per hour = 588.1 (192) = 112,900 B.t.u.

(c) Reference to tables or diagrams will serve to show that this is isentropic compression.

h leaving compressor (150 lbs., 209°). . . . . = 714   B.t.u.
h entering compressor (39 lbs., 30°). . . . . = 626.6

Heat equivalent of work per pound of ammonia. . . . . = 87.4 B.t.u.

$\qquad$ Compressor I.Hp. = $\dfrac{87.4\,(192)}{2544}$ = 6.6.

(d) Coefficient of performance = $\dfrac{500.2}{87.4}$ = 5.72.

(e) h leaving compressor. . . . . = 714.0 B.t.u.
h entering condenser. . . . . = 702.9

Heat from pipe line. . . . . = 11.1 B.t.u.

h entering expansion valve. . . . . = 120.5
h leaving condenser. . . . . = 114.8

Heat gain in pipe line and receiver. . . . . = 5.7 B.t.u.

h entering compressor. . . . . = 626.6
h leaving evaporator. . . . . = 620.7

Heat gain, evaporator to compressor. . . . . = 5.9 B.t.u.

(f) Heat balance on basis of one pound of ammonia:

Energy received by system:

In evaporator. . . . . = 500.2 B.t.u.
From evaporator to compressor. =   5.9
In compressor. . . . . =   87.4
In receiver and piping. . . . . =   5.7

Total energy in. . . . . = 599.2 B.t.u.

Energy rejected by system:

From compressor to condenser. . . . . = 11.1 B.t.u.
In condenser. . . . . = 588.1

Total energy out. . . . . = 599.2 B.t.u.

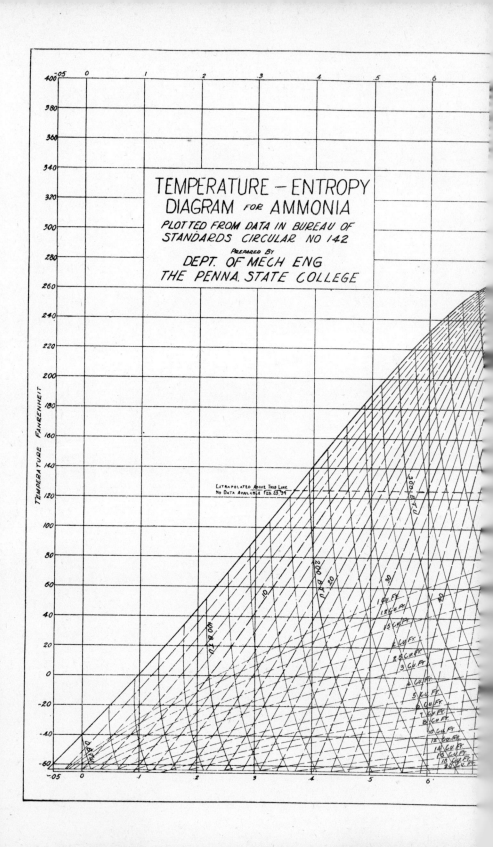

TEMPERATURE – ENTROPY
DIAGRAM FOR AMMONIA
PLOTTED FROM DATA IN BUREAU OF
STANDARDS CIRCULAR NO 142
PREPARED BY
DEPT. OF MECH ENG
THE PENNA. STATE COLLEGE

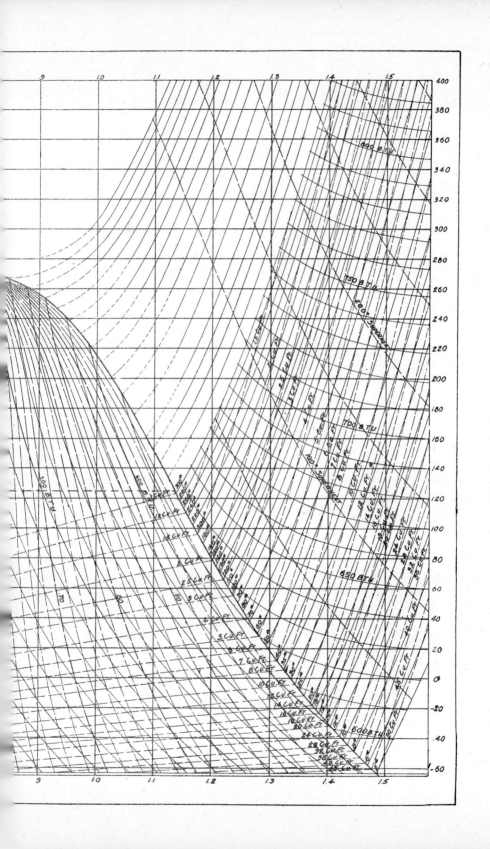

REFRIGERATION 387

PROPERTIES OF SATURATED ANHYDROUS AMMONIA*

Absolute Pressure, pounds per square inch	Temperature, degrees Fahrenheit	Specific Volume, cubic feet		Heat Content, above −40° F.			Entropy from −40° F.		
		Saturated Liquid	Saturated Vapor	Saturated Liquid	Evaporation	Saturated Vapor	Saturated Liquid	Evaporation	Saturated Vapor
5.0	−63.1	0.0227	49.31	−24.5	612.8	588.3	−0.0599	1.5456	1.4857
10.0	−41.3	0.0232	25.81	− 1.4	598.5	597.1	−0.0034	1.4310	1.4276
15.0	−27.3	0.0235	17.67	13.6	588.8	602.4	0.0318	1.3620	1.3938
20.0	−16.6	0.0238	13.50	25.0	581.2	606.2	0.0578	1.3122	1.3700
25.0	− 8.0	0.0240	10.96	34.3	574.8	609.1	0.0787	1.2728	1.3515
30.0	− 0.6	0.0242	9.24	42.3	569.3	611.6	0.0962	1.2402	1.3364
35.0	5.9	0.0243	7.99	49.3	564.3	613.6	0.1113	1.2123	1.3236
40.0	11.7	0.0245	7.05	55.6	559.8	615.4	0.1246	1.1879	1.3125
45.0	16.9	0.0247	6.31	61.3	555.6	616.9	0.1366	1.1661	1.3027
50.0	21.7	0.0248	5.71	66.5	551.7	618.2	0.1475	1.1464	1.2939
120.0	66.0	0.0262	2.48	116.0	512.4	628.4	0.2452	0.9749	1.2201
130.0	70.5	0.0263	2.29	121.1	508.1	629.2	0.2548	0.9584	1.2132
140.0	74.8	0.0265	2.13	126.0	503.9	629.9	0.2638	0.9430	1.2068
150.0	78.8	0.0266	1.99	130.6	499.9	630.5	0.2724	0.9285	1.2009
160.0	82.6	0.0267	1.87	135.0	496.1	631.1	0.2804	0.9148	1.1952
170.0	86.3	0.0269	1.76	139.3	492.3	631.6	0.2881	0.9019	1.1900
180.0	89.8	0.0271	1.67	143.3	488.7	632.0	0.2954	0.8896	1.1850
190.0	93.1	0.0272	1.58	147.2	485.2	632.4	0.3024	0.8778	1.1802
200.0	96.3	0.0273	1.50	150.9	481.8	632.7	0.3090	0.8666	1.1756
210.0	99.4	0.0275	1.43	154.6	478.4	633.0	0.3154	0.8559	1.1713

* Abstracted from "Thermodynamic Properties of Ammonia," *U. S. Bur. Standards, Circ.* 142.

XIII-10. **Other Vapor Refrigerants.**—Although water would serve as a refrigerant, there are other fluids which have characteristics rendering them more suitable. The hypothetical "ideal" refrigerant would have certain definite characteristics, the most important of which are: (1) A sufficiently low boiling point for the evaporator at a pressure slightly above atmospheric; (2) a sufficiently high boiling point for condensation at moderate pressure; (3) high latent heat of vaporization in order to reduce the amount to be circulated for a given refrigerating effect; (4) small specific volume which, with 3, will result in small piston displacement of the compressor; (5) non-inflammable; (6) non-corrosive; (7) non-toxic; (8) no effect on lubricants; (9) chemical stability. The three commercial refrigerants which seem best to satisfy these requirements are:

1. Ammonia (NH_3)—medium pressures; high latent heat and medium

THERMODYNAMICS

PROPERTIES OF SUPERHEATED AMMONIA

Absolute Pressure, pounds per square inch		Temperature, degrees Fahrenheit						
		−20°	−10°	0°	10°	20°	30°	40°
15	Specific volume	18.01	18.47	18.92	19.37	19.82	20.26	20.70
	Enthalpy	606.4	611.9	617.2	622.5	627.8	633.0	638.2
	Entropy	1.4031	1.4154	1.4272	1.4386	1.4497	1.4604	1.4709
25	Specific volume			11.19	11.47	11.75	12.03	12.30
	Enthalpy			613.8	619.4	625.0	630.4	635.8
	Entropy			1.3616	1.3738	1.3855	1.3967	1.4077
35	Specific volume				8.078	8.287	8.493	8.695
	Enthalpy				616.1	622.0	627.7	633.4
	Entropy				1.3289	1.3413	1.3532	1.3646
45	Specific volume					6.363	6.530	6.694
	Enthalpy					618.8	624.9	630.8
	Entropy					1.3068	1.3193	1.3313
		130°	150°	170°	190°	210°	230°	250°
140	Specific volume	2.460	2.569	2.675	2.779	2.880	2.981	3.080
	Enthalpy	667.4	679.9	692.0	704.0	715.8	727.5	739.2
	Entropy	1.2738	1.2945	1.3141	1.3328	1.3507	1.3679	1.3846
160	Specific volume	2.125	2.224	2.319	2.411	2.502	2.591	2.679
	Enthalpy	664.4	677.2	689.7	701.9	713.9	725.8	737.6
	Entropy	1.2542	1.2757	1.2958	1.3148	1.3331	1.3506	1.3675
180	Specific volume	1.865	1.955	2.042	2.126	2.208	2.288	2.367
	Enthalpy	661.3	674.6	687.3	699.8	712.0	724.1	736.1
	Entropy	1.2364	1.2586	1.2792	1.2987	1.3172	1.3350	1.3521
200	Specific volume	1.656	1.740	1.820	1.897	1.972	2.046	2.118
	Enthalpy	658.1	671.8	684.9	697.7	710.1	722.4	734.5
	Entropy	1.2200	1.2429	1.2641	1.2840	1.3029	1.3209	1.3382

specific volumes giving medium piston displacement; not dangerously inflammable; non-corrosive to iron and steel—corrosive to copper alloys; non-toxic but highly irritating; no effect on lubricants; chemically stable under normal pressures and temperatures.

2. Sulphur dioxide (SO$_2$)—medium pressures (lower than NH$_3$); medium latent heat and specific volume giving medium piston displacements (greater than NH$_3$); non-inflammable; non-corrosive when pure—

highly corrosive with moisture; non-toxic but extremely irritating; possesses lubricating properties of itself and has no effect on mineral oils; chemically stable.

3. Carbon dioxide (CO_2)—extreme pressures; low latent heat but such a small specific volume that the result is very small piston displacement; non-inflammable; non-corrosive; non-toxic and non-irritating; no effect on lubricants; chemically stable.

It may be seen that, although none of the three satisfies all the ideal requirements, ammonia probably is nearest and is the commercial refrigerant most generally used. Cost is also, of course, an important item, and, on this item, none of the above has any great advantage over the others.

Other refrigerants in general use are: butane; iso-butane; methyl chloride; ethyl chloride; propane; ethane; dichloroethylene; ether; dichlorodifluoromethane; and chloroform. These approach the ideal in varying degrees.

Complete tables of the properties of saturated and superheated ammonia, sulphur dioxide, and carbon dioxide are available in A.S.R.E. Data Book.

XIII–11. Refrigerating Machine Using Steam.—From the standpoint of pressure and temperature, as common a substance as water vapor or steam may be reasonably suitable for use as a refrigerant. A low pressure is required but not so low as to be impossible of attainment in practice. The steam tables show that for a boiling point of 32° F. the absolute pressure is .0887 lb. per sq. in.

A simple water vapor system can be made to work as follows. Suppose there to be a pipe coil in which a low pressure may be maintained by means of a vacuum pump. Into this coil water may be admitted through a valve in any desired quantity. If now, the coil be subjected to a vacuum such that the absolute pressure within is 0.10 lb. per sq. in. abs., the boiling point of the water will be the temperature corresponding to this pressure. Reference to the steam tables shows this temperature to be 35° F. So long, then, as water is present in the coil, and the pressure maintained at 0.10 lb., the temperature within the coil will be not more than 35°. The addition of heat from outside the coil will result in the evaporation of water but there will be no temperature rise. Thus, if the coil were to be surrounded by some substance at a temperature higher than 35°, heat would be abstracted from it continuously and supplied to the water within. Further, if the water be supplied at the boiling point corresponding to the pressure within the coil and be pumped out as dry and saturated vapor, the heat absorbed by each pound of vapor will be the latent heat of vaporization for that particular pressure. The steam tables show this to be, in this case, $h_{fg} = 1071.8$ B.t.u. Whatever the condition of the water entering or of the steam leaving, since the process takes place at constant pressure, the heat taken on by each pound will be the difference of heat contents leaving and entering. In this case, if the water were to enter at 50° F. instead of at 35°, the refrigerating effect per pound would be $h_{g\,35°} - h_{f\,50°} = 1074.8 - 18.06 = 1056.74$ B.t.u. (steam tables). The temperature within the coil could be reduced below 32° by a reduction in pressure below 0.0887 lb. per sq. in., the degree of cold being limited only by the practical difficulties in producing and maintaining a suitable vacuum. When carried below 32°, brine would be used instead of pure water in order to avoid difficulties due to freezing.

In practice, however, there are serious disadvantages in using water as a refrigerant. The principal ones are, the comparatively high vacuum that must be maintained with the attendant difficulty of excluding air, and the enormous specific volume of the vapor at the very low pressures. The specific volume of the steam in the example just discussed is 2946 cu. ft. per lb. Partial tables for most and complete tables for some of the other refrigerants have been compiled.

XIII–12. Various Methods for Graphically Representing Properties.— Diagrams for representing properties and state changes for refrigerants are similar in use and construction, and somewhat similar in appearance to those for steam. The diagrams most valuable from a thermodynamic and analytical viewpoint are the P–V and T–S, Fig. (XIII–9) (a), planes where the areas represent the two forms of energy in which we are interested—work and heat respectively. The H–S (heat content vs. entropy), Fig. (XIII–9) (b), and the P–H (pressure vs. heat content), Fig. (XIII–9 (c), diagrams are valuable in the solution of certain types of problems in that the properties for a given state may be determined with facility but the areas and, therefore, cyclic plots, have no meaning from the standpoint of energy relationships.

XIII–13. The Absorption System.—In the heat-pump systems discussed thus far, the energy to maintain the process has been supplied entirely in the form of work for compressing the vapor. If the refrigerant could be raised from the low pressure to the high *as a liquid* instead of as a vapor, the work required to do this would be only a fraction of that required in the vapor compression system. This is accomplished in the absorption system by dissolving the vapor as it comes from the evaporator, in a liquid, pumping the solution thus formed to the higher pressure, and releasing the refrigerant from the solution at that higher pressure. As just mentioned, the quantity of work required for this pumping process is, comparatively, very small but there are heat quantities involved in the forming and the dissociation of the solution which amount to about ten times the heat equivalent of the work done in the compression system. Thus the absorption system might be classified as a heat pump in which the energy to carry on

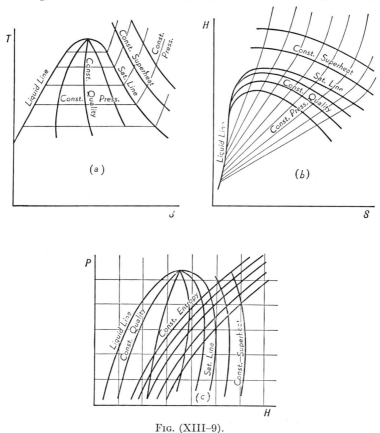

Fig. (XIII–9).

the process is supplied almost entirely in the form of heat instead of as work. The diagrammatic layout of the absorption system in Fig. (XIII–10) shows much similarity to the compression system. The only major change made has been the substitution of other apparatus for the compressor,—condenser, receiver, expansion valve, and evaporator remain exactly the same. For the compressor has been substituted an absorber, liquid pump, and generator. Back and forth between absorber and generator flows a water

and ammonia solution, or aqua ammonia. From the absorber to the
generator the solution is strong, that is, it possesses a high concentration of
ammonia. From the generator to the absorber, the aqua solution is
weaker because of the ammonia which has been set free in the generator.
The aqua may be said, then, to be the vehicle for carrying ammonia from
the low to the high-pressure side of the system through the medium of the
aqua pump. In the absorber, where the concentration of the solution is
increased by the addition of vapor from the evaporator, the process is one
of heat evolution and cooling must be carried on with water. On the other
hand, the reverse is true of the generator where the solution is broken
down and heat must be supplied. This is usually done by means of steam
supplied through coils within the generator. In a solution composed of a

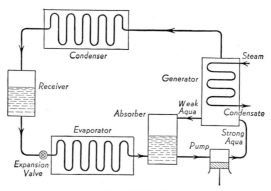

FIG. (XIII–10).

gas absorbed in a liquid, high pressure and low temperature are conducive
to a strong solution and vice versa. High pressure in the absorber and low
in the generator are not possible, of course, but this may be partially com-
pensated for by a great difference of temperature between the two—the
absorber being maintained at low temperature by means of cooling water,
and the generator at high temperature with steam. The heat quantities
involved in absorber and generator are further complicated by the fact
that the formation of a solution of ammonia and water results in an evolution of heat, and, inversely, the breakdown of the solution requires the
application of heat. This is the heat of association or dissociation, and,
for aqua ammonia, varies, depending upon the concentration of the solution, but, at the solution strengths used in practice, amounts to considerable. The heat removed from the absorber must be such as to cool the weak
aqua from the generator to absorber temperature, condense the ammonia

vapor from the evaporator, and remove the heat of solution. The heat supplied to the generator is used principally to heat the strong aqua from the absorber to generator temperature, evaporate the ammonia vapor removed from solution, and to supply the heat of solution for that ammonia which is freed.

The absorption system is advantageous where a source of heat which might otherwise be wasted, is available, such as exhaust steam; where the bulk of the apparatus is immaterial; where a minimum of moving parts is desired; or where the fluctuations in load are extreme.

On the basis of performance, the absorption system produces refrigeration to the extent of 25 per cent to 35 per cent of the heat energy supplied, whereas, it has been seen that a compression system will produce a refrigerating effect three to five times as great as the amount of work supplied. In this comparison it should be remembered, however, that high-grade energy in the form of work must be supplied to the compression system while low-grade heat energy operates the absorption system. With everything considered, the cost of operation is not radically different in either case.

XIII–14. Servel Electrolux (Munters-Platen) System.—This is an ingenious system which incorporates an interesting modification of the commercial absorption system and an admirable application of the law of partial pressures.

The object of this system is the complete elimination of moving parts which the standard absorption system had reduced to simply the small aqua pump. In order to do this, it is necessary to effect pressure equalization throughout the system while, at the same time, the ammonia must be at high pressure in the condenser and at low pressure in the evaporator in order that these may function. In the Servel system this is accomplished by subjecting the entire system to one pressure. In the condenser, this pressure is maintained by the ammonia alone, no other gas being present, while in the evaporator there is enough hydrogen present to maintain most of the total pressure, the partial pressure of the ammonia is then sufficiently low for evaporation to take place at low temperature. By keeping the hydrogen in the low-pressure side of the system, conditions may be maintained and circulation provided by the small differential pressure produced by the application of heat in the generator. This method has been applied to a large extent only to small plants and is advantageous where there is a lack of attendance and fully automatic control is desired.

XIII–15. Use of Refrigerating Machine as Heating Plant.—It has been mentioned that a heat pump may be useful for purposes of heating as well as for cooling. For instance, if a building is to be heated, it only becomes necessary to locate the unit rejecting heat inside where heat will be given up to the rooms, and the refrigerating coils outside where heat will be taken on from the outside. If a coefficient of performance of 6 be realized, based on the heat given up in the building, then it will be seen that five-sixths of the heat used in the building will have come from the low-temperature supply outside, the other sixth having come from the work of compression. As opposed to this, the conventional method of heating supplies all the heat from a fuel inside the building utilizing none of that from the outside surroundings. The advantage of taking most of the heat from outside with a heat pump is at present offset in most localities by the tremendous difference in cost per B.t.u. between electrical energy for driving the compressor and the energy in coal or oil. An example, however, will serve to show the advantage of the use of electricity to operate a refrigerating system over the use of electricity for direct heating as by radiant or glow heaters.

XIII–16. Illustrative Example on Heating.—It is desired to maintain a building at 70° F. with an outside temperature of −10° F. by use of an ammonia compression system and to compare the cost with that for direct electrical heating. Cost of electrical energy = 1½¢ per kw.-hr. Heat required = 60,000 B.t.u. per hour. Use theoretical system and neglect temperature differences* for heat transfer.

Solution.—Condenser pressure = 130 lbs. abs. Evaporator pressure = 23 lbs. Using dry compression, h_A (Fig. (XIII–7)) = 608; h_B = 715; h_C = 121.

Coefficient of performance, based on heat rejected $= \dfrac{715-121}{715-608} = \dfrac{594}{107} = 5.55$.

Heat equivalent of work of compression $= \dfrac{60,000}{5.55} = 10,800$ B.t.u. per hour.

Assuming a combined mechanical and electrical efficiency of 75 per cent, electrical consumption $= \dfrac{10,800}{3413\,(.75)} = 4.22$ kw.-hr. per hour.

Cost per hour = 4.22 (1.5) = 6.34¢ or $1.52 per 24 hours.

Cost for direct heating $= \dfrac{60,000\,(1.5)}{3413} = 26.4$¢ per hour or $6.34 per day.

XIII–17. Very Low Temperatures.—For the attainment of very low temperatures necessary, for instance, in the liquefaction of gases, the Joule-Thomson effect is utilized, supplemented by the use of the principle

* Actually the heating element would be at a temperature considerably in excess of the temperature it was desired to maintain in the rooms, and the absorbing unit would be lower in temperature than the air from which it was receiving its heat. In this problem, in order to simplify the presentation, these differences are neglected.

of regenerative cooling. Fig. (XIII–11) shows apparatus for liquefying gases which would operate as follows: The gas is first compressed to a pressure of 2000 or 3000 lbs. per sq. in., then cooled just before entering the regenerative apparatus by means of some form of refrigeration. Following this, the gas traverses the inner tube of the apparatus and is throttled through the valve at A. This produces a drop in temperature of a few degrees, depending upon the Joule-Thomson coefficient for the particular condition, and the gas so cooled passes through the outer tube, *around the incoming gas*, to the atmosphere or back to the compressor for a repetition of the process. Thus the incoming gas is cooled by the outgoing and, since it always undergoes a *further* drop in temperature, due to throttling at the valve, becomes constantly colder. As the gas and the apparatus are thus cooled, heat leakage from the outside increases and, if not largely prevented, will check the process and cause the temperature to remain constant in a

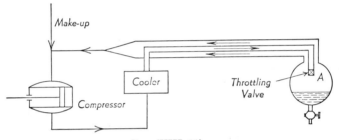

FIG. (XIII–11).

state of equilibrium far above the liquefaction temperature. If the transfer of heat be sufficiently retarded, as may be done by the use of suitable insulation, the machine will continue to lower the temperature until the liquefaction point is reached, whereupon any further withdrawal of heat by the expanding gas will not affect the temperature but will remove some latent heat of vaporization and condensation of a part of the gas will result, the moisture being separated mechanically and finally settling to the bottom of the vessel. The greater part of the gas entering will not be condensed but will pass from the apparatus, cooling the incoming gas as it does so.

Although this device is a refrigerating machine of a sort, it differs essentially from those previously discussed in that its cooling effect is cumulative and thus it is capable of producing exceedingly low temperatures, but with very small refrigerating capacity, while the other systems operating in a non-cumulative manner are limited to higher temperatures but have large capacities for cooling.

CHAPTER XIV

GENERAL THERMODYNAMIC RELATIONS

XIV-1. Need for General Mathematical Treatment.—Willard Gibbs is quoted as saying that "Mathematics is a language," an admirably concise statement, for all mathematical formulae and equations are simply shorthand presentations of relationships believed to exist. There are none but what can be stated in words though it may be at a sacrifice of clarity.

Accordingly when we deal with a considerable number of variables only a few of which may be directly observable experimentally, it is very helpful to establish mathematical relations which permit the data directly observed to be translated into terms of other properties, such, for example, as when, by the Clapyron relation (p. 410), it is possible from observations of temperature, pressure and latent heat to determine the specific volume of a vapor; or by observing the saturation and boiling temperature of a liquid to determine the slope of a line of constant pressure in the H–S Mollier Diagram (p. 283). It is by such means that observations on a relatively small number of properties are made to serve for the compilation of the much larger number of properties included in present-day tables of properties of Vapors.

Much work has been done in developing a mathematical treatment of the general case and there is presented in this chapter only a brief summary of some of the most salient features. The presentation lays no claim to originality but, to the author, represents the irreducible minimum with which any student of present-day thermodynamics as applied to engineering problems should be familiar.

XIV-2. Basic Assumptions.—The entire structure of modern thermodynamics is reared upon three foundational supports: the first and second laws of thermodynamics and the assumption that there can be only two independent variables in any equation of state, or, expressed differently, that a state is determined when any *two* independent properties are fixed.

Of the foregoing three the first is a statement of an experimental fact, the second a negation, and the third an assumption. The first is capable of direct experimental verification, the last two are not and justification for

396

them lies only in the fact that they have never been disproven. When assumptions at variance with them are made, the conclusions reached are absurd and differ from the observed facts.

The first law of thermodynamics may be expressed mathematically as $dQ = dU + \dfrac{dW}{J}$ and the second law as $\int dS = 0$ for a reversible cycle. The third basic relation may be generalized as $z = f(x, y)$ or $T = f(P, V)$, $U = f(T, S)$, etc.

XIV-3. Known Variables.—The variables dealt with in the mathematical discussion are the various properties which the fluids possess and the energy quantities Q (heat supplied) and W (external work done). These are of two sorts mathematically speaking, the *first* completely determined by the state and independent of previous history as illustrated by pressure or temperature and the *second*, quantities not completely defined by the state but which need for their evaluation information on how that state was achieved as illustrated by Q and W.

The first group are called explicit or point functions and the second implicit or path functions. The first can be dealt with as exact differentials but the second group are inexact differentials. All the true properties belong to the first group. The only common ones in the second group are Q and W.

Equivalent descriptive nomenclature for the two groups might be tabulated as follows:

Group I	*Group II*
Explicit function	Implicit function
Point function	Path function
Exact differential	Inexact differential
Properties	Performances

Thus for differentials of any of the *properties* it is allowable to obtain the integration directly as $\int_1^2 dP = P_2 - P_1$ or $\int_1^2 dH = H_2 - H_1$ but for the path functions this cannot be done till the path is specified, for example, we may not write $\int_1^2 dQ = Q_2 - Q_1$ or $\int_1^2 dW = W_2 - W_1$, as it cannot be integrated till the path is specified. If, however, a change occurs at, say, constant pressure, then the integration can be performed as

$$\int_1^2 dW = \int_1^2 P dV = P \int_1^2 dV = P(V_2 - V_1).$$

Of the properties commonly dealt with, four, P, V, T, U are obviously functions of the state only; for example, a substance at a certain pressure is quite unaffected so far as pressure is concerned by how that pressure was achieved. Of the other two common properties H and S, the first is by definition equal to $U + APV$, each term of which is a function of state only* and thus the sum must be. That entropy should be a property, however, is not so obvious, as by definition for a reversible process, it was

$$dS = \frac{dQ}{T}$$ and dQ is a path function, not a function of state. It is, however,

an energy function, as was earlier noted (p. 37), being a measure of the unavailable energy for any given state, and according to that should have a definite value for any given state. Another commonly presented proof is to show that the entropy change for any reversible cycle is zero, thus the

$$\int \frac{dQ}{T} = 0$$ and therefore $\dfrac{dQ}{T}$ must be an exact differential and dS a point

function; thus S is a function of state only and a true property.

XIV–4. Few Properties Directly Measurable.—Of all the properties which are commonly dealt with there are surprisingly few capable of direct measurement, only pressure, temperature, and volume. Of these the first is most easily and accurately measured. Temperature is usually measured by the mercurial thermometer or thermocouples and is capable of being determined with reasonable precision at the spot where the measuring unit is located. However, temperature differences may exist even in a fairly quiescent mass of fluid and in flowing vapors, temperature measurements are apt to be seriously affected by droplets or condensation films. Volume is capable of measurement in the experimental laboratory but not easily. Thus out of the six commonly used properties (P, V, T, U, H, S) there are but two which are conveniently measurable, P and T, and the others must be tied in with these either directly or indirectly before they can be readily evaluated.

XIV–5. Compound Properties.—Since by definition a property is an attribute of state only, there could be evolved an infinite number of properties by combining the foregoing in various ways. For example, as P, V and T are all properties there might be evolved a new compound property, $P + V + T$, or $PV + T$, etc. Each would be a function of state only and if it served a useful purpose its creation would be justified and probably a new name assigned. It was such reasoning that led Willard Gibbs to

---

* For a given state there can be but one P and one V, therefore only one PV product and thus the product of the two is also a property.

create three new properties, which he wisely refrained from naming, calling them "thermodynamic potentials" or thermodynamic functions and denoting each by a Greek letter, as follows:

(Psi) $\Psi = U - TS$

(Chi) $X = U + APV$

(Zeta) $Z = U - TS + APV.$

Of these the second (Chi) is the familiar property (H) so useful in the study of flowing fluids and heat drop, and variously named, or rather misnamed, by later users as, Total Heat, Heat Content, or Enthalpy. The other two fortunately have not been seriously handicapped with falsely descriptive titles, usually being called as Gibbs presented them* the Psi or Zeta functions.

The Psi function $(U - TS)$, however, was christened "Free energy" by Helmholtz, a descriptive appellation of doubtful service.

All three are extremely useful and it is preferable for the student to consider them as useful mathematical expressions evolved for particular purposes and defined as such. The true definition of each is its mathematical expression and as long as this definition is adhered to and the use of it facilitates mathematical analysis, its creation has been warranted. It is folly to attempt to picturize mentally what these compound properties might be like, as was done with the Chi function when it was miscalled Total Heat or Heat Content. It is far better to recognize it as a convenient thermodynamic property, compounded of familiar ingredients, it is true, but combined into one item for a definite mathematical objective and let it go at that.†

Thus there are available as recognized properties, functions only of the existing state of the fluid eight commonly used quantities.

Pressure $= P$

Volume $= V$

Temperature $= T$

---

* Gibbs, zeta function with its sign reversed is called G by some British writers and values for it tabulated in current British steam tables.

$$G = -Z = -(U + APV - TS) = TS - H.$$

† Tardy recognition of this has resulted in the meaningless name of Enthalpy being proposed for the use of those who must have a specific title other than that proposed by Gibbs.

Intrinsic energy $= U$

$$\text{Entropy} = S = \int \frac{dQ}{T}$$

Psi function, $\Psi = U - TS$

Heat content, $H = X = U + APV$

Zeta function $Z = U - TS + APV$ or $H - TS$.

Of these the first four are defined by physical conceptions and the last four by mathematical equations. All are point functions, and their derivatives are perfect differentials.

In addition to these the two quantities, External Work (W) and Heat Supplied (Q), must be dealt with and as these are path functions their derivatives are imperfect differentials.

XIV–6. Partial Derivatives.—Because we are dealing with two independent variables, partial differentiation and the solution of partial differential equations are most convenient mathematical tools. The student is assumed to be familiar with the methods of the calculus, and the following is presented as a matter of restatement and review.

When a quantity is a function of two variables as

$$Z = f(X, Y),$$

if each of the variables is successively treated as constant while the other is differentiated, the result of each step would be termed the partial differential, for example, if

$$Z = X \cdot Y,$$

treating X as a constant and differentiating

$$(dZ)_x = X dY$$

also treating Y as a constant, we have

$$(dZ)_y = Y dX.$$

The subscripts indicating which variable has been assumed constant in the process.

As the number of independent variables has been limited to two (p. 396), the characteristic equations give characteristic *surfaces*. These surfaces, truly enough, differ for a given substance depending upon which combination of these properties is taken for the coordinate axes, but they are nevertheless all *surfaces,* not lines or volumes.   Thus it is true that in going from state 1 to state 2 the journey might have been made in two parts, each in succession parallel to one of the coördinate planes, the total change on the surface itself would be equal to the sum of these two partial changes.   In other words, the total differential is equal to the sum of the partial differentials—a mathematical fact.

$$dZ = (dZ)_X + (dZ)_Y,$$

or as more commonly written,

$$dZ = \left(\frac{dZ}{dY}\right)_X dY + \left(\frac{dZ}{dX}\right)_Y dX.$$

Applying this to the illustrative example

$$dZ = XdY + YdX,$$

which agrees with the orthodox rule for differentiating a product.

Another way of expressing partial derivatives is by use of the Greek letter delta (δ) to indicate that the differentiation has been but partial, as

$$\frac{\delta Z}{\delta Y} = X$$

and

$$\frac{\delta Z}{\delta X} = Y;$$

in which case the total differential is expressed as

$$dZ = \frac{\delta Z}{\delta X} dX + \frac{\delta Z}{\delta Y} dY.$$

Two additional features of partial differentiation are so commonly used as the basis of operations that their reiteration here may be helpful.   One is that the order of differentiation is immaterial, i.e.,*

$$\frac{d(dZ)}{dXdY} = \frac{d(dZ)}{dYdX} \quad \text{or} \quad \frac{\delta^2 Z}{\delta X \delta Y} = \frac{\delta^2 Z}{\delta Y \delta X},$$

* The differential of the first coefficient with respect to the second variable is always equal to the differential of the second coefficient with respect to the first variable when dZ is an exact differential in the equation, $dZ = MdX + NdY$.

and the other is that for any three functions of state, the product of the three partial differential coefficients is equal to -1.

$$\left(\frac{dZ}{dX}\right)_Y \left(\frac{dX}{dY}\right)_Z \left(\frac{dY}{dZ}\right)_X = -1.$$

From the first, if a certain relation is known to exist, the second differentials are equal, and conversely if the second differentials are known to be equal we can conclude that the original function is a perfect differential and therefore represents a true property of the substance. The second is always true for any three functions of the state (true properties) of the substance.

XIV-7. The Interrelationship Between Property Changes.—Application of the foregoing to thermodynamic cases leads directly to a large number of differential equations involving the various properties, for example, considering the properties P, V, and T we may express T as a function of the other two

$$T = f(P, V)$$

and immediately write

$$dT = \left(\frac{dT}{dP}\right)_V dP + \left(\frac{dT}{dV}\right)_P dV, \qquad (A)$$

or, if we prefer to write, $V = f(P, T)$.

$$dV = \left(\frac{dV}{dP}\right)_T dP + \left(\frac{dV}{dT}\right)_P dT. \qquad (B)$$

As we commonly deal with six properties, P, V, T, H, U, S, there are available fifteen (15) combinations giving different pairs,

PV	VT	TH*	HU*	US
PT	VH	TU*	HS	
PH	VU	TS		
PU	VS			
PS				

Each of these pairs may be taken as the independent variables and combined with any of the four remaining properties to give differential equations of the foregoing sort.

In the pairs indicated by asterisks the properties are not always independent of each other, as in perfect gases where heat content and intrinsic energy are interrelated and also directly tied in with temperature.

To illustrate, selecting at random we may choose $S = f(P, V)$ or $S = f(P, T)$ or $S = f(P, H)$ or $S = f(P, U)$, all of which are correct statements and lead at once to equations similar to (A) and (B).

Thus there are available 60 expressions by the various combinations of the six original properties. If instead of restricting the original list of properties to six we increase it to eight by including the other two Gibbs Potentials (X and Z) (p. 400), the number of resulting differential equations jumps to ($28 \times 4 = 112$). Furthermore, the list of properties may be increased at will by defining any number of new compound properties. Thus it is evident that we are apt to be confronted from the outset with a multiplicity of data that may be appalling; in fact, our principal objective is the selection and development of only a very few equations expressing relations which are particularly useful and convenient.

Up to this point the interrelationship of the various properties only has been discussed, they are all functions of state, perfect differentials, and fixing any two properties definitely establishes the state.

XIV–8. Introduction of the Energy Equation.—*Maxwell's Relations.*— The general energy equation is

$$dQ = dU + \frac{dW}{J},$$

and as both dQ and dW are path functions, inexact differentials, it is preferable to substitute for them terms which permit exact manipulation. To simplify the mathematical operations consider heat quantities as expressed in work units, thus eliminating use of A and J in subsequent equations.

For all reversible operations

$$dQ = TdS$$

and

$$dW = PdV.$$

Hence we may write

$$dU = TdS - PdV. \tag{1}$$

The three Gibbs potentials (X, Ψ and Z) as defined on p. 400 are essentially energy quantities and their introduction into the general energy equation produces four important equations, known as Maxwell's Thermodynamic Relations. The steps are as follows:

By definition,

$$X = U + APV = H$$
$$\Psi = U - TS$$
$$Z = U + APV - TS = X - TS.$$

Differentiating X,
$$dX = dU + PdV + VdP.$$

Substituting for dU from (1),
$$dX = TdS + VdP. \tag{2}$$
Differentiating Ψ,
$$d\Psi = dU - TdS - SdT.$$

Substituting for dU from (1)
$$d\Psi = TdS - PdV - TdS - SdT$$
$$= -PdV - SdT. \tag{3}$$
Differentiating Z,
$$dZ = dX - TdS - SdT$$
$$= TdS + Vdp - TdS - SdT$$
$$= VdP - SdT \tag{4}$$

From the foregoing (Eqs. 1, 2, 3, 4) by applying the criterion that the sequence of successive differentiation has no effect on the result, as all four properties are perfect differentials, there results,

From Equation (1) $\qquad \left(\dfrac{dT}{dV}\right)_S = -\left(\dfrac{dP}{dS}\right)_V \tag{5}$

From Equation (2) $\qquad \left(\dfrac{dT}{dP}\right)_S = \left(\dfrac{dV}{dS}\right)_P \tag{6}$

From Equation (3) $\qquad \left(\dfrac{dP}{dT}\right)_V = \left(\dfrac{dS}{dV}\right)_T \tag{7}$

From Equation (4) $\qquad \left(\dfrac{dV}{dT}\right)_P = -\left(\dfrac{dS}{dP}\right)_T \tag{8}$

Also from the basic equations, 1–4, the following useful relations are readily obtainable:

From Equation (1) $\qquad \left(\dfrac{dU}{dS}\right)_V = T,$ and $\left(\dfrac{dU}{dV}\right)_S = -P.$

From Equation (2) $\qquad \left(\dfrac{dX}{dS}\right)_P = T,$ and $\left(\dfrac{dX}{dP}\right)_S = V$

From Equation (3) $\left(\dfrac{d\Psi}{dV}\right)_T = -P,$ and $\left(\dfrac{d\Psi}{dT}\right)_V = -S.$

From Equation (4) $\left(\dfrac{dZ}{dP}\right)_T = V,$ and $\left(\dfrac{dZ}{dT}\right)_P = -S.$

From which

$$\left(\frac{dX}{dS}\right)_P = T = \left(\frac{dU}{dS}\right)_V. \qquad (9)$$

$$\left(\frac{dX}{dP}\right)_S = V = \left(\frac{dZ}{dP}\right)_T \qquad (10)$$

$$\left(\frac{d\Psi}{dV}\right)_T = -P = \left(\frac{dU}{dV}\right)_S \qquad (11)$$

$$\left(\frac{d\Psi}{dT}\right)_V = -S = \left(\frac{dZ}{dT}\right)_P \qquad (12)$$

Aside from measuring simultaneous instantaneous values of the properties (usually P.V.T.) there are two other means of experimentally obtaining data useful for computing the characteristics of a fluid. One is to measure simultaneously the *changes* occurring in its properties, and the other is to cause an energy change, as by supplying heat, and record the resulting changes in properties. The former method can utilize the direct relationships derived as explained in the foregoing paragraph and the latter the relations developed by augmenting the scope of the mathematical treatment to include the general energy equation. The commonest laboratory experimental data is obtained from the addition (or rejection) of heat to the fluid under consideration and noting changes in the measurable properties. The quantity of heat which is supplied to produce a unit property change in the substance is called its thermal capacity, but such a definition is incomplete until rendered specific by information as to how the heat has been added, by which property we are measuring the unit increase, and the location on the characteristic surface of the initial and final state points. If dQ were a perfect differential, Q could be established as a function of any two of the properties selected for independent variables and it would be possible to write (selecting T and V as the independent variables)

$$dQ = \left(\frac{dQ}{dT}\right)_V dT + \left(\frac{dQ}{dV}\right)_T dV. \qquad (13)$$

Moreover, even though the integral equation cannot be written, the differential expression is true if its limitations are borne in mind. Such reasoning lead the earlier writers to establish equations like 13 and the two following (14 and 15), using other combinations of P, V and T for independent variables

(Using T and P as independent variables),

$$dQ = \left(\frac{dQ}{dT}\right)_P dT + \left(\frac{dQ}{dP}\right)_T dP \tag{14}$$

(Using P and V as independent variables),

$$dQ = \left(\frac{dQ}{dP}\right)_V dP + \left(\frac{dQ}{dV}\right)_P dV \tag{15}$$

and to denote these six partial derivatives as *Thermal Capacities*. They are usually assigned individual symbols for convenience in mathematical manipulation and three have been given semi-descriptive names.

The partial derivatives $\left(\frac{dQ}{dT}\right)_V$ and $\left(\frac{dQ}{dT}\right)_P$ represent the amount of heat required to raise the temperature of a unit weight of fluid by one unit when the heating is done at constant volume or constant pressure respectively, and will be recognized as the specific heats C_V and C_P of earlier definition. The partial derivative $\left(\frac{dQ}{dV}\right)_T$ represents the amount of heat required for a unit weight of substance to have its volume increased by one unit when the heating is at constant temperature. It has been given the name Latent Heat of Expansion (l). Like much of the other terminology in thermodynamics this is an inheritance from earlier and cruder conceptions and is more of a misnomer than a truly descriptive title, as the expression is frequently used in discussing changes which do not involve changes of phase as from the liquid to the gaseous, for which the term *latent* heat was originally coined.

The others $\left(\frac{dQ}{dP}\right)_T$, $\left(\frac{dQ}{dP}\right)_V$ and $\left(\frac{dQ}{dV}\right)_P$ are usually denoted by the letters m, n, and o, respectively and are rarely assigned even pseudo-descriptive names, though the first (m) is sometimes termed the "Latent Heat of Pressure Change."

Obviously, it would be possible to augment enormously the number of thermal capacities by using other pairs of properties as the independent variables; however, there would be no material gain in developing such, as the six given above are all that are obtainable from combinations of pressure, volume and temperature, the only directly observable properties. Furthermore of the six thermal capacities actually used, but two, the specific heats, C_V and C_P, are of prime importance.

For convenience the definitive equations of the thermal capacities are repeated:

$$C_V = \left(\frac{dQ}{dT}\right)_V \qquad\qquad m = \left(\frac{dQ}{dP}\right)_T$$

$$C_P = \left(\frac{dQ}{dT}\right)_P \qquad\qquad n = \left(\frac{dQ}{dP}\right)_V$$

$$l = \left(\frac{dQ}{dV}\right)_T \qquad\qquad o = \left(\frac{dQ}{dV}\right)_P.$$

Equations 13, 14, and 15 then become

$$dQ = C_V dT + l\,dV \tag{16}$$

$$dQ = C_P dT + m\,dP \tag{17}$$

$$dQ = n\,dP + o\,dV. \tag{18}$$

The relations connecting the thermal capacities, particularly the specific heats, with pressure, volume and temperature are important. The evaluations for the two specific heats (C_P and C_V), their difference ($C_P - C_V$), and the adiabatic ratio $\dfrac{C_P}{C_V}$ follow, ... For evaluating C_V we may use equation 16, $dQ = C_V dT + l\,dV$.

But, $dQ = T\,dS$, and $l = \left(\dfrac{dQ}{dV}\right)_T dV,$

Substituting

$$T\,dS = C_V dT + T\left(\frac{dS}{dV}\right)_T dV.$$

Dividing by T,

$$dS = \frac{C_V}{T}\,dT + \left(\frac{dS}{dV}\right)_T dV.$$

But by Equation 7,

$$\left(\frac{dS}{dV}\right)_T = \left(\frac{dP}{dT}\right)_V.$$

Substituting

$$dS = \frac{C_V dT}{T} + \left(\frac{dP}{dT}\right)_V dV.$$

dS is a perfect differential, thus the second derivatives are equal and

$$\left(\frac{d}{dV}\right)_T \frac{C_V}{T} = \frac{d}{dT}\left(\frac{dP}{dT}\right)_V.$$

Whence

$$\left(\frac{dC_V}{dV}\right)_T = T\left(\frac{d^2P}{dT^2}\right)_V \qquad (19)$$

Similar treatment of equation 17 yields for the evaluation of C_P,

$$\left(\frac{dC_P}{dP}\right)_T = -T\left(\frac{d^2V}{dT^2}\right)_P \qquad (20)$$

An expression for the difference in the specific heats may be had by combining equations 16 and 17:

$$C_V dT + l dV = C_P dT + m dP$$

$$(C_P - C_V)dT = l dV - m dP.$$

Imposing the condition of a constant pressure, $dP = 0$ and

$$(C_P - C_V) = l\left(\frac{dV}{dT}\right)_P.$$

From p. 407,

$$l = \left(\frac{dQ}{dV}\right)_T.$$

$$= T\left(\frac{dS}{dV}\right)_T.$$

From Equation 7

$$= T\left(\frac{dP}{dT}\right)_V.$$

Substituting

$$C_P - C_V = T\left(\frac{dP}{dT}\right)_V \left(\frac{dV}{dT}\right)_P. \qquad (21)$$

For the adiabatic ratio $\dfrac{C_P}{C_V}$ equations 16 and 17 may be modified and combined. Imposing the condition of constant volume on 16 and constant pressure on 17 we have

$$(dQ)_V = C_V dT \quad \text{and} \quad (dQ)_P = C_P dT.$$

Substituting $T dS$ for dQ,

$$C_V = T \left(\frac{dS}{dT} \right)_V \quad \text{and} \quad C_P = T \left(\frac{dS}{dT} \right)_P.$$

Equation 16 may be written $\dfrac{dQ}{T} = dS = \dfrac{C_V dT}{T} + \dfrac{l dP}{T}$ for adiabatic action

$$dS = 0.$$

whence

$$0 = \frac{C_V dT}{T} + \frac{l dV}{T}$$

$$= \frac{C_V dT}{T} + \left(\frac{dQ}{T dV} \right)_T dV.$$

Substituting $T dS$ for dQ,

$$0 = \frac{C_V dT}{T} + \left(\frac{dS}{dV} \right)_T dV.$$

Whence

$$\frac{C_V}{T} \left(\frac{dT}{dV} \right)_S = - \left(\frac{dS}{dV} \right)_T.$$

From Equation 7,

$$\frac{C_V}{T} \left(\frac{dT}{dV} \right)_S = - \left(\frac{dP}{dT} \right)_V. \tag{22}$$

Similarly

$$\frac{C_P}{T} \left(\frac{dT}{dP} \right)_S = \left(\frac{dV}{dT} \right)_P \tag{23}$$

As dS is zero, use of the third principle of partial differentiation (p. 402) permits the statement

$$\left(\frac{dV}{dP} \right)_T \left(\frac{dP}{dT} \right)_V \left(\frac{dT}{dV} \right)_P = - 1,$$

which may be written

$$\left(\frac{dV}{dP} \right)_T = - \frac{\left(\frac{dV}{dT} \right)_P}{\left(\frac{dP}{dT} \right)_V} = \frac{\frac{C_P}{T} \left(\frac{dT}{dP} \right)_S}{\frac{C_V}{T} \left(\frac{dT}{dV} \right)_S} = \frac{C_P}{C_V} \left(\frac{dV}{dP} \right)_S$$

whence

$$\frac{C_P}{C_V} = \left(\frac{dV}{dP} \right)_T \left(\frac{dP}{dV} \right)_S \tag{24}$$

XIV-9. Other Relations.—From the foregoing it must be obvious that the number of mathematical equations involving the relations of the various properties and energy changes is almost infinite and no one has attempted a complete presentation. The nearest approach to such is a tabulation by Bridgman * in which the number of relations is 90 for first derivatives.

There are, however, a few like the foregoing of particular usefulness which should be mentioned, though their derivation will not be given. Some are identified by the name of the one who originally presented them, others by the process to which they apply.

Clapyron's Equation.—This is an equation developed for a mixture of a liquid and its vapor in equilibrium, i.e., at the same temperature and pressure, and expresses the change in specific volume which accompanies the vaporization process. It can be developed from equation 6 and is usually stated as follows:

$$V_g - V_f = \frac{H_{fg}}{T}\frac{dT}{dP}. \tag{25}$$

This is sometimes written in a more general form applying to any state of vaporization process,

$$\frac{V_g - V_f}{V} = -\frac{H_{fg}}{T^2}\left(\frac{dT}{dS}\right)_h. \tag{25a}$$

In this V denotes the specific volume at the beginning of the vaporization process, i.e., $V = xV_g + (1-x)V_f$. The slope of a line of constant heat content in the wet region of the Mollier HS diagram is given by the term $\left(\frac{dT}{dS}\right)_H$.

Joule-Thomson Effect.—Much use has been made of the equation developed for the *cooling* effect accompanying the throttling flow of the porous plug experiments conducted by Joule and Thomson. The expression is as follows:

$$\left(\frac{dT}{dP}\right)_H = \frac{1}{C_P}\left[T\left(\frac{dV}{dT}\right)_P - V\right]. \tag{26}$$

The first term is the drop in temperature per unit drop in pressure experienced by a fluid flowing through a device which produces an adiabatic

* "Condensed Collection of Thermodynamic Formulas," P. W. Bridgman, Harvard University Press.

expansion doing no useful external work—(a true throttling)—as in the flow of gas through a porous plug. It has been termed the Joule-Thomson effect, and its direct measurement is comparatively easy in the laboratory. The Joule-Thomson effect is zero when the term in the brackets (Eq. 26) is zero, i.e., when $\left(\dfrac{dV}{dT}\right)_P = \dfrac{V}{T}$. For perfect gases this equality holds and there is no cooling effect. For actual gases, however, this is true at only one temperature. Below that temperature $\left(\dfrac{dV}{dT}\right)_P$ is greater than $\dfrac{V}{T}$ and hence the cooling effect is positive. Above that temperature the cooling effect is negative and a throttling results in a heating of the gas. Thus the Joule-Thomson effect may be either positive or negative, dependent on whether the expansion is initiated at a temperature lower than, or higher than, the temperature of inversion. Above the temperature of inversion the effect is negative, i.e., a heating effect, and below the temperature of inversion it is positive, i.e., a cooling effect. In most of the gases commonly dealt with the temperature of inversion is so high that most experimental work deals with cooling effects (air, oxygen, nitrogen, water vapor, etc.). Hydrogen, however, is an exception as the inversion of the Joule-Thomson effect occurs at $-112°$ F. and any throttling flow at temperatures above that produces heating.

Unresisted Expansion.—Distinguished from the foregoing change which occurred at constant heat content and applies in general to flowing fluids, there is the sort of change experienced by a fluid expanding into a chamber of finite volume but zero pressure—a truly unresisted expansion. This was the type of change occurring in Joule's original apparatus before the Joule-Thomson continuous flow experiments with porous plugs. Here expansion occurred from one chamber at high pressure into another chamber highly evacuated. For such a change the property remaining constant is the intrinsic energy instead of the heat content. For unresisted expansion the equation is

$$-\left(\frac{dT}{dV}\right)_U = \frac{1}{C_V}\left[T\left(\frac{dP}{dT}\right)_V - P\right]. \tag{27}$$

Slopes of Property Graphs.—The graphical representation of properties of fluids is quite common and it is frequently very convenient to be able to evaluate the slope of the lines representing such properties.

$$\left(\frac{dH}{dS}\right)_P = T. \tag{28}$$

From Equation 2, which states that the slope of a line of constant pressure
in the Mollier heat content-entropy chart is equal to the absolute temperature. Without going into details as to derivation others are as follows:

$$\left(\frac{dH}{dS}\right)_T = T - V\left(\frac{dT}{dV}\right)_P. \tag{29}$$

$$= T + V\left(\frac{dP}{dS}\right)_T. \tag{29a}$$

$$\left(\frac{dH}{dS}\right)_V = T + V\left(\frac{dP}{dS}\right)_V. \tag{30}$$

$$= T - V\left(\frac{dT}{dV}\right)_S. \tag{30a}$$

The foregoing give the slopes of lines of constant pressure, constant
temperature and constant volume, respectively, in the heat content-entropy
diagram.

For the temperature-entropy diagram the slopes of lines of constant
volume, constant pressure, and constant total heat are as follows:

$$\left(\frac{dT}{dS}\right)_V = \frac{T}{C_V}. \tag{31}$$

$$\left(\frac{dT}{dS}\right)_P = \frac{T}{C_P}. \tag{32}$$

$$\left(\frac{dT}{dS}\right)_H = \frac{T}{C_P} - \frac{T^2}{V}\left(\frac{dV}{dH}\right)_P. \tag{33}$$

For the heat content-entropy chart the slopes of lines of constant entropy,
constant temperature, and constant volume, respectively, follow:

$$\left(\frac{dH}{dP}\right)_S = V. \tag{34}$$

$$\left(\frac{dH}{dP}\right)_T = V - T\left(\frac{dV}{dT}\right)_P. \tag{35}$$

$$\left(\frac{dH}{dP}\right)_V = V - T\left(\frac{dV}{dT}\right)_S. \tag{36}$$

XIV-10. List of Useful General Relations.—

$$dU = TdS - PdV. \tag{1}$$

$$dX = TdS + VdP. \tag{2}$$

$$d\Psi = - PdV - SdT. \tag{3}$$

$$dZ = VdP - SdT. \tag{4}$$

$$\left(\frac{dT}{dV}\right)_S = - \left(\frac{dP}{dS}\right)_V. \tag{5}$$

$$\left(\frac{dT}{dP}\right)_S = \left(\frac{dV}{dS}\right)_P. \tag{6}$$

$$\left(\frac{dP}{dT}\right)_V = \left(\frac{dS}{dV}\right)_T. \tag{7}$$

$$\left(\frac{dV}{dT}\right)_P = - \left(\frac{dS}{dP}\right)_T. \tag{8}$$

$$\left(\frac{dX}{dS}\right)_P = T = \left(\frac{dU}{dS}\right)_V. \tag{9}$$

$$\left(\frac{dX}{dP}\right)_S = V = \left(\frac{dZ}{dP}\right)_T. \tag{10}$$

$$\left(\frac{d\Psi}{dV}\right)_T = - P = \left(\frac{dU}{dV}\right)_S. \tag{11}$$

$$\left(\frac{d\Psi}{dT}\right)_V = - S = \left(\frac{dZ}{dT}\right)_P. \tag{12}$$

$$dQ = \left(\frac{dQ}{dT}\right)_P dT + \left(\frac{dQ}{dP}\right)_T dP = C_V dT + l dV. \tag{14 \& 16}$$

$$dQ = \left(\frac{dQ}{dP}\right)_V dP + \left(\frac{dQ}{dV}\right)_P dV = C_P dT + m dV. \tag{15 \& 17}$$

$$dQ = n dP + o dV. \tag{18}$$

$$\left(\frac{dC_V}{dV}\right)_T = T \left(\frac{d^2P}{dT^2}\right)_V. \tag{19}$$

$$\left(\frac{dC_P}{dP}\right)_T = - T\left(\frac{d^2V}{dT^2}\right)_P.$$ (20)

$$C_P - C_V = T\left(\frac{dP}{dT}\right)_V\left(\frac{dV}{dT}\right)_P.$$ (21)

$$\frac{C_V}{T}\left(\frac{dT}{dV}\right)_S = -\left(\frac{dP}{dT}\right)_V.$$ (22)

$$\frac{C_P}{T}\left(\frac{dT}{dP}\right)_S = \left(\frac{dV}{dT}\right)_P.$$ (23)

$$\frac{C_P}{C_V} = \left(\frac{dV}{dP}\right)_T\left(\frac{dP}{dV}\right)_S.$$ (24)

$$V_g - V_f = \frac{H_{fg}}{T}\frac{dT}{dP}.$$ (25)

$$\frac{V_g - V_f}{V} = -\frac{H_{fg}}{T^2}\left(\frac{dT}{dS}\right)_H.$$ (25a)

$$\left(\frac{dT}{dP}\right)_H = \frac{1}{C_P}\left[T\left(\frac{dV}{dT}\right)_P - V\right].$$ (26)

$$\left(\frac{dT}{dV}\right)_U = \frac{1}{C_V}\left[T\left(\frac{dP}{dT}\right)_V - P\right].$$ (27)

$$\left(\frac{dH}{dS}\right)_P = T.$$ (28)

$$\left(\frac{dH}{dS}\right)_T = T - V\left(\frac{dT}{dV}\right)_P = T + V\left(\frac{dP}{dS}\right)_T.$$ (29 & 29a)

$$\left(\frac{dH}{dS}\right)_V = T + V\left(\frac{dP}{dS}\right)_V = T - V\left(\frac{dT}{dV}\right)_S.$$ (30 & 30a)

$$\left(\frac{dT}{dS}\right)_V = \frac{T}{C_V}.$$ (31)

$$\left(\frac{dT}{dS}\right)_P = \frac{T}{C_P}.$$ (32)

$$\left(\frac{dT}{dS}\right)_H = \frac{T}{C_P} - \frac{T^2}{V}\left(\frac{dV}{dH}\right)_P.$$ (33)

$$\left(\frac{dH}{dP}\right)_S = V.$$
(34)

$$\left(\frac{dH}{dP}\right)_T = V - T\left(\frac{dV}{dT}\right)_P.$$
(35)

$$\left(\frac{dH}{dP}\right)_V = V - T\left(\frac{dV}{dT}\right)_S$$
(36)

Abridged from "Thermodynamic Properties of Steam" by Joseph H. Keenan and Frederick G. Keyes
Copyright, 1937, by Joseph H. Keenan and Frederick G. Keyes
Published by John Wiley & Sons, Inc., New York

TABLE I., SATURATION: TEMPERATURES

Temp. Fahr.	Abs.Press. Lb. Sq.In.	Specific Volume Sat. Liquid	Evap.	Sat. Vapor	Enthalpy Sat. Liquid	Evap.	Sat. Vapor	Entropy Sat. Liquid	Evap.	Sat. Vapor	Temp. Fahr.
t	p	v_f	v_{fg}	v_g	h_f	h_{fg}	h_g	s_f	s_{fg}	s_g	t
32°	0.08854	0.01602	3306	3306	0.00	1075.8	1075.8	0.0000	2.1877	2.1877	32°
35	0.09995	0.01602	2947	2947	3.02	1074.1	1077.1	0.0061	2.1709	2.1770	35
40	0.12170	0.01602	2444	2444	8.05	1071.3	1079.3	0.0162	2.1435	2.1597	40
45	0.14752	0.01602	2036.4	2036.4	13.06	1068.4	1081.5	0.0262	2.1167	2.1429	45
50	0.17811	0.01603	1703.2	1703.2	18.07	1065.6	1083.7	0.0361	2.0903	2.1264	50
60°	0.2563	0.01604	1206.6	1206.7	28.06	1059.9	1088.0	0.0555	2.0393	2.0948	60°
70	0.3631	0.01606	867.8	867.9	38.04	1054.3	1092.3	0.0745	1.9902	2.0647	70
80	0.5069	0.01608	633.1	633.1	48.02	1048.6	1096.6	0.0932	1.9428	2.0360	80
90	0.6982	0.01610	468.0	468.0	57.99	1042.9	1100.9	0.1115	1.8972	2.0087	90
100	0.9492	0.01613	350.3	350.4	67.97	1037.2	1105.2	0.1295	1.8531	1.9826	100
110°	1.2748	0.01617	265.3	265.4	77.94	1031.6	1109.5	0.1471	1.8106	1.9577	110°
120	1.6924	0.01620	203.25	203.27	87.92	1025.8	1113.7	0.1645	1.7694	1.9339	120
130	2.2225	0.01625	157.32	157.34	97.90	1020.0	1117.9	0.1816	1.7296	1.9112	130
140	2.8886	0.01629	122.99	123.01	107.89	1014.1	1122.0	0.1984	1.6910	1.8894	140
150	3.718	0.01634	97.06	97.07	117.89	1008.2	1126.1	0.2149	1.6537	1.8685	150
160°	4.741	0.01639	77.27	77.29	127.89	1002.3	1130.2	0.2311	1.6174	1.8485	160°
170	5.992	0.01645	62.04	62.06	137.90	996.3	1134.2	0.2472	1.5822	1.8293	170
180	7.510	0.01651	50.21	50.23	147.92	990.2	1138.1	0.2630	1.5480	1.8109	180
190	9.339	0.01657	40.94	40.96	157.95	984.1	1142.0	0.2785	1.5147	1.7932	190
200	11.526	0.01663	33.62	33.64	167.99	977.9	1145.9	0.2938	1.4824	1.7762	200
210°	14.123	0.01670	27.80	27.82	178.05	971.6	1149.7	0.3090	1.4508	1.7598	210°
212	14.696	0.01672	26.78	26.80	180.07	970.3	1150.4	0.3120	1.4446	1.7566	212
220	17.186	0.01677	23.13	23.15	188.13	965.2	1153.4	0.3239	1.4201	1.7440	220
230	20.780	0.01684	19.365	19.382	198.23	958.8	1157.0	0.3387	1.3901	1.7288	230
240	24.969	0.01692	16.306	16.323	208.34	952.2	1160.5	0.3531	1.3609	1.7140	240
250°	29.825	0.01700	13.804	13.821	218.48	945.5	1164.0	0.3675	1.3323	1.6998	250°
260	35.429	0.01709	11.746	11.763	228.64	938.7	1167.3	0.3817	1.3043	1.6860	260
270	41.858	0.01717	10.044	10.061	238.84	931.8	1170.6	0.3958	1.2769	1.6727	270
280	49.203	0.01726	8.628	8.645	249.06	924.7	1173.8	0.4096	1.2501	1.6597	280
290	57.556	0.01735	7.444	7.461	259.31	917.5	1176.8	0.4234	1.2238	1.6472	290
300°	67.013	0.01745	6.449	6.466	269.59	910.1	1179.7	0.4369	1.1980	1.6350	300°
310	77.68	0.01755	5.609	5.626	279.92	902.6	1182.5	0.4504	1.1727	1.6231	310
320	89.66	0.01765	4.896	4.914	290.28	894.9	1185.2	0.4637	1.1478	1.6115	320
330	103.06	0.01776	4.289	4.307	300.68	887.0	1187.7	0.4769	1.1233	1.6002	330
340	118.01	0.01787	3.770	3.788	311.13	879.0	1190.1	0.4900	1.0992	1.5891	340
350°	134.63	0.01799	3.324	3.342	321.63	870.7	1192.3	0.5029	1.0754	1.5783	350°
360	153.04	0.01811	2.939	2.957	332.18	862.2	1194.4	0.5158	1.0519	1.5677	360
370	173.37	0.01823	2.606	2.625	342.79	853.5	1196.3	0.5286	1.0287	1.5573	370
380	195.77	0.01836	2.317	2.335	353.45	844.6	1198.1	0.5413	1.0059	1.5471	380
390	220.37	0.01850	2.0651	2.0836	364.17	835.4	1199.6	0.5539	0.9832	1.5371	390
400°	247.31	0.01864	1.8447	1.8633	374.97	826.0	1201.0	0.5664	0.9608	1.5272	400°
410	276.75	0.01878	1.6512	1.6700	385.83	816.3	1202.1	0.5788	0.9386	1.5174	410
420	308.83	0.01894	1.4811	1.5000	396.77	806.3	1203.1	0.5912	0.9166	1.5078	420
430	343.72	0.01910	1.3308	1.3499	407.79	796.0	1203.8	0.6035	0.8947	1.4982	430
440	381.59	0.01926	1.1979	1.2171	418.90	785.4	1204.3	0.6158	0.8730	1.4887	440
450°	422.6	0.0194	1.0799	1.0993	430.1	774.5	1204.6	0.6280	0.8513	1.4793	450°
460	466.9	0.0196	0.9748	0.9944	441.4	763.2	1204.6	0.6402	0.8298	1.4700	460
470	514.7	0.0198	0.8811	0.9009	452.8	751.5	1204.3	0.6523	0.8083	1.4606	470
480	566.1	0.0200	0.7972	0.8172	464.4	739.4	1203.7	0.6645	0.7868	1.4513	480
490	621.4	0.0202	0.7221	0.7423	476.0	726.8	1202.8	0.6766	0.7653	1.4419	490
500°	680.8	0.0204	0.6545	0.6749	487.8	713.9	1201.7	0.6887	0.7438	1.4325	500°
520	812.4	0.0209	0.5385	0.5594	511.9	686.4	1198.2	0.7130	0.7006	1.4136	520
540	962.5	0.0215	0.4434	0.4649	536.6	656.6	1193.2	0.7374	0.6568	1.3942	540
560	1133.1	0.0221	0.3647	0.3868	562.2	624.2	1186.4	0.7621	0.6121	1.3742	560
580	1325.8	0.0228	0.2989	0.3217	588.9	588.4	1177.3	0.7872	0.5659	1.3532	580
600°	1542.9	0.0236	0.2432	0.2668	617.0	548.5	1165.5	0.8131	0.5176	1.3307	600°
620	1786.6	0.0247	0.1955	0.2201	646.7	503.6	1150.3	0.8398	0.4664	1.3062	620
640	2059.7	0.0260	0.1538	0.1798	678.6	452.0	1130.5	0.8679	0.4110	1.2789	640
660	2365.4	0.0278	0.1165	0.1442	714.2	390.2	1104.4	0.8987	0.3485	1.2472	660
680	2708.1	0.0305	0.0810	0.1115	757.3	309.9	1067.2	0.9351	0.2719	1.2071	680
700°	3093.7	0.0369	0.0392	0.0761	823.3	172.1	995.4	0.9905	0.1484	1.1389	700°
705.4	3206.2	0.0503	0	0.0503	902.7	0	902.7	1.0580	0	1.0580	705.4

TABLE 2. SATURATION: PRESSURES

Abs.Press. Lb. Sq. In.	Temp. Fahr.	Specific Volume Sat. Liquid	Sat. Vapor	Enthalpy Sat. Liquid	Evap.	Sat. Vapor	Entropy Sat. Liquid	Evap.	Sat. Vapor	Internal Energy Sat. Liquid	Sat. Vapor	Abs.Press. Lb. Sq. In.
P	t	v_f	v_g	h_f	h_{fg}	h_g	s_f	s_{fg}	s_g	u_f	u_g	P
1.0	101.74	0.01614	333.6	69.70	1036.3	1106.0	0.1326	1.8456	1.9782	69.70	1044.3	1.0
2.0	126.08	0.01623	173.73	93.99	1022.2	1116.2	0.1749	1.7451	1.9200	93.98	1051.9	2.0
3.0	141.48	0.01630	118.71	109.37	1013.2	1122.6	0.2008	1.6855	1.8863	109.36	1056.7	3.0
4.0	152.97	0.01636	90.63	120.86	1006.4	1127.3	0.2198	1.6427	1.8625	120.85	1060.2	4.0
5.0	162.24	0.01640	73.52	130.13	1001.0	1131.1	0.2347	1.6094	1.8441	130.12	1063.1	5.0
6.0	170.06	0.01645	61.98	137.96	996.2	1134.2	0.2472	1.5820	1.8292	137.94	1065.4	6.0
7.0	176.85	0.01649	53.64	144.76	992.1	1136.9	0.2581	1.5586	1.8167	144.74	1067.4	7.0
8.0	182.86	0.01653	47.34	150.79	988.5	1139.3	0.2674	1.5383	1.8057	150.77	1069.2	8.0
9.0	188.28	0.01656	42.40	156.22	985.2	1141.4	0.2759	1.5203	1.7962	156.19	1070.8	9.0
10	193.21	0.01659	38.42	161.17	982.1	1143.3	0.2835	1.5041	1.7876	161.14	1072.2	10
14.696	212.00	0.01672	26.80	180.07	970.3	1150.4	0.3120	1.4446	1.7566	180.02	1077.5	14.696
15	213.03	0.01672	26.29	181.11	969.7	1150.8	0.3135	1.4415	1.7549	181.06	1077.8	15
20	227.96	0.01683	20.089	196.16	960.1	1156.3	0.3356	1.3962	1.7319	196.10	1081.9	20
25	240.07	0.01692	16.303	208.42	952.1	1160.6	0.3533	1.3606	1.7139	208.34	1085.1	25
30	250.33	0.01701	13.746	218.82	945.3	1164.1	0.3680	1.3313	1.6993	218.73	1087.8	30
35	259.28	0.01708	11.898	227.91	939.2	1167.1	0.3807	1.3063	1.6870	227.80	1090.1	35
40	267.25	0.01715	10.498	236.03	933.7	1169.7	0.3919	1.2844	1.6763	235.90	1092.0	40
45	274.44	0.01721	9.401	243.36	928.6	1172.0	0.4019	1.2650	1.6669	243.22	1093.7	45
50	281.01	0.01727	8.515	250.09	924.0	1174.1	0.4110	1.2474	1.6585	249.93	1095.3	50
55	287.07	0.01732	7.787	256.30	919.6	1175.9	0.4193	1.2316	1.6509	256.12	1096.7	55
60	292.71	0.01738	7.175	262.09	915.5	1177.6	0.4270	1.2168	1.6438	261.90	1097.9	60
65	297.97	0.01743	6.655	267.50	911.6	1179.1	0.4342	1.2032	1.6374	267.29	1099.1	65
70	302.92	0.01748	6.206	272.61	907.9	1180.6	0.4409	1.1906	1.6315	272.38	1100.2	70
75	307.60	0.01753	5.816	277.43	904.5	1181.9	0.4472	1.1787	1.6259	277.19	1101.2	75
80	312.03	0.01757	5.472	282.02	901.1	1183.1	0.4531	1.1676	1.6207	281.76	1102.1	80
85	316.25	0.01761	5.168	286.39	897.8	1184.2	0.4587	1.1571	1.6158	286.11	1102.9	85
90	320.27	0.01766	4.896	290.56	894.7	1185.3	0.4641	1.1471	1.6112	290.27	1103.7	90
95	324.12	0.01770	4.652	294.56	891.7	1186.2	0.4692	1.1376	1.6068	294.25	1104.5	95
100	327.81	0.01774	4.432	298.40	888.8	1187.2	0.4740	1.1286	1.6026	298.08	1105.2	100
110	334.77	0.01782	4.049	305.66	883.2	1188.9	0.4832	1.1117	1.5948	305.30	1106.5	110
120	341.25	0.01789	3.728	312.44	877.9	1190.4	0.4916	1.0962	1.5878	312.05	1107.6	120
130	347.32	0.01796	3.455	318.81	872.9	1191.7	0.4995	1.0817	1.5812	318.38	1108.6	130
140	353.02	0.01802	3.220	324.82	868.2	1193.0	0.5069	1.0682	1.5751	324.35	1109.6	140
150	358.42	0.01809	3.015	330.51	863.6	1194.1	0.5138	1.0556	1.5694	330.01	1110.5	150
160	363.53	0.01815	2.834	335.93	859.2	1195.1	0.5204	1.0436	1.5640	335.39	1111.2	160
170	368.41	0.01822	2.675	341.09	854.9	1196.0	0.5266	1.0324	1.5590	340.52	1111.9	170
180	373.06	0.01827	2.532	346.03	850.8	1196.9	0.5325	1.0217	1.5542	345.42	1112.5	180
190	377.51	0.01833	2.404	350.79	846.8	1197.6	0.5381	1.0116	1.5497	350.15	1113.1	190
200	381.79	0.01839	2.288	355.36	843.0	1198.4	0.5435	1.0018	1.5453	354.68	1113.7	200
250	400.95	0.01865	1.8438	376.00	825.1	1201.1	0.5675	0.9588	1.5263	375.14	1115.8	250
300	417.33	0.01890	1.5433	393.84	809.0	1202.8	0.5879	0.9225	1.5104	392.79	1117.1	300
350	431.72	0.01913	1.3260	409.69	794.2	1203.9	0.6056	0.8910	1.4966	408.45	1118.0	350
400	444.59	0.0193	1.1613	424.0	780.5	1204.5	0.6214	0.8630	1.4844	422.6	1118.5	400
450	456.28	0.0195	1.0320	437.2	767.4	1204.6	0.6356	0.8378	1.4734	435.5	1118.7	450
500	467.01	0.0197	0.9278	449.4	755.0	1204.4	0.6487	0.8147	1.4634	447.6	1118.6	500
550	476.94	0.0199	0.8424	460.8	743.1	1203.9	0.6608	0.7934	1.4542	458.8	1118.2	550
600	486.21	0.0201	0.7698	471.6	731.6	1203.2	0.6720	0.7734	1.4454	469.4	1117.7	600
650	494.90	0.0203	0.7083	481.8	720.5	1202.3	0.6826	0.7548	1.4374	479.4	1117.1	650
700	503.10	0.0205	0.6554	491.5	709.7	1201.2	0.6925	0.7371	1.4296	488.8	1116.3	700
750	510.86	0.0207	0.6092	500.8	699.2	1200.0	0.7019	0.7204	1.4223	498.0	1115.4	750
800	518.23	0.0209	0.5687	509.7	688.9	1198.6	0.7108	0.7045	1.4153	506.6	1114.4	800
850	525.26	0.0210	0.5327	518.3	678.8	1197.1	0.7194	0.6891	1.4085	515.0	1113.3	850
900	531.98	0.0212	0.5006	526.6	668.8	1195.4	0.7275	0.6744	1.4020	523.1	1112.1	900
950	538.43	0.0214	0.4717	534.6	659.1	1193.7	0.7355	0.6602	1.3957	530.9	1110.8	950
1000	544.61	0.0216	0.4456	542.4	649.4	1191.8	0.7430	0.6467	1.3897	538.4	1109.4	1000
1100	556.31	0.0220	0.4001	557.4	630.4	1187.8	0.7575	0.6205	1.3780	552.9	1106.4	1100
1200	567.22	0.0223	0.3619	571.7	611.7	1183.4	0.7711	0.5956	1.3667	566.7	1103.0	1200
1300	577.46	0.0227	0.3293	585.4	593.2	1178.6	0.7840	0.5719	1.3559	580.0	1099.4	1300
1400	587.10	0.0231	0.3012	598.7	574.7	1173.4	0.7963	0.5491	1.3454	592.7	1095.4	1400
1500	596.23	0.0235	0.2765	611.6	556.3	1167.9	0.8082	0.5269	1.3351	605.1	1091.2	1500
2000	635.82	0.0257	0.1878	671.7	463.4	1135.1	0.8619	0.4230	1.2849	662.2	1065.6	2000
2500	668.13	0.0287	0.1307	730.6	360.5	1091.1	0.9126	0.3197	1.2322	717.3	1030.6	2500
3000	695.36	0.0346	0.0858	802.5	217.8	1020.3	0.9731	0.1885	1.1615	783.4	972.7	3000
3206.2	705.40	0.0503	0.0503	902.7	0	902.7	1.0580	0	1.0580	872.9	872.9	3206.2

417

TABLE 3. SUPERHEATED VAPOR

Abs.Press. Lb./Sq.In. (Sat.Temp) — Temperature-Degrees Fahrenheit

Press. (Sat.Temp)		200°	300°	400°	500°	600°	700°	800°	900°	1000°	1100°	1200°	1400°	1600°
1 (101.74)	v	392.6	452.3	512.0	571.6	631.2	690.8	750.4	809.9	869.5	929.1	988.7	1107.8	1227.0
	h	1150.4	1195.8	1241.7	1288.3	1335.7	1383.8	1432.8	1482.7	1533.5	1585.2	1637.7	1745.7	1857.5
	s	2.0512	2.1153	2.1720	2.2233	2.2702	2.3137	2.3542	2.3923	2.4283	2.4625	2.4952	2.5566	2.6137
5 (162.24)	v	78.16	90.25	102.26	114.22	126.16	138.10	150.03	161.95	173.87	185.79	197.71	221.6	245.4
	h	1148.8	1195.0	1241.2	1288.0	1335.4	1383.6	1432.7	1482.6	1533.4	1585.1	1637.7	1745.7	1857.4
	s	1.8718	1.9370	1.9942	2.0456	2.0927	2.1361	2.1767	2.2148	2.2509	2.2851	2.3178	2.3792	2.4363
10 (193.21)	v	38.85	45.00	51.04	57.05	63.03	69.01	74.98	80.95	86.92	92.88	98.84	110.77	122.69
	h	1146.6	1193.9	1240.6	1287.5	1335.1	1383.4	1432.5	1482.4	1533.2	1585.0	1637.6	1745.6	1857.3
	s	1.7927	1.8595	1.9172	1.9689	2.0160	2.0596	2.1002	2.1383	2.1744	2.2086	2.2413	2.3028	2.3598
14.696 (212.00)	v		30.53	34.68	38.78	42.86	46.94	51.00	55.07	59.13	63.19	67.25	75.37	83.48
	h		1192.8	1239.9	1287.1	1334.8	1383.2	1432.3	1482.3	1533.1	1584.8	1637.5	1745.5	1857.3
	s		1.8160	1.8743	1.9261	1.9734	2.0170	2.0576	2.0958	2.1319	2.1662	2.1989	2.2603	2.3174
20 (227.96)	v		22.36	25.43	28.46	31.47	34.47	37.46	40.45	43.44	46.42	49.41	55.37	61.34
	h		1191.6	1239.2	1286.6	1334.4	1382.9	1432.1	1482.1	1533.0	1584.7	1637.4	1745.4	1857.2
	s		1.7808	1.8396	1.8918	1.9392	1.9829	2.0235	2.0618	2.0978	2.1321	2.1648	2.2263	2.2834
40 (267.25)	v		11.040	12.628	14.168	15.688	17.198	18.702	20.20	21.70	23.20	24.69	27.68	30.66
	h		1186.8	1236.5	1284.8	1333.1	1381.9	1431.3	1481.4	1532.4	1584.3	1637.0	1745.1	1857.0
	s		1.6994	1.7608	1.8140	1.8619	1.9058	1.9467	1.9850	2.0212	2.0555	2.0883	2.1498	2.2069
60 (292.71)	v		7.259	8.357	9.403	10.427	11.441	12.449	13.452	14.454	15.453	16.451	18.446	20.44
	h		1181.6	1233.6	1283.0	1331.8	1380.9	1430.5	1480.8	1531.9	1583.8	1636.6	1744.8	1856.7
	s		1.6492	1.7135	1.7678	1.8162	1.8605	1.9015	1.9400	1.9762	2.0106	2.0434	2.1049	2.1621
80 (312.03)	v			6.220	7.020	7.797	8.562	9.322	10.077	10.830	11.582	12.332	13.830	15.325
	h			1230.7	1281.1	1330.5	1379.9	1429.7	1480.1	1531.3	1583.4	1636.2	1744.5	1856.5
	s			1.6791	1.7346	1.7836	1.8281	1.8694	1.9079	1.9442	1.9787	2.0115	2.0731	2.1303
100 (327.81)	v			4.937	5.589	6.218	6.835	7.446	8.052	8.656	9.259	9.860	11.060	12.258
	h			1227.6	1279.1	1329.1	1378.9	1428.9	1479.5	1530.8	1582.9	1635.7	1744.2	1856.2
	s			1.6518	1.7085	1.7581	1.8029	1.8443	1.8829	1.9193	1.9538	1.9867	2.0484	2.1056
120 (341.25)	v			4.081	4.636	5.165	5.683	6.195	6.702	7.207	7.710	8.212	9.214	10.213
	h			1224.4	1277.2	1327.7	1377.8	1428.1	1478.8	1530.2	1582.4	1635.3	1743.9	1856.0
	s			1.6287	1.6869	1.7370	1.7822	1.8237	1.8625	1.8990	1.9335	1.9664	2.0281	2.0854
140 (353.02)	v			3.468	3.954	4.413	4.861	5.301	5.738	6.172	6.604	7.035	7.895	8.752
	h			1221.1	1275.2	1326.4	1376.8	1427.3	1478.2	1529.7	1581.9	1634.9	1743.5	1855.7
	s			1.6087	1.6683	1.7190	1.7645	1.8063	1.8451	1.8817	1.9163	1.9493	2.0110	2.0683
160 (363.53)	v			3.008	3.443	3.849	4.244	4.631	5.015	5.396	5.775	6.152	6.906	7.656
	h			1217.6	1273.1	1325.0	1375.7	1426.4	1477.5	1529.1	1581.4	1634.5	1743.2	1855.5
	s			1.5908	1.6519	1.7033	1.7491	1.7911	1.8301	1.8667	1.9014	1.9344	1.9962	2.0535
180 (373.06)	v			2.649	3.044	3.411	3.764	4.110	4.452	4.792	5.129	5.466	6.136	6.804
	h			1214.0	1271.0	1323.5	1374.7	1425.6	1476.8	1528.6	1581.0	1634.1	1742.9	1855.2
	s			1.5745	1.6373	1.6894	1.7355	1.7776	1.8167	1.8534	1.8882	1.9212	1.9831	2.0404
200 (381.79)	v			2.361	2.726	3.060	3.380	3.693	4.002	4.309	4.613	4.917	5.521	6.123
	h			1210.3	1268.9	1322.1	1373.6	1424.8	1476.2	1528.0	1580.5	1633.7	1742.6	1855.0
	s			1.5594	1.6240	1.6767	1.7232	1.7655	1.8048	1.8415	1.8763	1.9094	1.9713	2.0287
220 (389.86)	v			2.125	2.465	2.772	3.066	3.352	3.634	3.913	4.191	4.467	5.017	5.565
	h			1206.5	1266.7	1320.7	1372.6	1424.0	1475.5	1527.5	1580.0	1633.3	1742.3	1854.7
	s			1.5453	1.6117	1.6652	1.7120	1.7545	1.7939	1.8308	1.8656	1.8987	1.9607	2.0181
240 (397.37)	v			1.9276	2.247	2.533	2.804	3.068	3.327	3.584	3.839	4.093	4.597	5.100
	h			1202.5	1264.5	1319.2	1371.5	1423.2	1474.8	1526.9	1579.6	1632.9	1742.0	1854.5
	s			1.5319	1.6003	1.6546	1.7017	1.7444	1.7839	1.8209	1.8558	1.8889	1.9510	2.0084
260 (404.42)	v				2.063	2.330	2.582	2.827	3.067	3.305	3.541	3.776	4.242	4.707
	h				1262.3	1317.7	1370.4	1422.3	1474.2	1526.3	1579.1	1632.5	1741.7	1854.2
	s				1.5897	1.6447	1.6922	1.7352	1.7748	1.8118	1.8467	1.8799	1.9420	1.9995
280 (411.05)	v				1.9047	2.156	2.392	2.621	2.845	3.066	3.286	3.504	3.938	4.370
	h				1260.0	1316.2	1369.4	1421.5	1473.5	1525.8	1578.6	1632.1	1741.4	1854.0
	s				1.5796	1.6354	1.6834	1.7265	1.7662	1.8033	1.8383	1.8716	1.9337	1.9912
300 (417.33)	v				1.7675	2.005	2.227	2.442	2.652	2.859	3.065	3.269	3.674	4.078
	h				1257.6	1314.7	1368.3	1420.6	1472.8	1525.2	1578.1	1631.7	1741.0	1853.7
	s				1.5701	1.6268	1.6751	1.7184	1.7582	1.7954	1.8305	1.8638	1.9260	1.9835
350 (431.72)	v				1.4923	1.7036	1.8980	2.084	2.266	2.445	2.622	2.798	3.147	3.493
	h				1251.5	1310.9	1365.5	1418.5	1471.1	1523.8	1577.0	1630.7	1740.3	1853.1
	s				1.5481	1.6070	1.6563	1.7002	1.7403	1.7777	1.8130	1.8463	1.9086	1.9663
400 (444.59)	v				1.2851	1.4770	1.6508	1.8161	1.9767	2.134	2.290	2.445	2.751	3.055
	h				1245.1	1306.9	1362.7	1416.4	1469.4	1522.4	1575.8	1629.6	1739.5	1852.5
	s				1.5281	1.5894	1.6398	1.6842	1.7247	1.7623	1.7977	1.8311	1.8936	1.9513

TABLE 3. SUPERHEATED VAPOR (Continued)

Abs.Press.
Lb./Sq.In.
(Sat.Temp)

Temperature-Degrees Fahrenheit

Abs.Press. (Sat.Temp)		500°	550°	600°	620°	640°	660°	680°	700°	800°	900°	1000°	1200°	1400°	1600°
450 (456.28)	v	1.1231	1.2155	1.3005	1.3332	1.3652	1.3967	1.4278	1.4584	1.6074	1.7516	1.8928	2.170	2.443	2.714
	h	1238.4	1272.0	1302.8	1314.6	1326.2	1337.5	1348.8	1359.9	1414.3	1467.7	1521.0	1628.6	1738.7	1851.9
	s	1.5095	1.5437	1.5735	1.5845	1.5951	1.6054	1.6153	1.6250	1.6699	1.7108	1.7486	1.8177	1.8803	1.9381
500 (467.01)	v	0.9927	1.0800	1.1591	1.1893	1.2188	1.2478	1.2763	1.3044	1.4405	1.5715	1.6996	1.9504	2.197	2.442
	h	1231.3	1266.8	1298.6	1310.7	1322.6	1334.2	1345.7	1357.0	1412.1	1466.0	1519.6	1627.6	1737.9	1851.3
	s	1.4919	1.5280	1.5588	1.5701	1.5810	1.5915	1.6016	1.6115	1.6571	1.6982	1.7363	1.8056	1.8683	1.9262
550 (476.94)	v	0.8852	0.9686	1.0431	1.0714	1.0989	1.1259	1.1523	1.1783	1.3038	1.4241	1.5414	1.7706	1.9957	2.219
	h	1223.7	1261.2	1294.3	1306.8	1318.9	1330.8	1342.5	1354.0	1409.9	1464.3	1518.2	1626.6	1737.1	1850.6
	s	1.4751	1.5131	1.5451	1.5568	1.5680	1.5787	1.5890	1.5991	1.6452	1.6868	1.7250	1.7946	1.8575	1.9155
600 (486.21)	v	0.7947	0.8753	0.9463	0.9729	0.9988	1.0241	1.0489	1.0732	1.1899	1.3013	1.4096	1.6208	1.8279	2.033
	h	1215.7	1255.5	1289.9	1302.7	1315.2	1327.4	1339.3	1351.1	1407.7	1462.5	1516.7	1625.5	1736.3	1850.0
	s	1.4586	1.4990	1.5323	1.5443	1.5558	1.5667	1.5773	1.5875	1.6343	1.6762	1.7147	1.7846	1.8476	1.9056
700 (503.10)	v		0.7277	0.7934	0.8177	0.8411	0.8639	0.8860	0.9077	1.0108	1.1082	1.2024	1.3853	1.5641	1.7405
	h		1243.2	1280.6	1294.3	1307.5	1320.3	1332.8	1345.0	1403.2	1459.0	1513.9	1623.5	1734.8	1848.8
	s		1.4722	1.5084	1.5212	1.5333	1.5449	1.5559	1.5665	1.6147	1.6573	1.6963	1.7666	1.8299	1.8881
800 (518.23)	v		0.6154	0.6779	0.7006	0.7223	0.7433	0.7635	0.7833	0.8763	0.9633	1.0470	1.2088	1.3662	1.5214
	h		1229.8	1270.7	1285.4	1299.4	1312.9	1325.9	1338.6	1398.6	1455.4	1511.0	1621.4	1733.2	1847.5
	s		1.4467	1.4863	1.5000	1.5129	1.5250	1.5366	1.5476	1.5972	1.6407	1.6801	1.7510	1.8146	1.8729
900 (531.98)	v		0.5264	0.5873	0.6089	0.6294	0.6491	0.6680	0.6863	0.7716	0.8506	0.9262	1.0714	1.2124	1.3509
	h		1215.0	1260.1	1275.9	1290.9	1305.1	1318.8	1332.1	1393.9	1451.8	1508.1	1619.3	1731.6	1846.3
	s		1.4216	1.4653	1.4800	1.4938	1.5066	1.5187	1.5303	1.5814	1.6257	1.6656	1.7371	1.8009	1.8595
1000 (544.61)	v		0.4533	0.5140	0.5350	0.5546	0.5733	0.5912	0.6084	0.6878	0.7604	0.8294	0.9615	1.0893	1.2146
	h		1198.3	1248.8	1265.9	1281.9	1297.0	1311.4	1325.3	1389.2	1448.2	1505.1	1617.3	1730.0	1845.0
	s		1.3961	1.4450	1.4610	1.4757	1.4893	1.5021	1.5141	1.5670	1.6121	1.6525	1.7245	1.7886	1.8474
1100 (556.31)	v			0.4532	0.4738	0.4929	0.5110	0.5281	0.5445	0.6191	0.6366	0.7503	0.8716	0.9885	1.1031
	h			1236.7	1255.3	1272.4	1288.5	1303.7	1318.3	1384.3	1444.5	1502.2	1615.2	1728.4	1843.8
	s			1.4251	1.4425	1.4583	1.4728	1.4862	1.4989	1.5535	1.5995	1.6405	1.7130	1.7775	1.8363
1200 (567.22)	v			0.4016	0.4222	0.4410	0.4586	0.4752	0.4909	0.5617	0.6250	0.6843	0.7967	0.9046	1.0101
	h			1223.9	1243.9	1262.4	1279.6	1295.7	1311.0	1379.4	1440.7	1499.2	1613.1	1726.9	1842.5
	s			1.4052	1.4243	1.4413	1.4568	1.4710	1.4843	1.5409	1.5879	1.6293	1.7025	1.7672	1.8263
1400 (587.10)	v			0.3174	0.3390	0.3580	0.3753	0.3912	0.4062	0.4714	0.5281	0.5805	0.6789	0.7727	0.8640
	h			1193.0	1218.4	1240.4	1260.3	1278.5	1295.5	1369.1	1433.1	1493.2	1608.9	1723.7	1840.0
	s			1.3639	1.3877	1.4079	1.4258	1.4419	1.4567	1.5177	1.5666	1.6093	1.6836	1.7489	1.8083
1600 (604.90)	v				0.2733	0.2936	0.3112	0.3271	0.3417	0.4034	0.4553	0.5027	0.5906	0.6738	0.7545
	h				1187.8	1215.2	1238.7	1259.6	1278.7	1358.4	1425.3	1487.0	1604.6	1720.5	1837.5
	s				1.3489	1.3741	1.3952	1.4137	1.4303	1.4964	1.5476	1.5914	1.6669	1.7328	1.7926
1800 (621.03)	v					0.2407	0.2597	0.2760	0.2907	0.3502	0.3986	0.4421	0.5218	0.5968	0.6693
	h					1185.1	1214.0	1238.5	1260.3	1347.2	1417.4	1480.8	1600.4	1717.3	1835.0
	s					1.3377	1.3638	1.3855	1.4044	1.4765	1.5301	1.5752	1.6520	1.7185	1.7786
2000 (635.82)	v					0.1936	0.2161	0.2337	0.2489	0.3074	0.3532	0.3935	0.4668	0.5352	0.6011
	h					1145.6	1184.9	1214.8	1240.0	1335.5	1409.2	1474.5	1596.1	1714.1	1832.5
	s					1.2945	1.3300	1.3564	1.3783	1.4526	1.5139	1.5603	1.6384	1.7055	1.7660
2500 (668.13)	v							0.1484	0.1686	0.2294	0.2710	0.3061	0.3678	0.4244	0.4784
	h							1132.3	1176.8	1303.6	1387.8	1458.4	1585.3	1706.1	1826.2
	s							1.2687	1.3073	1.4127	1.4772	1.5273	1.6088	1.6775	1.7389
3000 (695.36)	v								0.0984	0.1760	0.2159	0.2476	0.3018	0.3505	0.3966
	h								1060.7	1267.2	1365.0	1441.8	1574.3	1698.0	1819.9
	s								1.1966	1.3690	1.4439	1.4984	1.5837	1.6540	1.7163
3206.2 (705.40)	v									0.1583	0.1981	0.2288	0.2806	0.3267	0.3703
	h									1250.5	1355.2	1434.7	1569.8	1694.6	1817.2
	s									1.3508	1.4309	1.4874	1.5742	1.6452	1.7080
3500	v								0.0306	0.1364	0.1762	0.2058	0.2546	0.2977	0.3381
	h								780.5	1224.9	1340.7	1424.5	1563.3	1689.8	1813.6
	s								0.9515	1.3241	1.4217	1.4723	1.5615	1.6336	1.6968
4000	v								0.0287	0.1052	0.1462	0.1743	0.2192	0.2581	0.2943
	h								763.8	1174.8	1314.4	1406.8	1552.1	1681.7	1807.2
	s								0.9347	1.2757	1.3827	1.4482	1.5417	1.6154	1.6795
4500	v								0.0276	0.0798	0.1226	0.1500	0.1917	0.2273	0.2602
	h								753.5	1113.9	1286.5	1388.4	1540.8	1673.5	1800.9
	s								0.9235	1.2204	1.3529	1.4253	1.5235	1.5990	1.6640
6000	v								0.0268	0.0593	0.1036	0.1303	0.1696	0.2027	0.2329
	h								746.4	1047.1	1256.5	1369.5	1529.5	1665.3	1794.5
	s								0.9152	1.1622	1.3231	1.4034	1.5066	1.5839	1.6499
6500	v								0.0262	0.0463	0.0880	0.1143	0.1516	0.1825	0.2106
	h								741.3	985.0	1224.1	1349.3	1518.2	1657.0	1788.1
	s								0.9090	1.1093	1.2930	1.3821	1.4908	1.5699	1.6369

Logarithms to the Base e

These two pages give the natural (hyperbolic, or Napierian) logarithms of numbers between 1 and 10, correct to four places. Moving the decimal point *n* places to the right (or left) in the number is equivalent to adding *n* times 2.3026 (or *n* times 3̄.6974) to the logarithm.

1	2.3026	1	0.6974 − 3
2	4.6052	2	0.3948 − 5
3	6.9078	3	0.0922 − 7
4	9.2103	4	0.7897 − 10
5	11.5129	5	0.4871 − 12
6	13.8155	6	0.1845 − 14
7	16.1181	7	0.8819 − 17
8	18.4207	8	0.5793 − 19
9	20.7233	9	0.2767 − 21

	0	1	2	3	4	5	6	7	8	9	10	Tenths of the Tabular Difference 1 2 3 4 5
1.0	0.0000	0100	0198	0296	0392	0488	0583	0677	0770	0862	0.0953	10 19 29 38 48
1.1	0953	1044	1133	1222	1310	1398	1484	1570	1655	1740	1823	9 17 26 35·44
1.2	1823	1906	1989	2070	2151	2231	2311	2390	2469	2546	2624	8 16 24 32 40
1.3	2624	2700	2776	2852	2927	3001	3075	3148	3221	3293	3365	7 15 22 30 37
1.4	3365	3436	3507	3577	3646	3716	3784	3853	3920	3988	4055	7 14 21 28 34
1.5	4055	4121	4187	4253	4318	4383	4447	4511	4574	4637	4700	6 13 19 26 32
1.6	4700	4762	4824	4886	4947	5008	5068	5128	5188	5247	5306	6 12 18 24 30
1.7	5306	5365	5423	5481	5539	5596	5653	5710	5766	5822	5878	6 11 17 23 29
1.8	5878	5933	5988	6043	6098	6152	6206	6259	6313	6366	6419	5 11 16 22 27
1.9	6419	6471	6523	6575	6627	6678	6729	6780	6831	6881	0.6931	5 10 15 21 26
2.0	0.6931	6981	7031	7080	7129	7178	7227	7275	7324	7372	7419	5 10 15 20 24
2.1	7419	7467	7514	7561	7608	7655	7701	7747	7793	7839	7885	5 9 14 19 23
2.2	7885	7930	7975	8020	8065	8109	8154	8198	8242	8286	8329	4 9 13 18 22
2.3	8329	8372	8416	8459	8502	8544	8587	8629	8671	8713	8755	4 9 13 17 21
2.4	8755	8796	8838	8879	8920	8961	9002	9042	9083	9123	9163	4 8 12 16 20
2.5	9163	9203	9243	9282	9322	9361	9400	9439	9478	9517	9555	4 8 12 16 20
2.6	9555	9594	9632	9670	9708	9746	9783	9821	9858	9895	0.9933	4 8 11 15 19
2.7	0.9933	9969	∫0006	0043	0080	0116	0152	0188	0225	0260	1.0296	4 7 11 15 18
2.8	1.0296	0332	0367	0403	0438	0473	0508	0543	0578	0613	0647	4 7 11 14 18
2.9	0647	0682	0716	0750	0784	0818	0852	0886	0919	0953	1.0986	3 7 10 14 17
3.0	1.0986	1019	1053	1086	1119	1151	1184	1217	1249	1282	1314	3 7 10 13 16
3.1	1314	1346	1378	1410	1442	1474	1506	1537	1569	1600	1632	3 6 10 13 16
3.2	1632	1663	1694	1725	1756	1787	1817	1848	1878	1909	1939	3 6 9 12 15
3.3	1939	1969	2000	2030	2060	2090	2119	2149	2179	2208	2238	3 6 9 12 15
3.4	2238	2267	2296	2326	2355	2384	2413	2442	2470	2499	2528	3 6 9 12 14
3.5	2528	2556	2585	2613	2641	2669	2698	2726	2754	2782	2809	3 6 8 11 14
3.6	2809	2837	2865	2892	2920	2947	2975	3002	3029	3056	3083	3 5 8 11 14
3.7	3083	3110	3137	3164	3191	3218	3244	3271	3297	3324	3350	3 5 8 11 13
3.8	3350	3376	3403	3429	3455	3481	3507	3533	3558	3584	3610	3 5 8 10 13
3.9	3610	3635	3661	3686	3712	3737	3762	3788	3813	3838	1.3863	3 5 8 10 13
4.0	1.3863	3888	3913	3938	3962	3987	4012	4036	4061	4085	4110	2 5 7 10 12
4.1	4110	4134	4159	4183	4207	4231	4255	4279	4303	4327	4351	2 5 7 10 12
4.2	4351	4375	4398	4422	4446	4469	4493	4516	4540	4563	4586	2 5 7 9 12
4.3	4586	4609	4633	4656	4679	4702	4725	4748	4770	4793	4816	2 5 7 9 11
4.4	4816	4839	4861	4884	4907	4929	4951	4974	4996	5019	5041	2 4 7 9 11
4.5	5041	5063	5085	5107	5129	5151	5173	5195	5217	5239	5261	2 4 7 9 11
4.6	5261	5282	5304	5326	5347	5369	5390	5412	5433	5454	5476	2 4 6 9 11
4.7	5476	5497	5518	5539	5560	5581	5602	5623	5644	5665	5686	2 4 6 8 11
4.8	5686	5707	5728	5748	5769	5790	5810	5831	5851	5872	5892	2 4 6 8 10
4.9	5892	5913	5933	5953	5974	5994	6014	6034	6054	6074	1.6094	2 4 6 8 10

	0	1	2	3	4	5	6	7	8	9	10	Tenths of the Tabular Difference 1 2 3 4 5
5.0	1.6094	6114	6134	6154	6174	6194	6214	6233	6253	6273	6292	2 4 6 8 10
5.1	6292	6312	6332	6351	6371	6390	6409	6429	6448	6467	6487	2 4 6 8 10
5.2	6487	6506	6525	6544	6563	6582	6601	6620	6639	6658	6677	2 4 6 8 10
5.3	6677	6696	6715	6734	6752	6771	6790	6808	6827	6845	6864	2 4 6 7 9
5.4	6864	6882	6901	6919	6938	6956	6974	6993	7011	7029	7047	2 4 6 7 9
5.5	7047	7066	7084	7102	7120	7138	7156	7174	7192	7210	7228	2 4 5 7 9
5.6	7228	7246	7263	7281	7299	7317	7334	7352	7370	7387	7405	2 4 5 7 9
5.7	7405	7422	7440	7457	7475	7492	7509	7527	7544	7561	7579	2 3 5 7 9
5.8	7579	7596	7613	7630	7647	7664	7681	7699	7716	7733	7750	2 3 5 7 9
5.9	7750	7766	7783	7800	7817	7834	7851	7867	7884	7901	1.7918	2 3 5 7 8
6.0	1.7918	7934	7951	7967	7984	8001	8017	8034	8050	8066	8083	2 3 5 7 8
6.1	8083	8099	8116	8132	8148	8165	8181	8197	8213	8229	8245	2 3 5 7 8
6.2	8245	8262	8278	8294	8310	8326	8342	8358	8374	8390	8405	2 3 5 6 8
6.3	8405	8421	8437	8453	8469	8485	8500	8516	8532	8547	8563	2 3 5 6 8
6.4	8563	8579	8594	8610	8625	8641	8656	8672	8687	8703	8718	2 3 5 6 8
6.5	8718	8733	8749	8764	8779	8795	8810	8825	8840	8856	8871	2 3 5 6 8
6.6	8871	8886	8901	8916	8931	8946	8961	8976	8991	9006	9021	2 3 5 6 8
6.7	9021	9036	9051	9066	9081	9095	9110	9125	9140	9155	9169	1 3 4 6 7
6.8	9169	9184	9199	9213	9228	9242	9257	9272	9286	9301	9315	1 3 4 6 7
6.9	9315	9330	9344	9359	9373	9387	9402	9416	9430	9445	1.9459	1 3 4 6 7
7.0	1.9459	9473	9488	9502	9516	9530	9544	9559	9573	9587	9601	1 3 4 6 7
7.1	9601	9615	9629	9643	9657	9671	9685	9699	9713	9727	9741	1 3 4 6 7
7.2	9741	9755	9769	9782	9796	9810	9824	9838	9851	9865	1.9879	1 3 4 .6 7
7.3	1.9879	9892	9906	9920	9933	9947	9961	9974	9988 ⌠0001		2.0015	1 3 4 5 7
7.4	2.0015	0028	0042	0055	0069	0082	0096	0109	0122	0136	0149	1 3 4 5 7
7.5	0149	0162	0176	0189	0202	0215	0229	0242	0255	0268	0281	1 3 4 5 7
7.6	0281	0295	0308	0321	0334	0347	0360	0373	0386	0399	0412	1 3 4 5 7
7.7	0412	0425	0438	0451	0464	0477	0490	0503	0516	0528	0541	1 3 4 5 6
7.8	0541	0554	0567	0580	0592	0605	0618	0631	0643	0656	0669	1 3 4 5 6
7.9	0669	0681	0694	0707	0719	0732	0744	0757	0769	0782	2.0794	1 3 4 5 6
8.0	2.0794	0807	0819	0832	0844	0857	0869	0882	0894	0906	0919	1 2 4 5 6
8.1	0919	0931	0943	0956	0968	0980	0992	1005	1017	1029	1041	1 2 4 5 6
8.2	1041	1054	1066	1078	1090	1102	1114	1126	1138	1150	1163	1 2 4 5 6
8.3	1163	1175	1187	1199	1211	1223	1235	1247	1258	1270	1282	1 2 4 5 6
8.4	1282	1294	1306	1318	1330	1342	1353	1365	1377	1389	1401	1 2 4 5 6
8.5	1401	1412	1424	1436	1448	1459	1471	1483	1494	1506	1518	1 2 4 5 6
8.6	1518	1529	1541	1552	1564	1576	1587	1599	1610	1622	1633	1 2 3 5 6
8.7	1633	1645	1656	1668	1679	1691	1702	1713	1725	1736	1748	1 2 3 5 6
8.8	1748	1759	1770	1782	1793	1804	1815	1827	1838	1849	1861	1 2 3 5 6
8.9	1861	1872	1883	1894	1905	1917	1928	1939	1950	1961	2.1972	1 2 3 4 6
9.0	2.1972	1983	1994	2006	2017	2028	2039	2050	2061	2072	2083	1 2 3 4 6
9.1	2083	2094	2105	2116	2127	2138	2148	2159	2170	2181	2192	1 2 3 4 5
9.2	2192	2203	2214	2225	2235	2246	2257	2268	2279	2289	2300	1 2 3 4 5
9.3	2300	2311	2322	2332	2343	2354	2364	2375	2386	2396	2407	1 2 3 4 5
9.4	2407	2418	2428	2439	2450	2460	2471	2481	2492	2502	2513	1 2 3 4 5
9.5	2513	2523	2534	2544	2555	2565	2576	2586	2597	2607	2618	1 2 3 4 5
9.6	2618	2628	2638	2649	2659	2670	2680	2690	2701	2711	2721	1 2 3 4 5
9.7	2721	2732	2742	2752	2762	2773	2783	2793	2803	2814	2824	1 2 3 4 5
9.8	2824	2834	2844	2854	2865	2875	2885	2895	2905	2915	2925	1 2 3 4 5
9.9	2925	2935	2946	2956	2966	2976	2986	2996	3006	3016	2.3026	1 2 3 4 5

Problems

to accompany

THERMODYNAMICS

By H. A. EVERETT

TABLE OF VALUES OF NUMBERS RAISED TO THE 1.4 POWER AND 0.4 POWER

1.4 Power

	.0	0.1	0.2	0.3	0.4	0.5	0.6	0.7	0.8	0.9
0		.040	.105	.185	.277	.379	.489	.606	.732	.863
1	1.000	1.143	1.291	1.445	1.601	1.765	1.931	2.105	2.279	2.456
2	2.640	2.832	3.016	3.210	3.406	3.605	3.810	4.017	4.227	4.440
3	4.656	4.874	5.087	5.320	5.547	5.770	6.009	6.238	6.480	6.722
4	6.964	7.209	7.457	7.707	7.955	8.213	8.470	8.720	8.990	9.253
5	9.518	9.775	10.035	10.328	10.565	10.830	11.155	11.435	11.716	11.980
6	12.286	12.588	12.863	13.155	13.442	13.740	14.040	14.340	14.639	14.940
7	15.245	15.551	15.059	16.168	16.479	16.791	17.106	17.422	17.739	18.058
8	18.379	18.702	19.026	19.351	19.679	20.007	20.337	20.669	21.003	21.338
9	21.674	22.012	22.351	22.692	23.035	23.378	23.724	24.070	24.418	24.768
10	25.119									

0.4 Power

	.0	0.1	0.2	0.3	0.4	0.5	0.6	0.7	0.8	0.9
0		.398	.525	.617	.694	.758	.815	.868	.914	.959
1	1.000	1.039	1.076	1.111	1.144	1.176	1.207	1.237	1.265	1.293
2	1.320	1.346	1.371	1.395	1.419	1.443	1.466	1.488	1.510	1.531
3	1.552	1.572	1.592	1.613	1.632	1.651	1.669	1.688	1.706	1.724
4	1.741	1.758	1.775	1.792	1.809	1.825	1.841	1.857	1.873	1.888
5	1.904	1.919	1.934	1.949	1.963	1.978	1.992	2.006	2.020	2.034
6	2.048	2.061	2.075	2.088	2.101	2.114	2.127	2.140	2.153	2.165
7	2.178	2.190	2.203	2.215	2.227	2.239	2.251	2.263	2.274	2.286
8	2.297	2.309	2.320	2.332	2.343	2.354	2.365	2.376	2.387	2.398
9	2.408	2.419	2.430	2.440	2.451	2.461	2.471	2.482	2.492	2.502
10	2.512									

NOTE.—In the following problems the abbreviation p.s.i. denotes pound per square inch. Below is assembled for convenience a list of some of the most frequently used equivalents and constants, also a table of numbers raised to the 1.4 and 0.4 powers which will be found helpful in adiabatic relations problems for gases.

$$1 \text{ B.t.u.} = 778.3 \text{ ft. lbs.};$$
$$1 \text{ Horsepower} = 2544 \text{ B.t.u. per hour, or}$$
$$= 42.40 \text{ B.t.u. per min.}$$
$$1 \text{ Kilowatt} = 3413 \text{ B.t.u. per hour, or}$$
$$= 56.88 \text{ B.t.u. per min.}$$
$$1 \text{ Atmosphere} = 14.696 \text{ p.s.i., use } 14.7$$
$$1 \text{ Inch of mercury} = 0.4912 \text{ p.s.i., use } 0.491$$
$$\text{Universal gas constant} = MR = 1545$$
$$\text{Absolute temperature} = t \text{ (deg. F.)} + 459.7;$$
$$\text{Volume of 1 mol at } 32° \text{ F. and 1 atmos.} = 358.7 \text{ cu. ft.}$$
$$\text{Aprox. composition of air; by volume, } N_2 = 79\%; O_2 = 21\%$$
$$\text{by weight, } N_2 = 77\%; O_2 = 23\%$$

CHAPTER I

1. An airplane weighing 20,000 lbs. is flying at 150 miles per hour in quiet air. What kinetic energy with reference to the earth does it possess? What energy would be dissipated if it collided with another plane of equal weight and speed travelling in the opposite direction?

2. If an automobile weighing 2800 lbs. is travelling at 40 miles per hour and is brought to rest in a distance of 20 yds. what is the average tractive drag between the tires and the road and how much heat is dissipated in the brakes?

3. An anti-aircraft gun fires a projectile weighing one pound vertically upward. The muzzle velocity is 3000 ft. per sec. Neglecting friction, what is the initial kinetic energy and how high would the projectile ascend? What would be its kinetic and potential energies at $\frac{1}{4}$, $\frac{1}{2}$, and maximum height?

4. According to the mechanical theory of heat,

(a) is there such a thing as intermolecular friction?

(b) does the molecular activity have a tendency to run down?

(c) why are molecular paths curved in liquids and straight in gases?

5. Could heat be added to a gas without speeding up the molecules?

6. If 10 British Thermal Units (B.t.u.) are added to a pound of gas while the gas is expanding and raising a 100-lb. weight 7.78 ft. vertically, by how much is the intrinsic energy of the gas increased?

7. (a) If heat is added to a gas confined in a rigid sphere until the average velocity of its molecules is doubled, how is the increase of energy divided, i.e., by how much is the molecular *kinetic* energy increased and by how much is the molecular *potential* energy changed?

(b) If next the volume of the sphere were allowed to double at constant temperature what would be the relations of the new kinetic and potential energies to those of the original state?

(c) Which case would require the more heat to be supplied from the external source?

8. Explain in your own words why it is that for substances *passing through* the melting or boiling stages it is true that the addition of heat does not raise the temperature of the substances.

9. (a) How do we know energy exists?

(b) Can one *see* energy?

10. (a) Convert 7,943,000 ft.-lbs. into kilogram-meters, British Thermal Units, International Joules.

(b) Derive the factor for converting the molecular velocities quoted in the table on page 11 into feet per second.

11. A pound of ice at 32° F. melts into water at the same temperature and atmospheric pressure. For this change 144 B.t.u. are required. If the specific volume of ice was 34.5 cu. ins. and the volume decreases 12% by how much will the intrinsic energy of the water be increased?

12. Mercury weighs 0.491 p.s.i. What is the absolute pressure in p.s.i. in a retort where the pressure gage reads 2.42 lbs. when the barometer stands at 27.80 ins.? *Ans.* 16.07 p.s.i.

13. What is the absolute pressure in p.s.i. in a condenser where a vacuum gage reads 26.9 in. when the barometer reads 30.71 in.?

CHAPTER II

(Note.—For values of R for various gases see Table I page 69. Neglect friction in all problems.)

1. Using the data given in the table of Art. 1—6, compute the molecular velocities at 170° F. for the gases hydrogen, helium, and carbon monoxide.

2. Compute the pressure exerted by one pound of argon when at 32° F. and occupying a volume of 7 cu. ft. Do the same for helium and carbon monoxide.

3. Is it allowable to average the thermometer readings for the purpose of obtaining an average temperature? Why?

4. The specific volume of air at 32° F. and atmospheric pressure (14.7 p.s.i. abs.) is 12.389 cu. ft. From these data find the gas constant for air.

5. How much helium by weight is contained in 100 cu. ft. at a pressure of 15 p.s.i. abs. and a temperature of 40° F.?

6. How many pounds of air at 200 p.s.i. abs. and 240° F. is contained in a cylinder 6 ft. in diameter and 30 ft. long?

7. A tank contains 8 lbs. of helium at 20° C. and 250 lbs. gage pressure with the barometer at 29.0 in. What is the size of the container?

8. Compressed air is to be stored in tanks 9 in. in diameter and 10 ft. long. At 150° F. the maximum allowable pressure is 2000 p.s.i. abs. What weight of air can be stored in each tank? What volume would this air occupy before compression at atmospheric conditions of 31.0 in. barometric pressure and 60° F.?

9. What would be the relative sizes of two receivers provided for the storage of equal weights of helium and hydrogen? The conditions of storage are identical, viz., pressure 100 atmospheres and temperature 60° F.

10. A spherical balloon has a maximum capacity of 50,000 cu. ft. To permit expansion as the balloon rises, the bag is only partially filled. How

PROBLEMS   429

much hydrogen at 68° F. and 14.7 p.s.i. abs. should be put in for the balloon
to exert an upward pull on the anchor ropes of 100 lbs.?   The total weight
of the partially filled balloon, including its contained hydrogen, is 2800 lbs.
Assume external temperature and pressure the same as hydrogen temperature and pressure.   *Ans.*   38,500 cu. ft.

11. Compute the lifting force of one cubic foot of hydrogen at 32° F. and
14.7 p.s.i. abs. and compare with the lifting force of one cubic foot of helium
under the same conditions.   Assume external temperature the same as
hydrogen temperature.

12. A frictionless piston fitted in a non-conducting cylinder is forced
inward 6 in. with an average force of 180 lbs.   Would the intrinsic energy
of the gas in the cylinder be increased or decreased and by how much?   If
it were desirable that the intrinsic energy remain constant, what change
would have been necessary in the apparatus or procedure?

13. If it were possible to have a frictionless pump would the pump barrel get hot when pumping up an automobile tire?

14. 10 B.t.u. are supplied to a gas causing it to expand and push a 3000-
lb. weight vertically upward 9 ins.   How much has its intrinsic energy
changed?

15. In the foregoing problem, if the same external work had been done
but the gas had been kept at constant temperature throughout the expansion, how much heat would it have been necessary to supply?

16. A bullet is projected from a rifle by the expansion of the products of
combustion of the burning powder.   If the bullet had 11,650 ft.-lbs. of
kinetic energy when leaving the muzzle and there had been a 10% heat loss
by radiation, how much heat energy was liberated by the burning powder
charge?   The heat remaining in the products of combustion at the termination of the expulsion process was 75 B.t.u.

CHAPTER III

1. The thermal efficiency of any heat engine is the ratio of the work done
(expressed in heat units) to the heat supplied.   Bearing this in mind, if an
engine requires 11,000 B.t.u. per hour to produce one horsepower at the
brake, what is its thermal efficiency?

2. (*a*) If the makers of the foregoing engine claimed that the engine
could produce one horsepower on a consumption of 2000 B.t.u. per hour,
would the statement violate the first law of thermodynamics?   Would it
violate the second law?

(*b*) If the economy claimed were 2544 B.t.u. per hour, would this be in
violation of either law?

3. A power plant produces 1 kilowatt hour of electrical energy from 1.75 lbs. of coal. The heat set free by burning one pound of the coal is 14,000 B.t.u. What is the thermal efficiency of the plant?

Ans. 13.9%.

4. A new power-producing device is invented and the inventor claims that by the direct action of a mysterious chemical on coal, electrical energy is produced. The economy claimed is one-quarter of a pound of coal per hour to produce one kilowatt-hour. The coal has a heating value of 13,620 B.t.u. per lb. Is such an economy possible? Why?

5. Would it be allowable to originate two new thermodynamic functions such as:

$$\omega \text{ (omega) } = TS + U \quad \text{and} \quad \epsilon \text{ (epsilon) } = QW + P$$

Would these be true properties? Why?

6. Could the functions of the preceding problem be differentiated? Why?

7. A graph of the thermodynamic change of a certain substance can be drawn on the P. V. coordinates. It is a curve extending downward and to the right. The area under this curve is 6 sq. ins. and the coordinates have the following scales, $1'' = 40$ p.s.i. and $1'' = 20$ cu. ft. How much work was performed by this substance? *Ans.* 691,200 ft.-lbs.

8. Compressing a gas gives a graph which goes upward and to the left from the initial state. Following this with a planimeter in the sequence generated results in a negative reading. Explain the significance of this.

9. (a) Are there in existence any completely reversible energy transformations?

(b) Are there any completely irreversible ones? Discuss briefly.

10. During a reversible process 260 B.t.u. are supplied to 3 lbs. of working substance at 400° F. (constant). Find the total change of entropy and the change per pound of working substance (i.e., change in specific entropy).

11. What is the change in entropy when 8 lbs. of water are heated from 70° to 210° F.? Assume specific heat of water to be unity and use $dQ = c dt$ in basic equation for entropy change. *Ans.* 1.88 units of entropy.

12. The coordinate scales for a temperature-entropy graph are: $1'' = 100°$ temp. F. and $1'' = 0.2$ unit of entropy. The area under the graph is 5 sq. ins. and lies to the right of the initial state. How much heat is represented and was it added or taken away from the working substance?

13. 97,030 B.t.u. are supplied at constant temperature causing 144.5 units increase of entropy in 100 lbs. of working substance. At what temper-

PROBLEMS 431

ature was the heat supplied?   Sketch a graph on the T. S. coordinates showing the process.

14. For a cooling at constant pressure determine the trend of the graphs showing the relations between any two of the following properties: P, V, T, U, H and S.

15. Same as Problem 14 but for an adiabatic expansion.

16. Does the statement, $\text{Work} = -\int_1^2 VdP$, hold for all cycles? Explain.

17. Sketch graphs on the P–V and T–S planes for a gas undergoing the following changes and show which process has the steeper graph.

Cooling at constant volume and cooling at constant pressure.

Compression at constant temperature and adiabatic compression.

18. An automobile engine consumes 0.6 lb. of gasoline per hour per horsepower. The heating value of the gasoline is 19,000 B.t.u. per pound. What is the thermal efficiency of the engine?

19. An engine has a thermal efficiency of 27%. It rejects 4000 B.t.u. every hour. How much heat is supplied to the engine?

Ans. 5480 B.t.u. per Hr.

20. An engine developing 250 hp. receives 42,400 B.t.u. each minute. What is its thermal efficiency and how much heat is rejected each minute?

21. A heat pump (reversed heat engine) is supplied with one kilowatt of power which enables it to withdraw 200 B.t.u. per minute from the lower temperature chamber. How much heat per minute is delivered to the higher temperature room?

22. A refrigerating machine delivers to its cooling system 32,000 B.t.u. per hour when using 0.5 kilowatt of electrical power. Neglecting heat leakages, how much heat is removed per hour from the cold chamber?

23. Set up the equation for steady flow for the following: (a) condenser; (b) boiler; (c) automotive engine; (d) throttling calorimeter; (e) turbine nozzle; (f) steam engine; (h) air compressor.

24. A steam engine uses 5000 lbs. of steam per hour. The steam has a heat content (enthalpy) of 1200 B.t.u. per lb. on entering the engine. The radiation loss from the engine is 25,000 B.t.u. per hour. What is the horsepower output of the engine? The enthalpy of the exit steam is 1050 B.t.u. per lb.

25. An air compressor compresses 300 cu. ft. of free air per minute. Air enters the compressor at 70° F. and leaves at 270° F.   20 lbs. of water pass through the compressor water jackets per minute increasing 10° F. in temperature as it passes through. Neglecting radiation calculate the

horsepower input. *Note:* For air, $h = c_p T$ and c_p (the specific heat at constant pressure) can be considered constant.   *Ans.*   30.2 Hp.

CHAPTER IV

1. Give mathematical statements of Boyle's Law, Charles' Law and Joules' Law.

2. A gas expands at constant temperature from an initial pressure of 150 p.s.i. abs. and a specific volume of 1.2 to a final pressure of 5 p.s.i. abs. What will be its final volume?

3. A gas originally at 60° F. and 15 p.s.i. abs. is heated in an hermetically sealed receiver until the pressure rises to 30 p.s.i. abs. What will be the temperature (deg. F.) in the final state?

4. A gas at 500 p.s.i. abs. is stored in a steel tank at 70° F. causing a stress in the steel shell of 8000 p.s.i. The storage building catches fire. As the steel tank is heated its strength diminishes and the gas pressure increases. Plot curves showing the progressively decreasing strength of the tank and the progressively increasing stress due to the pressure of the gas as the temperature rises, and predict the gas pressure at which the tank will explode.

Temp.	Strength of mild steel
70° F.	44,000 p.s.i.
400° F.	42,000 p.s.i.
700° F.	34,000 p.s.i.
1000° F.	14,000 p.s.i.
1200° F.	1,000 p.s.i.

Neglect any increase of tank volume due to pressure increase.
                    Ans.   1,295 lbs. per sq. in.

5. In the ideal Diesel engine, combustion is assumed to take place at constant pressure, i.e., the gases in the combustion chamber burn and force the piston outward at a rate such that the pressure on the piston remains constant. For such a process, assuming an initial pressure of 500 p.s.i. abs. and temperature of 1000° F., what will be the final volume, in terms of the initial volume, when the temperature has reached 3900° F.?
                    Ans.   2.98.

6. A captive balloon is completely filled with 40,000 cu. ft. of hydrogen at 60° F. It rises and as the day grows warmer the temperature of the hydrogen increases to 95° F. In order to maintain constant pressure in the balloon how much hydrogen at the higher temperature will it be necessary to let out?

7. A pound of air at 150 p.s.i. abs. occupies 3 cu. ft. What is its temperature?

8. Three cubic feet of argon exist at 200 p.s.i. abs. and 150° F. What is the weight?

9. Twenty pounds of helium occupy 2000 cu.ft. at a pressure of 5.3 lbs. sq. in. gage. What is its temperature in degrees F. and absolute?

10. Four pounds of a perfect gas, molecular weight 28, exist at 20 p.s.i. abs. and 500° F. What is its volume?   *Ans.* 73.5 cu. ft.

11. A mol of hydrogen is at a pressure of 4 in. of mercury above atmospheric. What is its volume if the temperature is 80° F.?

12. A mol of nitrogen at 15 p.s.i. gage and at a temperature of 85° F. occupies how many cubic feet?

13. Oxygen and hydrogen are to be stored in tanks 10 in. diameter and 35 in. long. At a maximum temperature of 110° F. the pressure must not exceed 250 lbs. gage. What weight of oxygen can be stored in one tank? What of hydrogen? What would be the volume of each at 14.7 lbs. absolute and 70° F.?

> *Ans.* The weight of oxygen 2.206 lbs.
> The weight of hydrogen .1387 lb.
> The volume of either gas 26.63 cu. ft.

14. The volume occupied by 23 lbs. of a certain gaseous compound is 555 cu. ft. at 15 p.s.i. abs. and 140° F. Its molecular weight is 23. Would we be justified in using the perfect gas equations for evaluating properties or changes? Why?

15. One mol of a gas at 32° F. and 14.7 p.s.i. abs. occupies 358 cu. ft. Can the gas be identified from these data? Why?

16. Using the data of table 1, p. 69, how many B.t.u. will be required to heat 15 lbs. of air at atmospheric pressure from 32° F. to 132° F. when the heating is (*a*) at constant volume, and (*b*) at constant pressure?

> *Ans.* (*a*) 257 B.t.u.
> (*b*) 360 B.t.u.

17. Twenty pounds of mercury vapor at 32° F. receive 40 B.t.u. at constant pressure. What is the rise in temperature?

18. Thirty pounds of atmospheric nitrogen require 58.6 B.t.u. to raise its temperature from 32° F. to 43° F. at constant volume. What is its mean specific heat under those conditions? If the temperature had been 3500° F. there would have been required 73.5 B.t.u. to raise it 10 degrees. What is its specific heat at 3500° F.?

19. Five B.t.u. are required to heat 3.0 lbs. of perfect gas 10 degrees F.

at constant volume. If the original temperature was 180° F., what has been the total increase in intrinsic energy?

20. If R for the above gas is 55, how much heat will be required to raise its temperature 20° F. at constant pressure?   *Ans.*   14.3 B.t.u.

21. For one pound of a gas whose molecular weight is 2.02 there is required 9.85 B.t.u. less to raise it 10 degrees F. at constant volume than at constant pressure. What is the value of R for this gas? What is the value of the universal gas constant, using the above data?

22. What are the molal specific heats at constant pressure and at constant volume for the following gases at 32° F.: Air, nitrogen, hydrogen, helium, argon?

23. Sketch graphs on the PV and TS coordinates of the following changes for a perfect gas. Adiabatic compression, constant volume cooling, isothermal expansion, constant pressure cooling.

24. A tank contains 2 cu. ft. of air at 70° F. and 100 p.s.i. abs. heat is added until the temperature becomes 170° F. Calculate: (*a*) Heat added, (*b*) Change in intrinsic energy, (*c*) Change in the $A P V$ term, (*d*) Change in heat content.

25. Same as Problem 24 but for a vertical cylinder having a piston loaded with a fixed weight.

26. Three pounds of oxygen are heated at constant pressure from an initial state of 15 p.s.i. abs. and 68° F. until the volume is doubled. Find the change in each of the properties P, V, T, U, H, and also the work done and heat supplied.

27. Find the change in P, V, T, U, H, and also the heat supplied and work done when four pounds of hydrogen change at constant pressure from an initial state of 20 p.s.i. gage and 40° F. to a final temperature of 540° F.

28. How much work must be done to compress 1000 cu. ft. of air from 14.5 p.s.i. to 145 p.s.i. without a change in temperature. How much heat must be removed during the compression?   *Ans.*   4,810,000 ft.-lbs.
                                                                          6180 B.t.u.

29. Two pounds of a perfect gas at 80° F. occupy 92.8 cu. ft. when at a pressure of 5 p.s.i. abs. How much work will be done if its expands at constant temperature to 300 cu. ft.? Will heat be added or withdrawn from the gas and by how much?

30. For the above gas the molecular weight is 25 and the specific heat at constant volume is 0.28. Determine the change in the properties P, v, T, u, and h.

31. Five hundred cu. ft. of air at 50° F. and under a barometric pressure of 31.0″ are to be compressed to 75 p.s.i. abs. How much heat must

be removed from it to prevent the temperature from rising during the process? How much work must be done to compress the air?

Ans. Ht. removed = 2247 B.t.u.

Work done = 1,748,000 ft.-lbs.

32. Four pounds of hydrogen expand adiabatically from 300 p.s.i. abs. and 150° F. to a final pressure of 50 p.s.i. abs. Find the change in P, v, T, u, h, the heat exchange and the work done.

33. Three pounds of air expand isentropically from 600° F. to 200° F. Calculate the external work done.

34. The value of the exponent for the compression taking place in the cylinder of an automobile engine is about 1.35 (i.e. $PV^{1.35}$ = const.) The ratio of the volume before to the volume after the compression (compression ratio) now ranges about 5.5. Assuming air is the working fluid and enters the cylinder at 11.0 p.s.i. abs. and 150° F. find the work done, heat exchange and change in properties P, v, T, u, h, for the compression process.

35. For the foregoing polytropic process what would be the specific heat? Using this calculate the heat exchange.

36. A tank, 10 cu. ft. capacity, contains 2 lbs. of air at 20.3 p.s.i. gage. If heat is added until the pressure is 55.3 p.s.i. gage, calculate the change in entropy.

37. A pound of air is cooled at constant pressure until its volume is one-fourth of its original volume. What is its change in entropy?

Ans. A decrease of 0.333 unit of entropy.

38. At 400° F., it requires 826 B.t.u. to change a pound of water into steam at the same temperature. Calculate the change in entropy.

39. Air is compressed from 14.5 p.s.i. abs., 60° F. to 100 p.s.i. abs. according to the law $PV^{1.33} = C$. Calculate the change in entropy.

40. A portable air compressor is fitted with a fusible plug melting at 450° F. What is the maximum allowable pressure if "n" for compression is 1.35? Initial temperature = 60° F, P_1 = atmos. *Ans.* 127 p.s.i.

41. In an air compressor, the compression line is represented by the equation $PV^{1.35} = C$. The temperature of the air is raised 200° F. How much heat is lost to the cylinder walls per lb. of air?

42. Find the exponent for the equation of an expansion line passing from the point $p = 28$, $v = 2.0$ to the point $p = 15$, $v = 9.6$. Find the work done during this expansion.

Ans. The required exponent is .398.

The work done is 21,040 ft.-lbs.

43. A perfect gas is throttled through an orifice from a pressure of

100 p.s.i. abs. to atmospheric. How large a drop in temperature will result? Why?

44. Had the gas in the previous problem been air, how large a temperature drop would have occurred?

45. One pound of CO exists at 40° F. and 8820 p.s.i. abs. Compute its true volume by use of Fig. IV–17. Also calculate its volume assuming it to be a perfect gas and also by use of Van der Waal's equation. (It may be well to solve Van der Waal's equation graphically by assuming various volumes.)

CHAPTER V

1. The inventor of a new internal combustion engine admits that 10% of the energy liberated by combustion is used to overcome mechanical friction. However he claims that all of the remainder of the heat energy is transformed into useful work. Is such a claim (a) possible, (b) probable (c) why?

2. A new gasoline turbine is being marketed. In this a carburetted mixture explodes and the products of combustion drive the turbine vanes. Losses due to mechanical friction are small (2%) and as the entire unit is well insulated the radiation losses are kept to a minimum (3%). Using gasoline with a heating value of 19,000 B.t.u. per pound it is claimed that one horsepower can be produced on 0.141 lb. of fuel per hour. Is such a claim (a) possible, (b) probable, (c) why?

3. If we know the maximum temperature in the cylinder of an internal combustion engine cannot exceed 4500° F. abs., and the temperature of the air to which the engine must exhaust is 520° F. abs., what percentage of the energy supplied at the higher temperature can be considered available for doing work? Actually we rarely obtain exhaust temperatures much below 1000° F. abs. For such, what is the percentage of available energy?

4. Is the transfer of heat from flue gas to water in a boiler an example of a reversible process? The water in the boiler receives heat at a constant temperature of 450° F. abs. The flue gases are at 2500° F.

5. In the cases illustrated by Figs. V–1 and V–2 could the ball be stopped in any intermediate position and remain stationary unassisted? If there were a step in the curved hill surface would the processes then be reversible? Why?

6. If Carnot had been a believer in the caloric theory of heat would his reasoning concerning an engine of maximum efficiency still have held? Why?

7. In problem 2 if it were known that the temperature of combustion was 3540° F. and the temperature of the exhaust 540° F., what would have been the absolute maximum economy, i.e., the least fuel consumption per horsepower hour, using fuel oil having a heating value of 19,000 B.t.u. per pound?

8. In problem 2 if the heat is supplied at 3500° F. and the temperature of the exhaust is 600° F. (a) what is the Carnot efficiency and (b) what is the lowest possible fuel rate, i.e., the maximum possible economy for the ideal engine?

9. A steam plant generates steam at 450° F. The temperature of the condenser where the exhaust steam gives up its heat is 90° F. What is the Carnot efficiency and the maximum economy expressed in pounds of coal (13,900 B.t.u. per pound) per horsepower per hour?

10. A Carnot engine working between 300° and 100° F. does 778,000 ft.-lbs. of work per cycle. How much heat is supplied and how much rejected per cycle? *Ans.* 3804 B.t.u. supplied; 2804 B.t.u. rejected.

11. An engine working on the Carnot cycle between 400° and 150° F. uses 1 lb. of gas. The maximum change in entropy is 0.2 of one unit. Find the efficiency, the heat received, the heat rejected and the work done per cycle.

12. In a Carnot cycle there is a change of 200° F. At the upper temperature, 339.3° F., 20 heat units are added. Find the efficiency, the work done and the heat rejected per cycle.

13. A Carnot engine working with air has at the beginning of the stroke a volume of 2 cu. ft., and a pressure of 500 lbs. absolute per sq. in. After isothermal expansion the volume is 20 cu. ft., and the temperature 539.3° F. If the maximum temperature range is 200° find (a) the heat received, (b) the heat rejected and (c) the work done per cycle, and (d) the efficiency. *Ans.* (a) 426 B.t.u.; (b) 341 B.t.u.; (c) 66,300 ft.-lbs.; (d) 20%.

14. An engine working on the Carnot cycle rejects 100 B.t.u. at 110° F. If the efficiency is 0.22, how much work is done per cycle and at what temperature is the heat received?

15. In a Carnot cycle 10 thermal units are converted into work and 42 are rejected at 50° F. At what temperature is the heat received?

16. A steam engine working between 350° and 126° F. requires 220 B.t.u. per I.Hp. per min. What is the relative efficiency of its cycle referred to the Carnot cycle for the same temperature limits? *Ans.* 69.8%.

17. Would you consider Carnot's Law a statement of the Second Law of Thermodynamics? Would you consider the expression for the efficiency of the Carnot engine a statement of the Second Law? Give reasons in both cases.

18. In a steam boiler plant the average flue gas temperature is 2200° F., the water and steam in the boiler are at 420° F. The lowest available temperature is that existing in the condenser where the exhaust steam gives up its heat and this is 102° F. Find the loss in available energy which has resulted from the transfer of 10,000 B.t.u. from the high temperature flue gases to the lower temperature boiler steam.

19. In the flow of a gas through a porous plug as described in Joule's work (Art. IV, 21), there is an irreversible adiabatic expansion without the doing of useful work. For such a case, using air, at 540° F., suppose the pressure drops from 150 p.s.i. abs. to 15 p.s.i. abs. and the specific entropy increases by 0.159 unit, what has been the decrease in available energy, considering atmospheric temperature of 60° F. as the lowest available temperature?   *Ans.* 82.7 B.t.u.

20. The temperature range in a Carnot cycle is 400° F. The heat transformed into work is 30% of that rejected. Calculate the temperatures at which heat is supplied and rejected.

21. An ideal Carnot cycle engine is to deliver 100 Hp. The source temperature is 600° F. and the cold body temperature is 100° F. Calculate the heat removed from the hot body and the heat rejected to the cold body per minute, also the change of entropy.

22. The temperature of an infinite source is 800° F. and the temperature of an infinite cold body is 60° F. 1000 B.t.u. are removed from the hot body and put into an engine of unknown efficiency. Heat not turned into work is rejected to the cold body. Calculate:

(a) B.t.u. available.

(b) Decrease in entropy of source.

(c) Minimum increase in entropy of the cold body. (max. eff.)

(d) Maximum increase in entropy of the cold body. (min. eff.)

CHAPTER VI

1. Sketch the thermodynamic cycle on the *PV* and *TS* planes of a machine which operates as follows: The charge of air in a cylinder is heated so that expansion at constant pressure takes place for one-half the stroke. The remainder of the stroke, the expansion is at constant temperature. After the piston has reached the end of its stroke, the charge is compressed and cooled at constant pressure for ¾ of its stroke. The completion of the return stroke is an adiabatic compression to the initial pressure. Label each process and number or letter similarly on both sets of coordinates.

2. In the foregoing example constancy of mass of the working fluid was assumed, i.e., no gas entered or left the cylinder. Consider now the mechanical cycle of a different engine and sketch the following operations on the PV plane. Air is drawn into the cylinder at high pressure for $\frac{1}{2}$ stroke. After cut-off isothermal expansion occurs for the completion of the stroke at which point the pressure has dropped to atmospheric. At the end of the stroke the exhaust valve opens and for $\frac{3}{4}$ of the return stroke, air is exhausted at constant pressure. The exhaust valve then closes and the rest of the travel ($\frac{1}{4}$ stroke) compresses adiabatically the remaining charge back to the initial pressure.

3. Draw the graph on both PV and TS planes for the thermodynamic changes occurring in the cylinder of Problem 2. Compare results with those of Problem 1 and explain differences, if any.

4. If the initial pressure for the cycle described in Problem 2 is 140 p.s.i. abs., compute the work of the cycle for one pound of air at cut-off. (Consider the clearance as 10% of the stroke.)

5. How many cubic feet of free air per minute can be compressed adiabatically from 14.7 p.s.i. abs. and 60° F. to 100 p.s.i. abs. if 50 hp. are available for driving the compressor? $Ans.$ 310 cu. ft.

6. How much more work per pound of air is required to compress air initially at 60° F. and 14.7 p.s.i. abs. to 294 p.s.i. abs. with adiabatic compression than with isothermal compression?

7. For a gasoline internal combustion engine the volumetric efficiency is the ratio of the weight of air actually drawn in, to the weight of free air represented by the piston displacement. A 6-cylinder automobile engine, $3'' \times 3\frac{1}{4}''$ stroke, draws in 110 cu. ft. of air per min. at 140° F. and 11 p.s.i. abs. pressure when running at 3600 r.p.m. External atmospheric conditions are 14.7 p.s.i. and 60° F. What is its volumetric efficiency?

8. An air compressor has a clearance of 10%. The pressure at end of suction is 14.0 p.s.i. abs. and 70 p.s.i. abs. at end of delivery. $n = 1.35$ for both compression and re-expansion.
Calculate:

(a) Volumetric eff. (Assume no heating during suction).

(b) Same as (a) but for 2% clearance.

(c) Same as (a) but for a pressure of 35 p.s.i. abs. at end of delivery.

$Ans.$ (a) 73.4%.
(b) 90.8%.
(c) 86%.

9. Air is compressed 5 atmospheres in a single stage compressor which has a clearance volume of 6%. (a) What is the volumetric efficiency?

$n = 1.34.$ (b) What are the volumetric efficiencies when compressing to 4 and to 6 atmospheres?

10. Neglecting clearance and friction, what will be the efficiency of compression for a single stage air compressor compressing to 5 atmospheres, (a) if $n = 1.3$, (b) if $n = 1.35$?

11. 500 cu. ft. per minute of free air (at 14.7 p.s.i. abs. and 60° F.) are to be compressed to 125 p.s.i. abs. using (a) a single stage compressor in which $n = 1.3$, and (b) a two stage compressor ($n = 1.3$) with intercooler which returns the air to 60° F. between stages. Find the horsepower for each case and the saving in power due to intercooling.

12. Air is to be compressed 10 atmospheres. What should be the intermediate pressure if the compression is carried out in two stages?

(b) If the final pressure were 500 lbs. and there were three stages, compute the intermediate pressures.

(c) If 2500 lbs. is to be obtained using four stages, compute the intermediate pressures.

13. For the cases of Problem 10 with adiabatic compression, compute the horsepower necessary to compress 500 cu. ft. of free air per minute.

14. An air compressor supplies 500 cu. ft. free air (14.7 p.s.i. and 60° F.) per minute at 200 p.s.i. abs. ($n = 1.33$). In the flasks the air cools back at constant pressure to 65° F. An air engine takes this air at 190 p.s.i. abs. and expands to atmospheric pressure ($n = 1.33$). Find (a) the horsepower to run the compressor, (b) the horsepower generated by the air engine and (c) the efficiency of power transmitted.

15. An air engine has two double acting cylinders each 8″ × 12″ stroke, and runs at 110 R.p.m. Air is supplied at 90 p.s.i. gage and 70° F. Cut-off occurs at ⅓ stroke and exhaust is to the atmosphere. Assume a card factor of .85. What is the probable M.E.P., the I.Hp., the B.Hp. ($E_m = .85$), and the air consumption expressed in cubic feet free air per B.Hp.?

16. Determine the proper dimensions for a single cylinder double acting compressed air engine using air at 65 p.s.i. gage at 65° F. cut-off ⅓ stroke and exhausting to atmosphere. The engine is to develop 50 I.Hp. at 200 R.p.m. Card factor .82. Ratio stroke to diameter = 1.25.

17. Determine the indicated and brake horsepowers of an 8-cylinder, 4-cycle int. comb. engine when running at 3300 R.p.m. Indicated M.E.P. = 92 p.s.i., Mech. Eff. = .86, Diam. cyl. = 3¼″, Stroke = 3⅜″.

18. A two-cycle engine of the same dimensions has an indicated M.E.P. of 55 p.s.i., otherwise the same dimensions as Problem 17. What is its I.Hp. and B.Hp.?

19. A gasoline engine (Otto cycle) has a 6 to 1 compression ratio. The charge has a heating value of 1150 B.t.u. per pound. The engine draws in 0.1 lb. of charge per cycle, at 14.5 p.s.i. abs., 70° F. Assuming the air standard, calculate:

(a) Pressure, volume, and temperature at the four points of cycle.

(b) Heat supplied and work done for each process.

(c) The net cycle work.

(d) Thermal efficiency. *Ans.* (d) 51.2% Thermal Eff.

20. A single-cylinder four-stroke Otto cycle gas engine has a bore of 12″ and a stroke of 18″. It operates at 280 R.p.m. and has a compression ratio of 4. The pressure at the end of the suction stroke is 15 p.s.i. and the temperature 50° F. The entering charge has a heating value of 1800 B.t.u. per pound. What is the theoretical horsepower (Air Standard)?

21. An engine which operates on the constant pressure cycle receives a carburetted mixture of 1200 B.t.u. per pound heating value at 370 p.s.i. abs. after an adiabatic compression of 10 to 1 from atmosphere ($p = 14.7, t = 60°$ F.). Assuming Air Standard, calculate:

(a) the pressure, volume and temperature at each of the 4 points of the cycle.

(b) heat supplied and work done for each process.

(c) the net cycle work per pound of mixture.

(d) the thermal efficiency.

22. A Diesel engine has a clearance of 8%. At the end of the suction stroke the air drawn in is at 13.7 p.s.i. and 90° F. Considering one pound of air, there is injected at the end of the compression stroke, 1/20 of a pound of fuel oil whose heating value is 18,800 B.t.u. per lb.

Assume air standard cycle and find:

(a) pressure, volume, and temperature for each point of the diagram; (b) the heat supplied or rejected and the work done on or by the gas during each process of the cycle; (c) the net work of the cycle; (d) the thermal efficiency.

23. The pressure at the start of compression in a Diesel cycle (air standard) is 14 p.s.i. abs. and the temperature is 140° F. If the compression ratio is 15 to 1 and the maximum temperature is 3140° F., calculate the temperature and pressure at end of expansion, also calculate, per pound, the heat received, the heat rejected, and the efficiency.

24. Given an automobile gasoline engine operating on the Otto cycle and having a compression ratio of 6. As this engine knocks badly, a larger gasket is inserted between the cylinder block and head which reduces the compression ratio to 5.4. What percentage reduction in mileage per gallon of gasoline should be expected?

25. If using an anti-knock fuel permits an increase in the compression ratio of a given gasoline engine (Otto cycle) from 4.7 to 5.5, without detonation, how much could the owner afford to pay for the anti-knock fuel if the undoped fuel was costing 17¢ per gallon?

26. Determine the instantaneous specific heat (c_p and c_v) of the following gases at 3000° F.

$$Air, \quad CO, \quad CH_4, \quad C_8H_{18} \text{ (gasoline)}$$

27. Five pounds of CO are heated at constant pressure from 60° F. to 2500° F. Taking cognizance of the variation in specific heat, calculate the heat necessary.

28. For the condition of the preceding problem find the change in (a) Intrinsic Energy, (b) Enthalpy, per pound.

29. Determine the mean specific heat at constant pressure of air over a range of temperatures from 60° F. to 1000° F. and over a range from 60° F. to 3000° F.

30. (a) Find the temperature of air after an adiabatic compression from 14.7 p.s.i. abs. to 2500 p.s.i. abs. Initial temperature was 60° F. Take cognizance of variable specific heat. (b) By how much does this differ from the temperature obtained by assuming the specific heat remains constant?

31. An air refrigerating machine is to withdraw 500 B.t.u. per minute. Air leaves the cold room at 20° F. The temperature of the circulating water available is 50° F. and the air leaves the cooling receiver at 60° F. The operating pressures are 200 p.s.i. abs. and 15 p.s.i. abs. Assume the ideal cycle of Fig. VI–38. Find (a) the pressure, temperature, and volume of the air at each point of the cycle, (b) the weight of air circulated per minute, (c) work done in compressor cylinder, (d) work done in expander cylinder, (e) net work and horsepower.

32. An air-refrigerating machine similar to that illustrated by Figs. VI–37 and 38 returns the following data. The temperature of the air in the cold room is 33° F., and the pressure 14.5 p.s.i. abs. The compressor delivers at 110 p.s.i. abs. The compressed air is reduced in temperature, in the cooling receiver to 80° F. Expansion then takes place to 14.5 p.s.i. abs. The exponent for the compression process is, $n = 1.26$ and for the expansion, $n = 1.34$.

(a) If 36,000 B.t.u. per hour are to be removed from the cold room, how many pounds of air per minute must be circulated?

(b) Neglecting clearances, what theoretical horsepower is used to run the compressor? How much is furnished by the expander? How much remains to be furnished by the motor?

(c) Make an energy balance showing the amounts of energy supplied to and withdrawn from the air per minute (neglecting losses) for each process.

Chapter VII

1. A mixture is made reversibly of the following gases each at a pressure of 15 p.s.i. and a temperature of 32° F.; 3 lb. of oxygen; 2 lb. of CO; ½ lb. of hydrogen; 1 lb. of helium; 3 lb. of nitrogen and ½ lb. of argon. Find the following properties for one pound of the mixture: intrinsic energy, heat content, specific heat, temperature, and pressure.

2. Determine the apparent molecular weight of the mixture in Problem 1.

3. Given the following analysis by volume of a gas, determine the apparent molecular weight.

Gas	Per cent by volume
CO_2	9
CO	2
O_2	12
N_2	77

Ans. 29.9.

4. Convert the following analysis by volume of a sample of Pittsburgh illuminating gas to an analysis by weight:

Gas	Per cent by volume
H_2	26.15
CO	0.90
CH_4	65.25
C_2H_4	6.30
O_2	0.80
CO_2	0.60

5. Convert the following analysis by weight to one by volume:

Gas	Per cent by weight
H_2	10.25
CO	16.25
CH_4	54.10
C_2H_4	5.40
CO_2	8.50
N_2	5.50

6. Determine the specific heat at constant pressure for the gases of Problems 4 and 5. Assume atmospheric pressure and 32° F.

7. Write the combustion equations for the combustion of the following

fuels, (a) in oxygen and (b) in air. Hydrogen (H_2), ethylene (C_2H_4), methyl alcohol (CH_4O), kerosene ($C_{12}H_{26}$).

8. Methyl alcohol (CH_4O) is burned in oxygen. Calculate:

(a) lbs. of oxygen per pound of alcohol

(b) volumetric analysis of products of combustion.

Ans. (a) 1.5 lbs. (b) $CO_2 = 33.3\%$.
$H_2O = 66.7\%$.

9. Methyl alcohol is burned in air. Calculate:

(a) lbs. of air per pound of alcohol

(b) lbs. of products per pound of alcohol

(c) cu. ft. products, 15.7 p.s.i. abs. 500° F. per mol alcohol.

10. Calculate the higher heating values per pound, at constant pressure, 62° F. of

(a) hydrogen

(b) carbon

(c) gasoline vapor.

11. 400 B.t.u. are added at constant pressure to a pound of nitrogen at 16 p.s.i. abs., 1000° F. By use of Fig. VII–5, determine the final temperature and volume.

12. Using the values of Table IX determine the lower heating value per pound at constant pressure and at constant volume of a mixture of the following composition by volume:

Gas	Per cent by volume
H_2	9
CH_4	80
C_2H_6	11

13. Using the Temperature-Entropy diagram of Fig. VII–5 for one mol of air from an initial state of 600° F. abs. and a pressure of 16 p.s.i. abs. find the final state (P, V, T) when

(a) adiabatically compressed to 1800 lbs.

(b) heated at constant volume by adding 16,000 B.t.u.

(c) heated at constant pressure by adding 16,000 B.t.u.

14. Using the Temperature-Entropy diagram of Fig. VII–5 find the work done when one mol of air at 3000° F. abs. and 1024 p.s.i. abs. expands isothermally to 16 p.s.i. abs. Compare with the work for a similar expansion assuming the specific heats to remain constant at atmospheric values.

15. Using Fig. VII–8 what temperature would result from heating air by the addition of 24,000 B.t.u. per mol (a) at constant volume and (b) at

constant pressure? The initial temperature at the beginning of the process was 1000° F. abs.

16. Carbon monoxide is burned in air with 20% excess air. What would be the percentage burned on reaching chemical equilibrium if the combustion were (a) adiabatic, (b) with 10% heat loss, and (c) with 20% heat loss? Obtain the same figures for the burning of hydrogen and compare with those obtained for CO.

17. Determine by the approximate method the maximum temperature attained by the adiabatic combustion, at constant volume, in air, of hydrogen. No excess air and original temperature 600° F. abs.

18. Determine the percentage chemical contraction occurring when kerosene ($C_{12}H_{26}$) is burned in air with 20% excess air.

CHAPTER VIII

1. Air in a duct is moving with a uniform velocity of 500 ft. per minute. It undergoes adiabatic expansion between sections at A and B. The temperatures at two sections, A and B, are 150° and 100° F. respectively. What has been the increase in velocity from section A to section B?

2. The pressures at sections A and B of Problem 1 were 100 p.s.i. abs. and 74 p.s.i. abs. respectively. The velocity past section A was 10,000 ft. per min. What would be the sectional areas of the duct at A and B to accommodate 200 lbs. of air per minute?

3. Air expands in a nozzle from 300 p.s.i. abs. 250° F. to 200 p.s.i. abs. At the point where the pressure is 200 p.s.i. abs., the nozzle area is 1 sq. in. Calculate the discharge in pounds per hour. No friction.

Ans. 20,700 lbs. per hr.

4. What will be the velocity of sound in the following gases at atmospheric pressure and 60° F.: air, argon, helium, hydrogen?

5. For the nozzles using the gases mentioned in Problem 4 determine the ratio of throat pressure to initial pressure.

6. For a nozzle to use superheated mercury vapor at 50 p.s.i. abs. and specific volume of 2.32 cu. ft., what would be the throat pressure and throat velocity?

7. Compare the results of Problem 6 with a steam nozzle using superheated steam at 200 p.s.i. abs. with a specific volume of 4.0 cu. ft. *Note:* Superheated steam at this state may be considered as approximately conforming to the laws of gaseous flow where $k = 1.3$.

8. Neglecting friction, compute the successive sectional areas at 20-lb. intervals for a nozzle to discharge 2 lbs. of air per second from a reservoir

at 175 p.s.i. abs. and 75° F. Assume pressure at exit to be 15 p.s.i. abs. Plot graphs showing the successive velocities, specific volumes, and areas.

9. Compare the computed throat pressure with the pressure at minimum sectional area (the throat) as obtained from the foregoing graph.

10. Compare the velocity at the throat from the graph of Problem 8 with the acoustic velocity.

11. Calculate the maximum discharge (lbs. per sec.) through a convergent nozzle receiving air at 100 p.s.i. abs., 200° F., and having an exit area of 2 sq. in. No friction.   *Ans.*   4.14 lbs. per sec.

12. Compute the throat and exit areas for data of Problem 8 but with 5% of the kinetic energy developed by expansion to the throat pressure reconverted by friction into heat and 15% of that developed by the total expansion to the exit pressure of 15 lbs. reconverted by friction.

13. Air is to be expanded from 160 p.s.i. abs, 200° F. to atmospheric pressure. If the flow is 3600 lbs. per hour, calculate the throat and mouth areas. No friction.   *Ans.*   Area throat = 0.306 sq. in.

Area mouth = 0.61 sq. in.

14. Repeat Problem 13, assuming the nozzle efficiency is 98% up to the throat and 92% over all.

15. Compare the discharge of Problems 8 and 11 with those obtained by using Fliegner's equation, p. 270. Discuss the difference.

CHAPTER IX

1. Explain by means of the kinetic theory why it is that during boiling the temperature of a liquid remains constant even though heat is continually being added to the boiling liquid.

2. According to the kinetic theory should we expect the temperature at which water will boil to increase as the pressure on the liquid is raised? Why?

3. From the data contained in Steam Table II (p. 417) plot the logarithm of the boiling (saturation) temperature on logs of absolute pressures for pressures up to 3200 p.s.i. abs. Does this relation between P and T follow any fixed law, i.e., is the exponent in PT^n = const. a constant? Use absolute temperatures only.

4. When considering vapors, (*a*) are *saturation temperature* and *boiling temperature* synonymous? (*b*) Are *saturation pressure* and *boiling pressure* synonomous? (*c*) Can one saturation temperature have more than one corresponding saturation pressure and vice versa?

5. When 1 lb. of water is heated at atmospheric pressure from 80° F. to its boiling temperature and a portion of it boiled off into steam, the heat

supplied for the entire change has been 617.2 B.t.u.   The increase in volume has been 13.39 cu. ft.   What has been the increase in intrinsic energy?

6. In the foregoing problem the increase in volume during the vaporization process was 13.37 cu. ft.   What was the quality?

7. Steam has a specific volume of 4 cu. ft. per pound at a pressure of 100 p.s.i. abs.   Specify its quality (i.e., its dryness or superheat).

8. Same as Problem 7, but for a specific volume of 5 cu. ft.

9. The heat content of 4 lbs. of steam at 400° F. is 4400 B.t.u.   Specify its quality.   *Ans.*   87.8%.

10. Same as Problem 9 but with a heat content of 4900 B.t.u.
                                              Ans.   61.3° superheat.

11. Steam at 180 p.s.i. abs. has a specific entropy of 1.45.   Specify its quality.

12. Same as Problem 11 but for an entropy of 1.736.

13. A tank, 4 cu. ft. capacity, contains steam at 200 p.s.i. abs., 90% quality.   Specify the entropy of total amount of steam.
                                              Ans.   2.81 units of entropy.

14. Steam has 200° superheat at 400 p.s.i. abs.   Specify its temperature, specific volume, heat content, and entropy.

15. Construct to scale a temperature-entropy diagram showing the following lines:

(*a*) Constant pressure lines for 1, 10, 50, 150 and 500 pounds per sq. in. abs.   In the superheat region, determine for each pressure, points at 50°, 100°, 150° and 200° superheat.

(*b*) Draw in the "liquid" and "saturation" lines.

(*c*) Draw in the lines for 95%, 50%, and 10% quality.

(*d*) Draw in the lines to represent constant superheats of 50°, 100°, 150° and 200°.

(*e*) Construct constant volume lines for 2, 5, and 20 cu. ft.

16. Construct to scale, an elementary heat content-entropy chart, showing the lines called for in Problem 15.

17. Given an initial state for 1 lb. of steam, of 200 p.s.i. abs. pressure and quality .90, list its initial properties, *P*, *V*, *S*, *t*, *H*, and *x* and determine its final properties (6) after each of the following changes:

(*a*) addition of 100 B.t.u. at constant pressure.

(*b*) addition of 100 B.t.u. at constant volume.

(*c*) adiabatic expansion to 1½ original volume.

(*d*) isothermal expansion to 1½ original volume.

18. Water exists at 2000 p.s.i. abs., 100° F. Specify its specific volume, heat content, and entropy.

19. Water enters a pump at 200 p.s.i. abs., 200° F., and leaves at 1500 p.s.i. abs., 205° F. Neglecting radiation, calculate the work per pound.
Ans. 6160 ft.-lbs. per lb.

20. For an initial state of 100° C. and dry saturated tell whether the state after adiabatic expansion to 40° C. will be superheated, dry saturated, or with moisture for the 7 substances for which the data are given in Fig. IX–8.

21. If the universal gas constant for any given fluid departs radically from the value 1545 it is safe to assume that the perfect gas laws and equations are inapplicable. Would you consider that steam at the following states might be amenable to the perfect gas laws?

P (p.s.i. abs.)	t (° F.)
2500	1000
2000	650
500	950
500	500
20	550
5	380
6	170

22. Assuming 10° superheat at exit as the minimum for satisfactory operation of a throttling calorimeter find the answer when the following throttling calorimeter data are taken:

Initial Press.	Final Press.	Final Temp. (° F.)
75 p.s.i. abs.	15 p.s.i. abs.	227
150	16	240
300	15	213

23. Data from a throttling calorimeter $P = 166$ p.s.i. gage; calorimeter pressure $= 4$ in. Hg above atmospheric; calorimeter temperature $= 240°$ F., barometer $= 28.45$ in. Find the quality of the steam entering the calorimeter. Ans. $x = 0.962$.

24. A throttling calorimeter has the exit pressure of 15 p.s.i. abs. If the initial pressures are 300, 200, 100, and 50 p.s.i. abs. and 10° of superheat at exit is required for accurate results find the maximum amount of moisture initially in the steam which can be determined by this experiment. Plot a curve of the results.

Chapter X

1. Considering the seven gases for which the saturation dome is shown in the Fig. IX–8 (p. 293) determine the final state (i.e., wet, dry, or super-heated) for an adiabatic expansion from the critical state (maximum saturation temperature) to 80° C.

2. A nozzle is to be designed to pass 1200 lbs. of steam per hour under the following conditions. Initial state: $P = 300$ p.s.i. abs., $t = 700°$ F., final pressure $= 14.7$ p.s.i. abs. Calculate the throat and mouth, or exit, areas for equilibrium flow without friction.

3. Adjust the calculations of the preceding example to allow for a 5% friction loss to the throat and a 12% total friction loss to exit.

4. The exit area of a convergent nozzle is 0.8 sq. in. If the nozzle receives steam at 200 p.s.i. abs., 500° F. and exhausts at 120 p.s.i. abs., calculate the discharge in pounds per hour. No friction.

Ans. 7800 lbs. per hr.

5. Repeat problem 4, assuming a nozzle efficiency of 95%.

6. A nozzle receiving steam at 200 p.s.i. abs., 600° F. and exhausting to the atmosphere, has a throat area of 0.6 sq. in. and a mouth area of 1.6 sq. in. Neglect friction to throat. Nozzle efficiency is 90% over all.

(a) Calculate discharge in lbs. per hour.

(b) Show by calculation whether or not mouth area is correct.

7. Compute the throat area for the nozzle of Problem 2 without friction but taking account of metastable expansion. Compare the areas obtained by the two methods.

8. A simple convergent nozzle of circular cross-section has an exit diameter of 0.75 in. The initial steam state is 240 p.s.i. abs. and 400° F. The back pressure to which the nozzle discharges is 180 p.s.i. abs. Calculate the steam discharged per hour

(a) by frictionless equilibrium expansion.

(b) by frictionless metastable expansion.

9. Calculate throat and mouth area of a nozzle receiving 4500 lbs. of steam per hour at 200 p.s.i. abs. and 390° F. and exhausting at 80 p.s.i. abs. Neglect friction to throat. Nozzle efficiency (over all) is 90%. Assume that supersaturation is present but that equilibrium is restored by the time the mouth is reached.

10. Four nozzles are to supply steam at 175 p.s.i. abs. and 500° F. to an impulse turbine which is to develop 160 Hp. The exhaust pressure is 15 p.s.i. The expected economy of the turbine is 18 pounds of steam per Hp. per hour. Find the throat and exit areas in square inches of each nozzle.

11. Calculate the orifice diameter to pass 30,000 lb. of steam per hour with a pressure drop of 20 p.s.i. The initial pressure is 300 p.s.i. abs. and the temperature is 600° F. Orifice coefficient (i.e., ratio of actual to theoretical discharge) is 0.6.

CHAPTER XI

1. Plot to scale on PV and TS coordinates the Carnot cycle for a plant using steam at 180 p.s.i. abs. dry saturated and expanding to 2 p.s.i. abs. Also plot the Rankine cycle for the same initial and final expansion states. Which obtains more work per lb. of steam circulated and which has the higher eff.?

2. An engine operates on the Rankine cycle between an initial pressure of 200 p.s.i. abs. and a back pressure of 1 p.s.i. abs. The quality of the initial steam is 0.98. (a) What is its thermal efficiency? (b) Steam consumption?   *Ans.* (a) 29.6%.

(b) 7.74 lbs. per Hp. per hr.

3. An engine uses 20 lb. of steam per Hp. per hour. The boiler supplies steam at 100 p.s.i. gage with 1% moisture and the condenser pressure is 7.5 p.s.i. abs. Find (a) the B.t.u. per Hp. per min. and (b) the Rankine cycle ratio.

4. Calculate the theoretical work per pound and the efficiency of the Rankine Cycle (neglecting work of the feed pump) for the following conditions:

	Initial press.						Exhaust
(a)	Initial press.	"	120 p.s.i. abs.			Dry	Atmospheric
(b)	"	"	120	"	"	90% qual.	"
(c)	"	"	120	"	"	Dry	1″ Hg
(d)	"	"	120	"	"	500° F.	Atmospheric
(e)	"	"	120	"	"	500° F.	1″ Hg
(f)	"	"	1400	"	"	Dry	Atmospheric
(g)	"	"	1400	"	"	800° F.	1″ Hg

5. Solve Problem 4 using the Doolittle chart, p. 325.

6. A steam engine test returned the following data: Boiler pressure 100 p.s.i. gage; moisture 2%; vacuum 25 in.; barometer 31 in.; total I.Hp. 110; B.t.u. per Hp. per minute 380. Find the steam consumption in lb. per Hp. per hr. and the actual thermal efficiency. Find the Rankine cycle ratio.

7. In a stage of an impulse turbine passing 15 lbs. of steam per second the steam velocity from the nozzles is 1400 ft. per second. The speed ratio is 0.4. Nozzle angle is 16°. Symmetrical blades and no losses. Sketch

the velocity diagram and find: (a) the relative velocity of the steam in the blade passages; (b) the blade angles; (c) the velocity and angle at which the steam leaves the plane of rotation; (d) the change in velocity of whirl; (e) the tangential force exerted on the blades; (f) the blade Hp.; (g) the diagram efficiency.

> *Ans.*   (a) 0.875; (b) 26°–10′; (c) 446 ft. per sec.; (d) 1570 ft. per sec.
> (e) 732 lbs.; (f) 745 Hp.; (g) 89.7%.

8. Data as in Problem 7, but using a blade velocity coefficient of 0.85. Parts a, b, c, d, e, f, g.

9. Considering the available range for a steam turbine to be from 260 p.s.i. abs., 700° F. to 1 p.s.i. abs., what would be the ratio of the peripheral velocity of a compound unit to that of a simple turbine for (a) velocity compound turbine using 3 rows of moving vanes; (b) pressure compound turbine using 4 pressure stages?

10. A pressure-compounded turbine is composed of ten stages.   Initial steam conditions 460 p.s.i. abs. and 800° F., and back pressure 1 p.s.i. abs. The reheat factor is 1.09.   Find the pressure in the first stage.

11. In a ten-stage pressure-compounded turbine, the actual heat available per stage is 26 B.t.u. per lb.   The reheat factor is 1.08.   Initial steam at 260 p.s.i. abs. and 600° F.   What is the exhaust pressure?

> *Ans.*   14.7 p.s.i.

12. In a six-stage pressure-compounded turbine, there are 40 B.t.u. per lb. actually available per stage.   The stage efficiency is 0.65 for all stages. Steam initially at 180 p.s.i. abs., 600° F.   Find: (a) the terminal state; (b) the reheat factor.   *Ans.*   (a) 14.0 p.s.i.   (b) 1.083.

13. A steam turbine operates with regenerative feed heating.   Steam is supplied at an initial pressure of 600 p.s.i. abs. and a temperature of 680° F. Exhaust pressure is 0.5 p.s.i. abs.   One extraction stage is used and heats the feed to a temperature equal to the saturation temperature of the pressure at which the adiabatic expansion line intersects the dry saturation line.   Determine the efficiency of the cycle and compare with that of the Rankine cycle between the same limits.

14. Steam at the initial state of Problem 13 is supplied to a turbine operating on the reheating cycle.   When the expansion reaches 200 p.s.i. abs. all of the steam passes through a resuperheater and is reheated to 680° F.   From the resuperheater it reenters the turbine and completes its expansion to 0.60 p.s.i. abs.

(a) Calculate the efficiency of the cycle and compare with that of the Rankine cycle.   Consider all expansions adiabatic and frictionless and the reheater condensate returned to the boiler without loss.

(*b*) Determine the pounds of reheat steam used per pound of main turbine steam.

15. An injector operates with steam at 160 p.s.i. abs. and 2% moisture. Temperature of suction water is 70° F. and of discharge is 160° F. Suction lift is 7 ft. and 12 lbs. of water are pumped per pound of steam supplied. What is its efficiency as a pump and as a combined pump and feed heater?

Chapter XII

1. A mixture at 30 p.s.i. abs. and 180° F. has the following composition by volume:

O_2	17.8%
N_2	67.1%
H_2O	15.1%

Calculate (*a*) analysis by weight; (*b*) apparent molecular weight; (*c*) apparent gas constant; (*d*) volume per mol and volume per pound; (*e*) partial pressures of constituents; (*f*) molal specific heats; (*g*) intrinsic energy per pound and per mol; (*h*) heat content per pound and per mol.

2. A scotch type cylindrical boiler is taken off service and allowed to cool down. When the temperature has reached 150° F. what is the pressure in the boiler? After cooling to 150° F. air is let into the steam space to break the vacuum and immediately comes to a temperature of 150° F. The valve is then closed and the boiler continues to cool until it reaches 90° F. At this point what is the pressure in the boiler and what percentage of air by volume is present? Compute the partial pressures of air and water vapor, the analysis by weight, and the specific volume of the mixture.

3. The wet bulb temperature is 62° F. when the dry bulb is 77° F. Calculate:

(*a*) partial pressure of water vapor.
(*b*) relative humidity.
(*c*) partial pressure of air.
(*d*) volume per pound of dry air.
(*e*) pounds of water vapor per pound of dry air.
(*f*) dew point.

4. 7000 cu. ft. of air at 70° F. has a relative humidity of 52%. Calculate:

(*a*) partial pressure of water vapor. *Ans.* (*a*) 0.189 p.s.i. abs.
(*b*) weight of water vapor present. (*b*) 4.2 lbs.
(*c*) partial pressure of dry air. (*c*) 14.51 p.s.i.
(*d*) weight of dry air present. (*d*) 518 lbs.
(*e*) weight per cu. ft. wet air. (*e*) 0.0746 lb. per cu. ft.

5. Saturated air at 40° F. is heated to 70° F.

Calculate:

(a) partial pressure of water vapor at 40° and 70° F.

(b) relative humidity at 70° F.

(c) partial pressure of air.

(d) volume per pound of dry air at 40° and 70° F.

(e) weight of water vapor per pound dry air, 40° F. and 70° F.

6. 1000 cu. ft. of air at 50° F., 40% relative humidity, are heated to 90° F. Calculate:

(a) pressure of water vapor.

(b) pressure of air.

(c) final volume of air.

(d) weight of water vapor present.

(e) final relative humidity.

7. A pound of air, 60% relative humidity, 72° F., is cooled to 40° F. Calculate:

(a) dew point temperature.

(b) initial and final pressures of water vapor.

(c) initial and final pressures of air.

(d) initial and final volumes of air.

(e) initial and final weights of water vapor.

(f) weight of water condensed per pound dry air.

8. 1000 cu. ft. of air 90° F. and 70% relative humidity, are cooled in a de-humidifier and then heated to 70° F. If the relative humidity at 70° F. is to be 50%, calculate:

(a) dew point of air leaving dehumidifier.

(b) weight of air entering dehumidifier.

(c) weight of vapor entering dehumidifier.

(d) volume of air leaving dehumidifier.

(e) weight of vapor leaving dehumidifier.

(f) weight of vapor condensed.

(g) heat removed from vapor.

(h) heat removed from air.

9. A house is supplied with 50,000 B.t.u. per hr. by air entering at 130° F. and cooling to 70° F. The air at 70° F. has a relative humidity of 45%. If the air is all fresh air, supplied to the heater at 20° F., 60% rel. hum., and the water added at 50° F. calculate:

(a) pounds vapor per lb. air in house.

(b) pounds dry air and vapor to heat house (per hour).

(c) pounds vapor per pound air, outside conditions.

(d) heat to be added in heater (per hour).

10. Air enters a drying chamber at 140° F., wet bulb temp. 95° F. If 50 pounds of water are to be removed by the air, calculate the weight of dry air required, assuming an adiabatic drier and that the air is saturated when it leaves.

11. If the air in Problem 10 leaves at 100° F., calculate the weight of air required.

12. 15 lbs. of air and 1 lb. of gasoline enter an engine cylinder where the total pressure is 13 p.s.i. abs. If the gasoline is completely vaporized, what is its partial pressure? (Assume gasoline to be C_8H_{18}.)

CHAPTER XIII

1. A mechanical refrigerating machine is operated by a motor of $\frac{1}{2}$ Hp. output. The refrigerating effect produced is the withdrawal of 10,000 B.t.u. per hour. Neglecting radiation and friction losses, how much heat is rejected at the higher temperature?

2. A refrigerating machine of 1 ton capacity requires 0.9 Hp. to operate it. What is its coefficient of performance?

3. If the foregoing were used as a heat pump to heat a chamber at the higher temperature, what then would be considered its coefficient of performance?

4. A refrigerating machine is rated at 25 tons. If the temperature of the water supplied to the machine is 60° F. and the ice when taken from the machine is at 20° F., how many tons of ice can be produced in 24 hours? Assume specific heat of ice to be 0.50 and a general heat leakage into the system of 20%.

5. Consider an ammonia compression refrigeration system as shown diagrammatically in Figs. XIII–6 and XIII–7. For this the following data are available.

At entrance to the compressor the pressure is 25 p.s.i. and temp. 30° F.

Leaving the compressor the pressure is 200 p.s.i. and temp. 210° F.

At entrance to the condenser the temp. is 190° F.

Leaving the condenser the temp. is 82.6° F.

At entrance to the throttling expansion valve the temp. is 78.8° F.

At exit from the expansion coils the temp. is 20° F.

From these data and the tables on pp. 387, 388, construct to scale a temp.-entropy diagram similar to Fig. XIII–7 showing the changes of state occurring throughout a complete circuit. The compression line on this diagram may be assumed to be a straight line.

Determine the following quantities per pound of ammonia and establish a complete heat balance. Specific heat of liquid ammonia may be taken as 1.1, of superheated ammonia vapor as .55 and .66 at 25 p.s.i. abs., and 200 p.s.i. abs. respectively.

(a) Heat removed from ammonia during compression.

(b) Heat removed from ammonia by radiation from pipe line from compressor to condenser.

(c) Heat removed from ammonia in condenser.

(d) Heat removed from ammonia by radiation from liquid pipe line and receiver on the way from condenser to expansion valve.

(e) Heat received by ammonia in expansion coils.

(f) Heat received by ammonia by warming effect of atmosphere on vapor pipe line from expansion coils to compressor.

(g) Heat equivalent of work done by the compressor upon the ammonia.

(h) The coefficient of performance of the system.

(i) If 1000 pounds of ammonia are circulated per hour, what is the refrigerating capacity of the plant in tons?

6. An ammonia compressor discharges vapor at 200 p.s.i. abs. and 230° F. The liquid ammonia leaves the condenser at 70.5° F. and enters the expansion valve at 74.8° F. The ammonia leaves the evaporator at 0° F. and enters the compressor at 10° F. The temperature in the evaporator coils is −8° F.

(a) Find the work per pound of ammonia by solving for n of compression; check by use of equation of steady flow and heat to jacket. Latter found by assuming compression line to be straight on the T-S plane.

(b) Make an energy balance for complete system.

(c) Calculate the theoretical Hp. per ton.

(d) Calculate the coefficient of performance.

Ans. (a) 133 B.t.u.

(c) 1 29 Hp. per ton. (d) 3.64.

7. It is desired to maintain a building at a temperature of 70.5° F. with an outside temperature of −0.6° F. using an ammonia compression machine as a heat pump. Heat to be withdrawn from the building amounts to 80,000 B.t.u. per hour and electrical energy costs 1¼ cents per kilowatt-hour. Theoretically considered (neglecting losses) compare the cost with heating by means of radiant electrical heaters.

INDEX

INDEX

459